THE ROLE OF VIRUSES
IN HUMAN CANCER

Proceedings of the First International Congress of Viral Oncology
of the T. and L. de Beaumont Bonelli Foundation for Cancer Research
held in Naples, Italy, September 21–23, 1979

Editors:

G. GIRALDO and E. BETH

Memorial Sloan-Kettering Cancer Center
New York, New York

ELSEVIER/NORTH-HOLLAND
NEW YORK · AMSTERDAM · OXFORD

Published by:

Elsevier North Holland, Inc.
52 Vanderbilt Avenue, New York, New York 10017

Sole distributors outside USA and Canada:

Elsevier/North-Holland Biomedical Press
335 Jan Van Galenstraat, PO Box 211
Amsterdam, The Netherlands

ISBN: 0-444-00440-8
ISSN: 0270-2118

Manufactured in the United States of America

Contents

Preface

This volume is based on the International Congress of Viral Oncology entitled "The Role of Viruses in Human Cancer," held in Naples in September 1979 and sponsored by the de Beaumont Bonelli Foundation for Cancer Research, with the enthusiastic support of Dr. Giulio Tarro, President of the Foundation.

The question of whether viruses cause cancer in man has been asked for twenty years by hundreds of scientists in many laboratories throughout the world. Although we know that viruses do, without doubt, cause various forms of cancer in animals under laboratory and natural conditions, and that specific viral vaccines have been applied in some of them with great success, we still cannot definitely say the same for man, although Epstein-Barr virus appears to be the most probable candidate. Genetic susceptibility, closely associated with immunologic responses, and environmental cocarcinogens are the most prominent features influencing these events. Cancer might be, indeed, the result of multifactorial events in which either heavy perinatal infections or chronic viral infections—like EBV in equatorial Africans or hepatitis B virus—could represent the initiating factor.

The purpose of this conference is to outline the main areas in which viruses can be or have been potentially associated with human malignancies, to draw attention to areas of research such as hepatitis B virus and hepatoma, to learn more about ongoing work on interferon as a possible therapeutic agent, and other new approaches like hybridomas or DNA recombinant technology. Furthermore, the demonstration and biochemical characterization of tumor-specific transplantation antigens (TSTA) might open the way toward a meaningful immunotherapeutic intervention in the control of human cancer.

We are indebted to Dr. Errico di Lorenzo who, in his function as Secretary of the Congress, has contributed significantly to the organization of this meeting. We thank the members of his department for their valuable assistance before and during the meeting. We express our sincere thanks to Ms. Mimi Halpern for her outstanding help and interest in the development of this publication. The cover design was based on a visual impression obtained from a figure kindly provided by the Abbott Laboratories, Diagnostic Division.

Gaetano Giraldo

Elke Beth

Foreword

The acuteness of the cancer problem and the fundamental importance of research aimed at uncovering its causes places the theme of viral involvement in cancer among the most interesting and urgent problems in the field of medical science today.

It is therefore an honor for me and a great privilege to speak about the commitment of the "T. and L. de Beaumont Bonelli Foundation for Cancer Research" in sponsoring the First International Congress of Viral Oncology entitled "The Role of Viruses in Human Cancer." Furthermore, the Foundation wishes to extend this commitment into the future: it is our intention to continue these conferences every three years. The topics to be selected shall cover a wide range and encompass the most up-to-date information on the multifactorial events which lead to cancer in man.

I would like to express my sincere thanks to the members of the Organizing Committee and to all who have contributed with their participation, help and interest in the success of this conference. I am delighted to thank Dr. Denis Burkitt for his participation in the Congress. It was his remarkable detective work and his intuition that opened the way to the discovery of the Epstein-Barr virus and its association with two human cancers—Burkitt's lymphoma and nasopharyngeal carcinoma.

The knowledge we have gained today concerning this virus and its involvement in human malignancies represents one of the most important breakthroughs in the advancement of human cancer research.

Giulio Tarro

Organizing Committee:

ELKE BETH
ERRICO DI LORENZO
GIOVAN GIACOMO GIORDANO
GAETANO GIRALDO
GIULIO TARRO

List of Contributors

Dr. Laure Aurelian
Division of Comparative Medicine, The Johns Hopkins School of Medicine, Room 220, G Building, 4940 Eastern Avenue, Baltimore, Maryland 21224, USA

Dr. Yechiel Becker
Laboratory for Molecular Virology, Hebrew University-Hadassah Medical School, Jerusalem, Israel

Dr. Elke Beth
Laboratory of Immuno-Virology, Memorial Sloan-Kettering Cancer Center, 1275 York Avenue, New York, New York 10021, USA

Dr. Denis P. Burkitt
Unit of Geographical Pathology, St. Thomas's Hospital Medical School, London, England SE1 7EH, United Kingdom

Dr. Antonio Cajano
Dipartimento di Medicina, Fondazione Senatore Pascale, Istituto per lo Studio e la Cura dei Tumori, Cappella dei Cangiani, Via M. Semmola, 80131 Naples, Italy

Dr. Antonio Caputo
Istituto Regina Elena per lo Studio e la Cura dei Tumori, Viale Regina Elena 291, 00161 Rome, Italy

Dr. Guy de-Thé
Programme CNRS, Faculté de Médecine Alexis Carrel, Rue Paradin, 69372 Lyon—Cedex 2, France

Dr. Alexandra H. Filipovich
Dept. of Pediatrics, Hematology and Oncology, University of Minnesota, Box 609 Majo Memorial Building, Minneapolis, Minnesota 55455, USA

Dr. Giovan Giacomo Giordano
Dipartimento di Patologia, Fondazione Senatore Pascale, Istituto per lo Studio e la Cura dei Tumori, Cappella dei Cangiani, Via M. Semmola, 80131 Naples, Italy

Dr. Gaetano Giraldo
Laboratory of Immuno-Virology, Memorial Sloan-Kettering Cancer Center, 1275 York Avenue, New York, New York 10021, USA

Dr. Ullrich Hämmerling
Laboratory of Immunochemistry, Memorial Sloan-Kettering Cancer Center, 1275 York Avenue, New York, New York 10021, USA

Dr. William D. Hardy, Jr.
Laboratory of Veterinary Oncology, Memorial Sloan-Kettering Cancer Center, 1275 York Avenue, New York, New York 10021, USA

Dr. Ariel C. Hollinshead
Department of Medicine, Div. of Hematology and Oncology, The George Washington University, Medical Center, Room 526, Ross Hall, 2300 Eye Street, Washington, D.C. 20037, USA

Dr. Abraham Karpas
Department of Haematological Medicine, University of Cambridge, School of Clinical Medicine, Hills Road, Cambridge, England CB2 2QQ, United Kingdom

Dr. Klaus Munk
Institut für Virusforschung, Deutsches Krebsforschungszentrum, Im Neuenheimer Feld 280, 6900 Heidelberg, Federal Republic of Germany

Dr. Billie L. Padgett
Department of Medical Microbiology, University of Wisconsin, Medical School, 470 North Charter Street, Madison, Wisconsin 53706, USA

Dr. Augusto Pederzini
Dipartimento di Immunologia Clinica, Ospedali Civili di Mantova, 46100 Mantova, Italy

Dr. Paul J. Price
Cell Culture Laboratory, U.S. Dept. of Health, Education and Welfare, Public Health Service, Center for Disease Control, Atlanta, Georgia 30333, USA

Dr. Alfred M. Prince
Laboratory of Virology, Lindsley F. Kimball Research Institute, The New York Blood Center, 310 East 67th Street, New York, New York 10021, USA

Dr. Kinglsey Sanders
Laboratory of Interferon Evaluation Program, Memorial Sloan-Kettering Cancer Center,
1275 York Avenue, New York, New York 10021, USA

Dr. Nurul H. Sarkar
Laboratory of Molecular Virology, Memorial Sloan-Kettering Cancer Center, 1275 York Avenue,
New York, New York 10021, USA

Dr. Ruppert Schmidt-Ullrich
Tufts-New England Medical Center, Department of Therapeutic Radiology, Division of Radiobiology,
171 Harrison Avenue, Boston, Massachusetts 02111, USA

Dr. Carlo Siriori
Fondazione Carlo Erba, Via C. del Duca 8, 20100 Milan, Italy

Dr. Giulio Tarro
Dipartimento di Virologia, Ospedale D. Cotugno, Via Gaetano Quagliariello, 80131 Naples, Italy

Dr. L. Vaczi
Department of Microbiology, University Medical School of Debrecen, Debrecen, Hungary

Dr. Vladimir Vonka
Department of Experimental Virology, Institute of Sera and Vaccine, Prague, Czechoslovakia

The Background to the Epstein-Barr Virus

Denis P. Burkitt

Unit of Geographical Pathology, St. Thomas's Hospital Medical School, London, England

Most great things have very small beginnings, and the now world-famous Epstein-Barr virus (EBV), first identified in 1954 by Epstein, Achong and Barr, is no exception.

A Serendipitous Encounter

On March 22, 1961, a little-known surgeon from Africa was to describe one of his research hobbies to the Surgical Department of the Middlesex Hospital Medical School in London. On previous home leaves, he had shared other aspects of his surgical experience in Africa with the Middlesex surgical staff and students. On this occasion he titled his talk "The Commonest Children's Cancer in Tropical Africa. A Hitherto Unrecognized Syndrome."

Something prompted a research virologist, Dr. M. A. Epstein, then working in the adjacent Bland-Sutton Institute, to slip in and sit near the back of this meeting primarily for surgeons.

The lecturer had not been speaking for long before Epstein recognized with a thrill of excitement that the subject being discussed contained the missing clues of the jig-saw puzzle on which he had been working. Here was just the evidence of an epidemiological nature to supplement his experimental studies aimed at showing that viruses could play a causative role in the induction of cancer in man. It had long been known that this was so in a variety of animal species, and although viral agents had not yet been demonstrated to be carcinogenic in humans, why should man differ from animals in this respect?

The evidence that appeared crucial to Epstein's trained and perceptive mind was that the particular form of cancer that the lecturer was describing in Africa had a geographical distribution related to the climatic factors of rainfall and temperature. To him, as to others, this proclaimed a dependence on some biological agent, probably an insect vector that might transmit a virus.

Tony Epstein approached me after the event, for I was the lecturer that day, and requested that I send him fresh tumor tissue removed from my patients in Africa, and offered to be responsible for the cost of transport. He would examine this tissue under the electron microscope for evidence of viral particles. Thus started a fruitful scientific cooperation and a valued personal friendship—and the EBV saga was launched.

As has been described in detail elsewhere, Epstein and his colleagues succeeded where others had failed, by growing the tumor cells in tissue culture before submitting them to electron microscopy.

It must have been some strange perception that perhaps history was being made that prompted Epstein to raise his hand and pull from the notice board the typewritten announcement of my lecture as he left the hall. A replica of this is the first illustration in the recent comprehensive publication, "The Epstein-Barr Virus," which describes the remarkable progress made over the decade and a half since this now famous virus was first observed.[1]

The story following this discovery has been told by others. My role in the drama was drawing to a close. I had been privileged to plant a seed, but had none of the knowledge and expertise required to nurture the plant towards flower and fruit. We each make our particular contribution and then must rejoice to hand the baton on to others. Some brilliant starters may find no one ready to grasp their baton, while hesitant starters may find eager and competent hands to carry their seemingly unremarkable achievements to undreamed-of fruition. So it was in the case of my serendipitous or providential first encounter with Tony Epstein. How did it come to pass that I should be lecturing in London on a children's cancer common in Africa?

The Discovery of a Tumor

One morning well-remembered but naturally not, at the time, recorded, but probably early in 1947, my friend and medical colleague, Dr. H. C. Trowell, then Senior Consultant Physician at Mulago Hospital, Kampala, Uganda, called me in consultation to see a puzzling case. Beginnings of major enterprises have often been insignificant and consequently difficult to date. The patient was a child with swellings in all four jaw quadrants, both sides of his maxilla and both sides of his mandible. This bizarre presentation was not in keeping with sepsis or cancer. I had been aware of single jaw tumors in children of undetermined nature, but not of multiple simultaneous lesions. A few weeks later when visiting a distant hospital, I found another child with four jaw tumors, and this convinced me that the first was not just a bizarre and unique case. These encounters prompted a careful search for tumors elsewhere in the body in children with jaw lesions, and they were almost invariably discovered. Before long it became increasingly apparent that tumors occurring in characteristic anatomical locations in children tended to be associated with one another in individual patients. The sites most commonly affected were the jaws, the orbit, the kidneys, the liver, the skeleton and, in girls, the ovaries. Moreover tumors in all these sites had a characteristic age distribution, peaking between six and eight years.[2,3]

These observations led to the conviction that rather than these multiple neoplastic deposits being different tumors, they must all be merely differing clinical manifestations of a single tumor. Formerly the orbital lesions were considered retinoblastomas; the ovarian tumors, granulosa-cell tumors; the kidney tumors, neuroblastomas; the long-bone tumors, Ewing's sarcomas—all tumors composed of small round cells.

Subsequently this conclusion, reached by deductive reasoning following clinical observations, was confirmed histologically by O'Conor and Davies,[4] who recategorized all these tumors as a form of lymphoma after review of histological material.

In view of this histological diagnosis, the rarity of peripheral lymph node involvement was particularly puzzling. Subsequently, Wright[5] was to identify the tumor on both histological and cytological criteria as a particular and distinct type of lymphoma.

Geographical Distribution

It soon became apparent that these tumors were by no means equally distributed throughout Uganda, and that they were all common or all rare together in different localities.

A providential visit to Kampala by South Africa's leading cancer epidemiolgist, George Oettlé, provided the opportunity to discuss these tumors with him. A remark of his that these tumors were not seen in South Africa proved seminal, in that it indicated the localized geographical distribution of the disease. This prompted the beginnings of studies throughout Africa, initially by postal questionnaires and subsequently by personal safaris throughout the continent to determine the geographical distribution of the tumor. This was found to consist of a horizontal belt across the continent between 15° North and South of the equator, but with tumor-free areas within this belt, and with a tail running down the east coast as far as the North of Natal.[3,6]

Climatic Dependence

Investigations in South, Central and East Africa revealed that the tumor rarely occurred above an altitude of 5,000 feet above sea level near the equator, above 3,000 feet 1,000 miles South of the equator, or above 1,000 feet further south in Mozambique. This altitude barrier was subsequently recognized to be a temperature barrier, the tumor only being common where the mean daily temperature did not fall below 60°F.[7,8] These studies entailed a 10,000 mile fact-finding tour through much of East, Central and South Africa which reached the pages of Readers' Digest[9] and was the central theme of a book by Bernard Glemser, "The Long Safari".[10]

Later studies in West Africa, a region with great contrasts in rainfall but not, as in East Africa, in altitude, indicated that the tumor rarely occurred where the annual rainfall was below about 20 inches.

The dependence of tumor occurrence on these two climatic parameters suggested the implication of some biological agent. The distribution of this tumor was in fact comparable to that of several known insect-borne diseases.

Viruses are agents which are known to be transmitted by insects, and known, at least in animals, to cause cancer. It was therefore postulated that the tumor being studied might be caused by a vectored virus.

The search for a virus which, as mentioned above, culminated in the identification of EBV, was initiated by a hypothesis which subsequently proved to be false. This virus was found to be ubiquitous, its distribution in no way corresponding to that of the tumor. Yet evidence steadily accumulated implicating this virus in the etiology of what subsequently became known as "Burkitt's lymphoma."

Remarkable Response to Therapy

A factor that added to the interest aroused in this tumor by its epidemiological features was its quite remarkable response to chemotherapy,[11,12] an observation consistent with what had been observed in virus-induced tumors in animals. This was partly explicable by the intense sensitivity of the tumor cells to cytotoxic drugs, and partly to the very strong immunological response mechanisms demonstrated in spontaneous remissions.[13]

Further Encounters with Prof. Epstein

Two further encounters with Professor Epstein deserve comment. It was with him that I realized the hazards often met in research in the tropics. I well remember visiting some islands on Lake Victoria with him in the hope of persuading local islanders to capture monkeys which could be examined for the presence of viruses. We were conveyed to the islands by motor launch, but for the ten-mile journey to shore long after dark, we had to entrust ourselves to a frail canoe with a temperamental outboard motor. This began to fail shortly after leaving our island and we didn't cherish the prospect of drifting without power in a hippopotamus-inhabited lake subject to sudden violent storms. Fortunately, careful coaxing kept the engine running in spite of many stops and starts, and in total darkness, with no navigational aids, we reached our destination ten miles from our site of departure!

The most recent encounter with Tony Epstein was the happy occasion when I stood before him listening to his oration, a highly embellished account of what this paper has been all about, when he presented me for the Honorary Doctorate in Medicine of Bristol University, where he currently holds the chair in pathology.

How the Eponym Originated

In January 1963, an international conference was held in Paris on the subject of lymphoreticular tumors in Africa. It was largely dominated by the subject "Lymphoma of Children in Africa," and contributions were made by workers in many parts of the continent. There was lack of agreement on the precise nature of the tumor, some participants being unwilling to accept it as a lymphoma. In the absence of any agreed histological terminology, it was agreed to call it Burkitt's tumor, a testimony to the generosity of my colleagues in East Africa who had, with characteristic unselfishness, used this name.[14] Subsequently it was possible to improve on "tumor" and replace this word with "lymphoma." A tumor doesn't necessarily imply cancer, as witness "Pott's puffy tumor."

Later Modification

When searching for an alternative hypothesis that would explain the epidemiological features of Burkitt's lymphoma (BL), an early suggestion by Gilbert Dalldorf was re-examined. He had postulated that the tumor only occurred commonly in regions where malaria was holo- or hyperendemic, which denotes intense transmission throughout the year. The distribution of BL in Africa and parts of Asia was observed to correspond closely to the regions in which malaria is still hyperendemic. The only tumor-free areas in warm, moist parts of Africa were Zanzibar and the environs of Kinshasa—places in which effective malarial control had been maintained. Detailed studies of Uganda showed a close relationship between the prevalence of BL and intensity of malarial infection.

These findings can be explained on the basis that the immunodepression of the lymphoreticular system, caused by intense and persistent malarial infection starting in childhood, renders this tissue more susceptible to malignant transformation in the presence of EBV than would otherwise be the case. This parallels the situation in which malignant lymphomas occur with undue frequency in patients under immunodepression following organ transplants.

At this stage epidemiological studies on Burkitt's lymphoma, to a large extent, yielded pride of place to the by-then exciting developments in the field of the Epstein-Barr virus.

References

1. Epstein, M.A. and Achong, B.G.; In: *The Epstein-Barr Virus,* M.A. Epstein and B.G. Achong (eds.), Springer-Verlag, Berlin, Heidelberg, New York, 1979.
2. Burkitt, D.P.: *Br. J. Surg.* 46:218, 1958.
3. Burkitt, D.P. and O'Conor, G.T.: *Cancer* 14:258, 1961.
4. O'Conor, G.T. and Davies, J.H.P.: *J. Pediat.* 56:526, 1960.
5. Wright, D.H.: *Br. J. Cancer* 17:50, 1963.
6. Burkitt, D.P.: In: *Symposium on Lymphoreticular Tumors in Africa,* F.C. Roulet (ed.), S. Karger, Basel, New York, 1964, p. 119.
7. Burkitt, D.P.: *Br. Med. J.* 2:1019, 1962.
8. Burkitt, D.P.: *Br. J. Cancer* 16:379, 1962.
9. Glemser, B.: In: *Readers' Digest,* US edition, September 1968, p. 119.
10. Glemser, B: *The Long Safari,* B. Glemser (ed.), Bodley Head, London, 1970.
11. Burkitt, D.P., Hutt, M.S.R., and Wright, D.H.: *Cancer* 18:399, 1965.
12. Clifford, P.: *E. Afr. Med. J.* 43:179, 1966.
13. David, J. and Burkitt, D.P.: *Br. Med. J.* 4:288, 1968.
14. Roulet, F.C.: In: *Symposium on Lymphoreticular Tumors in Africa,* F.C. Roulet (ed.), S. Karger, Basel, New York, 1964, p. 420.

The Epstein-Barr Virus and Human Cancer

Yechiel Becker

Hebrew University-Hadassah Medical School, Jerusalem, Israel

Epstein-Barr virus (EBV), a human herpesvirus, was first found in B lymphoblasts derived from a biopsy of an African Burkitt's lymphoma (BL) grown under *in vitro* conditions.[1] This discovery brought to light a virus which is resident in tumor lymphoblasts and led to the realization that the virus is a ubiquitous pathogen found in all human populations. The interaction between EBV and the human host leads to infection of the buccal cavity and to horizontal transmission of the virus from individual to individual. In seronegative young children, the virus causes an inapparent infection followed by seroconversion in most of the pharynx and its lymph nodes in young adolescence, and this results in a violent response of T lymphocytes to the infected B lymphocytes. Such an infection is called infectious mononucleosis (IM). Tumor development was noted in a very small number of children in the Burkitt's lymphoma belt in Uganda, namely 31 out of 42,000 children examined.[3] In those children who developed BL, high antibody titers to the EBV capsid antigen were noted early in childhood. However, outside the African lymphoma belt, infection of children with EBV never leads to the development of BL or any other lymphoproliferative disorders.

Studies on the relationship between EBV infection of B lymphocytes and tumor development have not as yet revealed the factors that lead to the development of a transformed clone of B lymphocytes which are able to escape host regulation of cell growth and develop into an invasive tumor. Studies on the interaction of EBV with B lymphocytes under *in vitro* conditions revealed that only B lymphocytes have receptors for EBV on the cell membrane.[4,5] The EBV DNA, which is linear in the virus itself, can integrate into chromosomal DNA and is also maintained in a circular form in the nuclei of infected B lymphocytes.[6,7] The presence of EBV in the lymphocytes allows them to grow under *in vitro* conditions, namely in the presence of fetal calf serum. The mechanism controlling EBV DNA in the nuclei of B lymphocytes and the molecular events that lead to the indefinite growth of lymphocytes under *in vitro* conditions, a phenomenon called immortalization,[8] are not yet understood.

The ability of B lymphocytes to restrict the replication of EBV has limited the pace of studies in this field. The EBV is produced only in a small number of cells in each culture derived from BL. In many instances, the metabolism of the host cell needs to be arrested to allow the escape of EBV DNA from host cell control, so that the replication of linear EBV DNA of the type needed for encapsidation into infectious virions can take place. Elucidation of the molecular processes of B lymphocytes, which restrict EBV DNA when the host cell is active and functioning, as well as the process of unrestricted growth of the host cell under *in vivo* and *in vitro* conditions might hold the key to solving the question of the involvement of EBV in human cancer.

The scope of this study is to analyze some of the processes which govern the interaction of EBV with B lymphocytes.

EBV is a Ubiquitous Human Pathogen

Infection of Permissive Cells In Vivo

Cells permissive for EBV must be present in the buccal cavity of infected individuals in order to allow the lytic cycle of the virus to take place. Pagano and Shaw[9] were able to identify epithelial cells in the pharynx of IM patients that contained large amounts of EBV DNA, using ^{3}H-cRNA[10,11] as a probe. Such permissive cells allow the replication of viral DNA, the expression of all virus functions, and the synthesis of infectious EBV. Unfortunately, it is not yet possible to grow the virus in cultured cells *in vitro*. As a result, little is known about the virus cycle and about the viral structural and nonstructural proteins produced in permissive cells. The development of a humoral antibody response to viral antigens like EBV-determined nuclear antigen (EBNA), membrane antigen (MA), early viral antigen (EA), and viral capsid antigen (VCA) indicates that lytically infected cells are disrupted at the end of the virus growth cycle and the viral antigens stimulate the immunological system to respond with antibody production (Table 1).

Children with antibodies to EBV are immune to the virus, but those who are still seronegative during young adulthood can be infected by EBV by horizontal transmission, since the virus is transferred by direct mouth-to-mouth contacts. In these individuals, EBV replicates in per-

Table 1.   Scheme of EBV Infection of "Permissive" Cells *In Vivo*

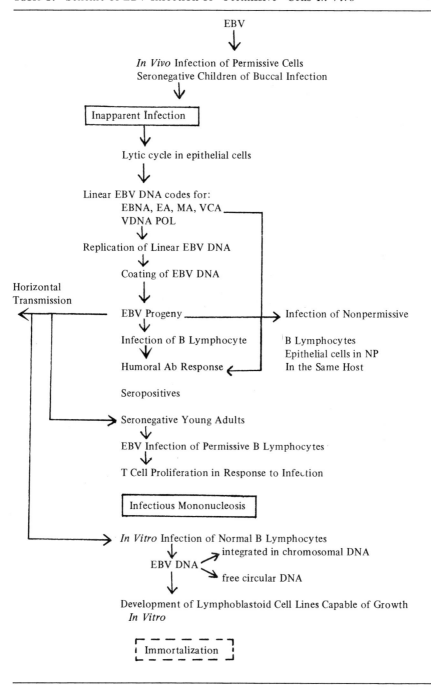

missive epithelial cells, and the viral antigens produced cause a violent proliferation of T cells and their appearance in large numbers in the peripheral blood. The role of EBV as the causative agent of IM was well established.[12–14]

Childhood Infection by EBV Leading to the Development of BL Tumors

Since BL is limited to the African tumor belt, de-Thé[3] and his associates searched for evidence of the relationship between EBV infection and the development of BL tumors in children in areas endemic for BL. It was found that 31 children out of 42,000 tested developed lymphomas. In the "pre-BL" diagnosis, high antibody titers to the viral capsid antigen were noted. It was concluded by de-Thé[3] that the degree of increased risk of developing BL in children with VCA titers two or more dilutions above the mean of the normal population was 30 times that of the general population. This study indicated that there may be a causal association between EBV and BL.

B lymphocytes derived from BL tumors constitute the major source of cell lines for the study of the relationship between EBV, its DNA, and the transformed cells. Since lymphomas are made of monoclonal cells,[15] it is possible that in each African child that develops BL, only one B lymphocyte which was infected with EBV became transformed and developed into a tumor. The mechanisms leading to the restriction of EBV DNA and cell transformation are unknown, although cofactors such as malarial infection of the children, as well as genetic factors, have been implicated in the development of BL.[3,16]

Latently-Infected B Lymphocytes in the Blood of Normal Individuals

Adults are mostly seropositives in respect to EBV which was acquired during childhood or young adolescence. Yet, when lymphocytes from adults are kept in culture medium containing fetal calf serum, lymphoblastoid cell lines can be established. This finding suggests that in the peripheral blood a few EBV-infected B lymphocytes are present. The cells are latently infected with EBV which is not expressed in the cells under in vivo conditions. When these cells are maintained under in vitro conditions, activation of EBV DNA takes place. The viral DNA codes for viral functions and the release of infectious EBV leads to the infection of other B lymphocytes and to the establishment of a lymphoblastoid cell line (Table 2).[16–18]

Since the life span of a normal B lymphocyte is limited, it must be concluded that latently-infected B lymphocytes are produced in the organism as a long-term event. The site of infection of the B lymphocytes is not known. Latently-infected B lymphocytes behave as normal cells

Table 2. Scheme of EBV Infection of "Nonpermissive" Cells *In Vivo*

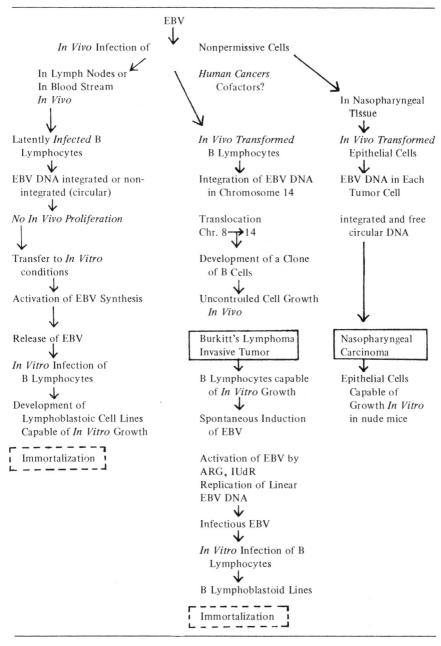

and do not proliferate *in vivo,* in spite of the fact that they contain EBV DNA. It is most likely that the B lymphocyte that becomes transformed in EBV-infected children and eventually develops into a tumorous clone is a latently-infected cell. Some event causing a change in the lymphocyte of the African child or in the oncogene of EBV will lead to transformation.

EBV DNA is Present in Transformed Lymphoblast Cell Lines from Most BL

The lymphoblasts present in BL are capable of *in vitro* growth, as initially observed by Epstein and Barr.[2] During the past fifteen years, many lymphoblastoid cell lines were established *in vitro*. The presence of EBV DNA in the cell lines was detected by molecular hybridization, with labeled complementary RNA and by the presence of EBV-coded nuclear antigen (EBNA). Although most of the lymphoblasts from BL biopsies that were established *in vitro* contain EBV DNA, several lines with no detectable EBV DNA were also obtained from typical African BL. The properties of these cell lines will be discussed later.

Induction of EBV in Lymphoblasts from BL

Epstein et al.[1] noted the presence of herpes-like virus particles in BL lymphoblasts cultured *in vitro,* mainly in dying cells. Henle and Henle[19] noted that incubation of BL lymphoblasts in an arginine deficient medium led to the appearance of viral antigens in 80% of the cells, while less than 10% of the cells had viral antigens when grown in complete medium. This result, as well as studies on the effect of arginine depletion on herpes simplex virus (HSV),[20] led us to the isolation of the first purified preparation of EBV. These results suggested that EBV DNA is controlled by the B lymphocyte in such a way that the synthesis of viral DNA and antigens is prevented when the cells are physiologically active. Only when molecular processes of the cells are affected, as in the absence of the essential amino acid arginine, can EBV escape host control and replicate (Figure 1). Experiments by Hamper et al.[21,22] also demonstrated that EBV can be induced by treatment of the lymphoblasts with IUdR (Table 2). Most of the studies on EBV were carried out with virus released from BL lymphoblasts.

EBV DNA in Virions and Cells

The initial isolation of DNA from EBV[20] revealed that the virions contain a linear DNA genome with a molecular weight of 100×10^6 daltons. Subsequent studies confirmed this finding. It was therefore of interest that growing lymphoblasts were found to contain circular EBV DNA.[23,24] All the free copies of EBV DNA present in the growing lymphoblasts

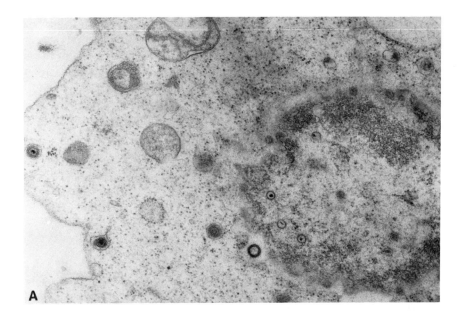

Figure 1A. Electron micrograph of a 895-8 lymphoblast. Note EBV nucleocapsids in the nuclei and enveloped virions in the cytoplasm. (×26,000)

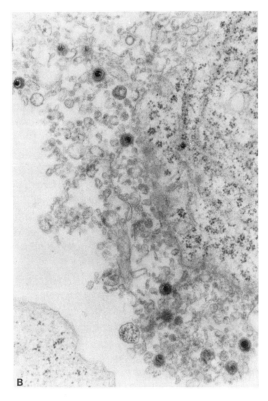

Figure 1B. Electron micrograph of a lymphoblast from a cell line developed from the peripheral blood of a patient (A.Y.) with ataxia telangiectasia (a recessive genetic disorder). The cell line was developed and maintained in culture. Note enveloped EB virions released from the cells.(× 23,000) (The electron micrographs were done by Dr. A. Friedmann, Department of Genetics, The Hebrew University of Jerusalem.)

from BL, as well as *in vitro*-infected B lymphocytes, contained free circular EBV DNA.

Adams et al.[25] demonstrated that part of the EBV DNA present in the nuclei of lymphoblastoid cells is integrated into the chromosomal DNA. This finding was confirmed by Becker et al.[26] Recently it was demonstrated by Yamamoto et al.[27] that EBV DNA which codes for EBNA is integrated or associated with chromosome 14 of human lymphoblasts. It was suggested by Becker et al.[26] that fragments of EBV DNA integrate into chromosomal DNA. However, the integration of complete EBV DNA genomes with cellular DNA cannot be ruled out. The mechanisms that lead to the integration of EBV DNA into cellular DNA are not known.

Resident EBV DNA Replicates During the S Phase of the Lymphoblastoid Cell Cycle

Studies by Becker and Weinberg[28] and Hampar et al.[29] demonstrated that EBV DNA is synthesized during the S phase in Burkitt lymphoblasts. Recent studies with the antiviral drug phosphonoacetic acid (PAA) revealed that the synthesis of the circular EBV DNA which is resident in the nucleus is not affected by the drug.[30,31] Since PAA inhibits the herpesvirus-coded DNA polymerase and not the cellular DNA polymerase α, β and λ (with the exception of a subfraction of DNA polymerase α),[32] it may be concluded that the circular EBV DNA is replicated by the cellular DNA polymerase. In Figure 2, the DNA polymerases extracted from the lymphoblastoid cell lines (P3HR-1 and B95-8) are shown. Only cellular DNA polymerases were found. In Figure 3, the chromatography of the cellular DNA polymerases and EBNA on benzoylated, napthoylated DEAE (BND)-cellulose columns is shown. EBNA is eluted from the column together with the cellular DNA polymerases.

Treatment of lymphoblasts with cycloheximide results in the disappearance of the free circular EBV DNA from the nuclei. Only the integrated EBV DNA, 1 or 2 genome equivalents, is retained in the cells.[33] Cycloheximide most probably inhibits the synthesis of the cellular DNA polymerases. The cells containing only integrated EBV DNA have growth properties similar to lymphoblasts containing the episomal EBV DNA.

Induction of the Synthesis of Linear EBV DNA

Arginine deprivation of BUdR treatment of Burkitt lymphoblasts grown *in vitro* lead to the production of EB virions. The resident episomal viral DNA molecules are circular; the virions contain linear viral DNA. Thus, it must be assumed that circular EBV DNA must be cleaved to yield linear DNA molecules which could replicate semiconservatively by a virus-induced DNA polymerase, as demonstrated for HSV.[34–38] The

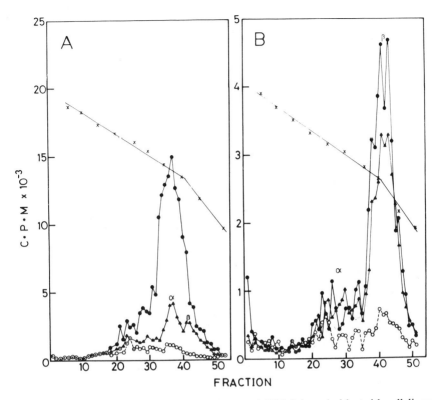

Figure 2. DNA polymerase from P3HR-1 and B95-8 lymphoblastoid cell lines. The DNA polymerases were extracted from 100×10^6 cells using the procedure of Hirai and Watanabe [54] as described by Fridlender et al. [32] The $(NH_4)_2SO_4$ precipitates were centrifuged in sucrose gradients and the position of the DNA polymerases was determined by incubation of 25 μl samples from each fraction with a reaction mixture containing the four deoxyribonucleoside triphosphates (the TTP was tritiated) and activated calf thymus DNA. The salt (KCl) concentration was 250 mM (to determine the presence of a virus-induced DNA polymerase and the DNA polymerase β) or 10 mM (to determine the presence of the DNA polymerase α). **A.** DNA polymerase from P3HR-1 cells. The major enzymatic activity is that of the DNA polymerase α. **B.** DNA polymerases from B95-8 cells. The major enzymatic activity is that of the DNA polymerase β. A low level of DNA polymerase α activity can also be seen.

finding that PAA inhibits the production of EB virions[31] indicates that EBV DNA codes for a viral DNA polymerase.

In our studies on the induction of EBV DNA replication in EB_3 cells (Becker, unpublished observations;[28]) it was noted that EBV DNA was synthesized in the nuclei of arginine-deprived lymphoblasts (Figure 4A-C). Lymphoblasts incubated in complete medium (Figure 4D) or medium without leucine (Figure 4E) did not synthesize EBV DNA. Treatment of

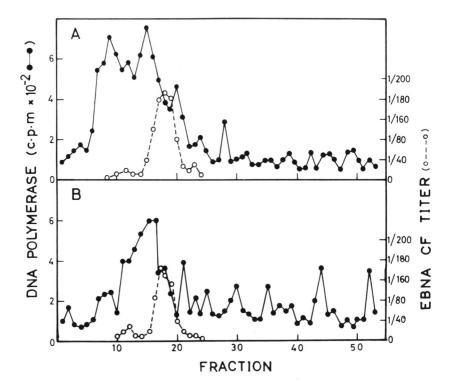

Figure 3 A, B. Chromatography of DNA polymerases and EBNA from PdHR-1 and B95-8 lymphoblast cell lines. Lymphoblasts from P3HR-1 (5×10^8) and B95-8 (1×10^9) cultures were harvested by centrifugation and washed twice with reticulocyte standard buffer (RSB) supplemented with 0.1 mM $CaCl_2$. The cells were resuspended in 8 ml Tris buffer (2 mM Tris pH 7.5) containing 8% sucrose. The cells were broken in a Dounce homogenizer, the nuclei were centrifuged down and resuspended in 8 ml of the same buffer and NaCl was added to a final concentration of 1.0 M to disrupt the nuclei. The DNA was digested with pancreatic DNAse (150 μg/ml in 10% glycerol, 0.24 mg/ml BSA, 0.07 μl/ml β-mercaptoethanol and 1.6 M NaCl). The solution was left at room temperature for 40 min and then centrifuged at 45,000 rpm for 30 min in a 50 Ti rotor in a Beckman ultracentrifuge. The supernatant fluids were dialyzed against the column buffer (50 mM Tris pH 7.9). The dialyzed material was layered onto a DEAE-Sephadex column and the DNA polymerases were eluted by a gradient of $(NH_4)_2SO_4$ ranging from 0.2-0.45 M. The DNA polymerase activity in each fraction was determined as described in Figure 2. (The EBNA content in each fraction was done by the complement fixation test in Prof. G. Klein's laboratory, Karolinska Institute, Stockholm, Sweden.)

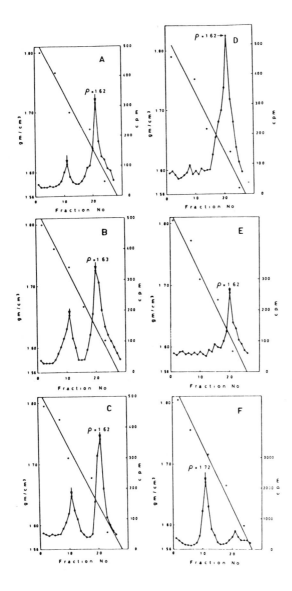

Figure 4A-F. Time course of EBV DNA replication in arginine-deprived Burkitt lymphoblasts. The cells were resuspended in arginine-deficient medium, incubated at 37°C and labeled for different time intervals with ³H-thymidine. Samples of cells were removed at 10 h (**A**), 20 h (**B**), and 30 h (**C**) after arginine deprivation. Lymphoblasts incubated in complete medium (**D**) or leucine-deficient medium (**E**), which served as controls, were labeled with ³H-thymidine for 30 h and their DNA was also analyzed by CsCl centrifugation. Herpes simplex virus DNA (**F**) served as a marker.

the arginine-deprived lymphocytes with puromycin, an inhibitor of protein biosynthesis, inhibited EBV DNA synthesis when added at the time of arginine deprivation. These results suggest that immediately after arginine deprivation the resident EBV DNA codes for the viral DNA polymerase. Addition of puromycin at this time will prevent the synthesis of EBV DNA. Addition of puromycin at a later time (Figure 5) did not completely prevent EBV DNA synthesis.

Figure 5A-D. Effect of puromycin on the induction of EBV DNA. Lymphoblasts were incubated in arginine-deficient medium and labeled with ³H-thymidine. One culture (**A**) served as a control, while puromycin was added to the others at 10 h (**B**), or at 20 h (**C**) after transfer to the arginine-deficient medium. The labeled DNA was prepared from the different cell samples and analyzed by centrifugation in CsCl density gradients.   =radioactivity; − =density.

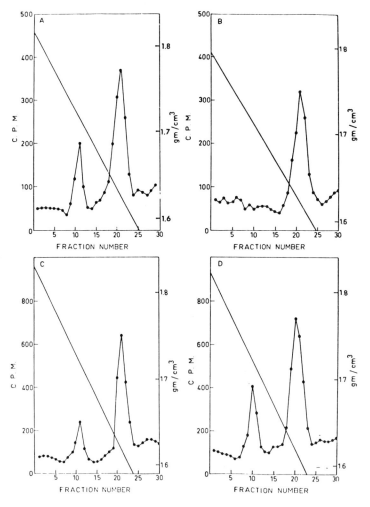

Since attempts to isolate the replicative intermediates from the nuclei of lymphoblastoid cell lines were unsuccessful, attempts were made to isolate the DNA released from EBV producing cells. The cell lines B95-8 and P3HR-1 were propagated in RPMI medium supplemented with 10% fetal calf serum and labeled with ^{3}H-thymidine. The DNA released from the cells to the medium was studied by chromatography on BND-cellulose columns. The results in Figure 6 reveal that labeled DNA present in the medium was adsorbed to the BND-cellulose and eluted with 1.0 M NaCl in buffer, suggesting that the DNA is double-stranded.[35,39] About 10% of the labeled DNA eluted with 2% caffein, a property of DNA molecules which are either completely or partially

Figure 6. BND-cellulose chromatography of labeled DNA from the growth medium of B95-8 cells. 100×10^6 B95-8 cells were labeled with 10 μCi/ml of ^{3}H-thymidine for one day, 24 h after feeding. The cells and debris were removed by centrifugation and the supernatant fluid was again centrifuged at 9,000 rpm for 90 min in a Sorvall centrifuge. The pellet was discarded. The supernatant fluid containing 0.1 M NET buffer was diluted with 0.3 M NET buffer to 0.2 M NET and loaded onto a BND-cellulose column (35). Elution was performed stepwise with 0.3 M NET, 1.0 M NET, 1.0 M NET plus 2% (w/v) caffeine and 1.0 M NET plus 50% (v/v) formamide. A portion of each fraction was taken to TCA and the radioactivity was determined.

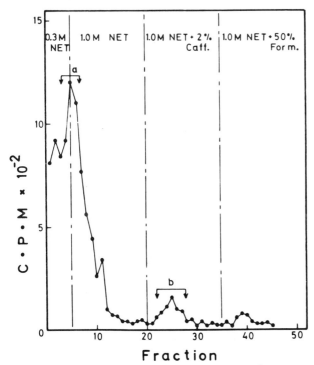

single-stranded. Centrifugation of the two DNA preparations obtained from the BND-cellulose column in CsCl density gradients (Figure 7) revealed that most of the double-stranded DNA molecules were viral (Figure 7B), while the rest was cellular DNA. Unfortunately, it cannot be concluded that the viral DNA molecules with single-stranded sequences are the replicative intermediates of EBV, since the analysis of EBV DNA from purified EB virions by chromatography on BND-cellulose columns showed that 25% of the virion DNA contains single-stranded sequences (Figure 8). Further experiments are needed to deter-

Figure 7a, b. CsCl density gradients of DNA isolated by chromatography on BND-cellulose columns. DNA eluted with 1.0 M NET buffer (**a,** region *a* in Figure 6) and 1.0 M NET plus 2% (w/v) caffeine (**b,** region *b* in Figure 6) was centrifuged in CsCl gradients at 35,000 rpm for 48 h at 20°C.

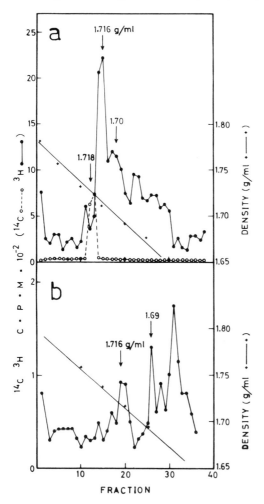

mine how the circular episomal EBV DNA molecules are converted to linear EBV DNA, the mechanism of EBV DNA replication, and the coding for the EBV DNA polymerase. Elucidation of conversion of linear EBV DNA in EBV-infected B lymphocytes into circular episomal DNA is of equal importance in understanding the molecular processes controlling EBV DNA in the B lymphocyte.

EBV DNA Controls the Ability of B Lymphocytes to Grow Under *In Vitro* Conditions

EBV Infection of EBV Negative Lymphoblasts

Some of the BL biopsies were found to consist of B lymphoblasts that lack EBV DNA. Upon establishment of cell lines from these BL biopsies, it was noted by Steinitz and Klein[40,41] that the cells grow poorly *in vitro*.

Figure 8. BND-cellulose chromatography of EBV DNA. EBV DNA from virus particles released from B95-8 cells was isolated in CsCl gradients. The DNA banding at a density of 1.716 g/ml was diluted 200 times in 0.3 M NET buffer and eluted stepwise from BND-cellulose using 1.0 M NET buffer, 1.0 M NET buffer containing 2% (w/v) caffeine and 1.0 M NET buffer containing 50% (v/v) formamide (35). The TCA precipitable radioactivity in each fraction was determined.

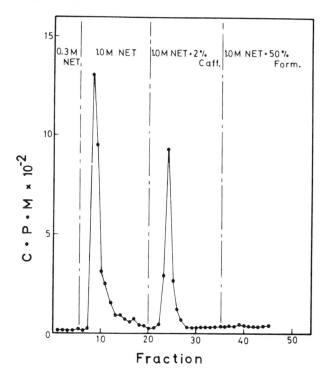

Infection of these cells with EBV under *in vitro* conditions yielded cells with the ability to proliferate *in vitro*. This study seems to indicate that tumor cells which proliferate *in vivo* have a limited ability to grow *in vitro*. It can also be concluded that BL can develop as a result of proliferation of B lymphoblasts that do not contain EBV DNA, although it can also be argued that these cells contained EBV DNA which disappeared during proliferation of the clone. Regardless of this and related arguments, the experiments of Steinitz and Klein[40,41] clearly indicate that it is advantageous for B lymphocytes to be infected with EBV, in order to grow in the presence of fetal calf serum *in vitro*.

EBV Infected B Lymphocytes Contain Receptors for Insulin

Lymphoblastoid cell lines have been reported to have cell surface receptors for insulin[42,43] as well as receptors for human growth hormone[44,45] and calcitonin.[45] BL lymphoblasts had fewer calcitonin receptors than lymphoblastoid cell lines *in vitro*.[46]

The presence of insulin receptors on lymphocytes infected with EBV is of interest, since insulin and somatomedin, the growth factor present in fetal calf serum, can bind to the same receptors. Indeed, in our studies (Becker and Wallach, unpublished data), it was found that addition of insulin to the medium can reduce the serum concentration required for cell proliferation (Figure 9). It may be possible that EBV infection of B lymphocytes could lead to an increased number of insulin receptors which can efficiently adsorb somatomedin supplied in the fetal calf serum. As a result, the cells acquire the ability to proliferate *in vitro* in the presence of fetal calf serum.

Burkitt's Lymphoblasts Require Cofactors for Transformation?

The Role of EBV

The rarity of the development of BL tumors in children in the endemic area (31 tumors in 42,000 children) raised the question of what leads to the development of tumors. Burkitt himself suggested that infection of children with malarial parasites is a cofactor. However, all the children in the study of de-Thé[3] were infected with malaria, and yet only a small number developed tumors. With the lack of an answer to this question, we can resort to the genetics of people living in the African tumor belt. However, since we know little of the genetics of these people, which is reflected in the properties of their lymphocytes, we are still left with the basic question: is EBV needed for cell transformation *in vivo*? In EBV DNA negative tumors the answer is complicated because the viral DNA may not be easily detectable. In EBV DNA-containing tumors, the

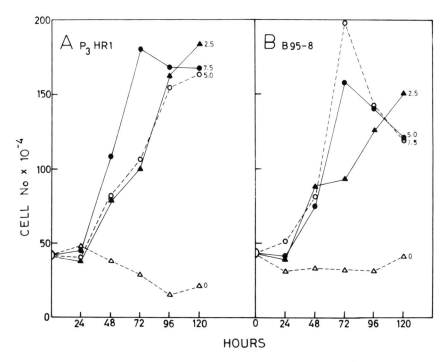

Figure 9A, B. Effect of insulin on the growth of P3HR-1 and B95-8 cells *in vitro*. Cells were washed and resuspended in RPMI medium (GIBCO) containing 0.1 U/ml insulin and different concentrations of serum. The number of the cells was determined by counting in a hemocytometer.

answer is no less complicated, since EBV can infect the tumor cell after transformation has already taken place. In any event, it is not only the rarity of the transformation event in one lymphocyte which causes the effect, but also the ability of the transformed cell to develop into a clone which proliferates to form a destructive tumor. The nature of these events is still not clear.

Lymphoblasts from EBV DNA Negative and Positive Tumors Contain a Retrovirus when Grown In Vitro

Studies from our laboratory[47–49] showed that a retrovirus can be induced in lymphoblasts (Figure 10). This was confirmed by Klucis et al.[50] Kufe et al.[51,52] reported on retrovirus-like RNA sequences in BL tumors and lymphoblast cell lines.

The retroviruses have not yet been fully identified, and it is not possible to relate this virus to the transformation event. These may be endogenous retroviruses of human lymphoblasts. In a recent study[49] it

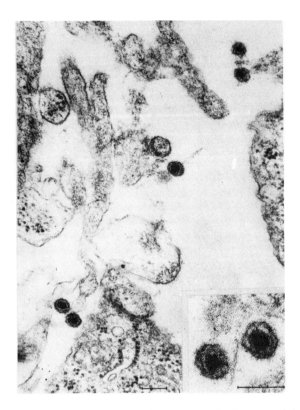

Figure 10. Electron microscopy of virus particles from arginine-deprived PdHR-1 cells. Particles resembling C-type virus particles are present in the extracellular space.(×58,000) **Inset:** Higher magnification of the virus particles.(× 117,000) Bar represents 100 nm.
Source: *Kotler et al: Proc. Natl. Acad. Sci. USA 72:4592, 1975.*

was shown that retroviruses were induced in EBV DNA negative BL lymphoblasts, but not in lymphoblastoid cells from ataxia telangiectasia and Down's syndrome patients, which had been immortalized *in vitro* by EBV. Retroviruses could be seen only in lymphoblasts derived from tumors and not yet in cell lines from patients with IM.

EBV and Nasopharyngeal Carcinoma (NPC) in the Chinese

Table 2 relates some of the possible events leading to the development of nasopharyngeal carcinoma in the Chinese. The tumor cells contain both episomal and integrated EBV DNA genomes.[24] Yet it should be recalled that in IM, epithelial cells in the buccal cavity are permissive for EBV.[9] Genetic factors may be involved in the transformation event, since these tumors are restricted to the southern Chinese.

The difficulty in determining the role of EBV in NPC is similar to that of the role of EBV in BL. The ability of EBV to cause malignant transformation when injected into cotton top marmosets and owl monkeys clearly suggests that EBV is capable of transforming B lymphoblasts, which are capable of developing into tumors in experimentally-infected animals.[53]

Summary

Studies on EBV and EBV DNA-containing cells have provided a great deal of information on the virus and its host cells, but the molecular processes that control the virus in the lymphoblasts are not known. Knowing some of the processes involved in the production of EBV is not enough to understand the viral genes and their function, assuming that there are 50 genes in a DNA genome of 103×10^6 daltons. The finding of EBV in Burkitt's lymphoblasts grown *in vitro* made possible the study of the ubiquity of the virus. Its ability to infect children and seronegative young adults, causing infectious mononucleosis, has been firmly established. The role of EBV in the human cancers—Burkitt's lymphoma and nasopharyngeal carcinoma—is merely implied, but has not been established. A causal association between EBV and BL was suggested by de-Thé[3] on the basis of his prospective study which indicated that the oncogenic potential of EBV for humans is expressed only under unusual environmental conditions. A similar argument can be used for the role of EBV in NPC.

References

1. Epstein, M.A., Achong, B.G., and Barr, Y.M.: *Lancet* 1:702, 1964.

2. Epstein, M.A. and Barr, Y.M.: *Lancet* 1:252, 1964.

3. De-Thé, G.: In: *The Epstein-Barr Virus,* M.A. Epstein and B.G. Achong (eds.), Springer-Verlag, Berlin, Heidelberg, New York, 1979, p. 417.

4. Jondal, M. and Klein, G.: *J. Exp. Med.* 138:1365, 1973.

5. Pattengale, P.K., Smith, R.W., and Gerber, P.: *Lancet* 2:93, 1973.

6. Kaschka-Dierich, C., Adams, A., Lindahl, T., Bornkamm, G.W., Bjursell, G., Klein, G., Giovanella, B.C., and Singh, S.: *Nature* 260:302, 1976.

7. Lindahl, T., Adams, A., Bjursell, G., Bornkamm, G.W., Kaschka-Dierich, C., and Jehn, U.: *J. Mol. Biol.* 102:511, 1976.

8. Miller, G., Robinson, J., Heston, L., and Lipman, M.: *Proc. Natl. Acad. Sci. USA* 71:4006, 1974.

9. Pagano, J.S. and Shaw, J.E.: In: *The Epstein-Barr Virus,* M.A. Epstein and B.G. Achong (eds.), Springer-Verlag, Berlin, Heidelberg, New York, 1979, p. 109.

10. Nonoyama, M. and Pagano, J.S.: *Nature New Biol.* 233:103, 1971.

11. Nonoyama, M. and Pagano, J.S.: *Nature* 242:44, 1973.

12. Henle, W. and Henle, G.: *J. Virol.* 2:182, 1968.
13. Henle, W., Henle, G., and Horwitz, C.A.: *Hum. Pathol.* 5:551, 1974.
14. Henle, W. and Henle, G.: In: *The Epstein-Barr Virus,* M.A. Epstein and B.G. Achong (eds.), Springer-Verlag, Berlin, Heidelberg, New York, 1979, p. 61.
15. Klein, G.: *Proc. Natl. Acad. Sci. USA* 69:1056, 1972.
16. Epstein, M.A. and Achong, B.G.: In: *The Epstein-Barr Virus,* M.A. Epstein and B. G. Achong (eds.), Springer-Verlag, Heidelberg, Berlin, New York, 1979, p. 321.
17. Crawford, D.H., Rickinson, A.B., Finerty, S., and Epstein, M.A.: *J. Gen. Virol.* 38:449, 1978.
18. Epstein, M.A. and Achong, B.G.: In: *The Epstein-Barr Virus,* M.A. Epstein and B.G. Achong (eds.), Springer-Verlag, Berlin, Heidelberg, New York, 1979, p. 1.
19. Henle, G., Henle, W., and Diehl, V.: *Proc. Natl. Acad. Sci. USA* 59:94, 1968.
20. Weinberg, A. and Becker, Y.: *Virology* 39:312, 1969.
21. Hampar, B., Derge, J.G., Martos, L.M., Tagamets, M.A. Chang, S.Y., and Charkrabarty, M.: *Nature New Biol.* 244:214, 1973.
22. Hampar, B.: In: *The Epstein-Barr Virus,* M.A. Epstein and B.G. Achong (eds.), Springer-Verlag, Berlin, Heidelberg, New York, 1979, p. 283.
23. Adams, A. and Lindahl, T.: In: *Oncogenesis and Herpesviruses II, IARC Scientific Publications No. 11,* G. de Thé, M.A. Epstein and H. zur Hausen (eds.), International Agency for Research on Cancer, Lyon, 1975, p. 125.
24. Adams, A.: In: *The Epstein-Barr Virus,* M.A. Epstein and B.G. Achong (eds.), Springer-Verlag, Berlin, Heidelberg, New York, 1979, p. 155.
25. Adams, A., Lindahl, T., and Klein, G.: *Proc. Natl. Acad. Sci. USA* 70:2888, 1973.
26. Becker, Y., Shlomai, Y., Weinberg, E., Ben-Zeev, A., and Olshevsky, U.: *Isr. J. Med. Sci.* 10:1454, 1974.
27. Yamamoto, K., Mizuno, F., Matsuo, T., Tanaka, A., Nonoyama, M., and Osaka, T.: *Proc. Natl. Acad. Sci. USA* 75:5155, 1978.
28. Becker, Y. and Weinberg, A.: *Isr. J. Med. Sci.* 7:561, 1971.
29. Hampar, B., Tanaka, A., Nonoyama, M., and Derge, J.G.: *Proc. Natl. Acad. Sci. USA* 71:631, 1974.
30. Nyormoi, O., Thorley-Lawson, D.A., Elkington, J., and Strominger, J.L.: *Proc. Natl. Acad. Sci. USA* 73:1745, 1976.
31. Summers, W.C. and Klein, G.: *J. Virol.* 18:151, 1976.
32. Fridlender, B., Chejanovsky, N., and Becker, Y.: *Antimicrob. Agents Chemother.* 13:124, 1978.
33. Tanaka, A., Nonoyama, M., and Hampar, B.: *Virology* 70:164, 1976.
34. Shlomai, J., Friedmann, H., and Becker, Y.: *Virology* 69:647, 1976.
35. Shlomai, J., Strauss, B., Asher, Y., Friedmann, A., and Becker, Y.: *J. Gen. Virol.* 32:189, 1976.
36. Shlomai, J., Asher, Y., and Becker, Y.: *J. Gen. Virol.* 34:223, 1977.
37. Friedmann, A., Shlomai, J., and Becker, Y.: *J. Gen. Virol.* 34:507, 1977.
38. Shlomai, J. and Becker, Y.: *J. Gen. Virol.* 37:429, 1977.
39. Kiger, J.A. and Sinsheimer, R.L.: *J. Mol. Biol.* 40:467, 1969.
40. Steinitz, M. and Klein, G.: *Proc. Natl. Acad. Sci. USA* 72:3518, 1975.
41. Steinitz, M. and Klein, G.: *Virology* 70:570, 1976.
42. Gavin, J.R., Buell, D.N., and Roth, J.: *Science* 178:168, 1972.

43. Gavin, J.R., Roth, J., Jen, P., and Freychet, P.: *Proc. Natl. Acad. Sci. USA* 69:747, 1972.

44. Lesniak, M.A., Roth, J., Gordon, P., and Gavin, J.R.: *Nature New Biol.* 241:20, 1973.

45. Lesniak, M.A., Gordon, P., Roth, J., and Gavin, J.R.: *J. Biol. Chem.* 249:1661, 1974.

46. Marx, S.J., Aurbach, G.D., Gavin, J.R., and Buell, D.W.: *J.Biol. Chem.* 249:6812, 1974.

47. Kotler, M., Balabanova, H., Weinberg, E., Friedmann, A., and Becker, Y.: *Proc. Natl. Acad. Sci. USA* 72:4592, 1975.

48. Kotler, M., Balabanova, H., Ben-Moyal, Z., Friedmann, A., and Becker, Y.: *J. Med. Sci.* 13:740, 1977.

49. Kotler, M., Balabanova, H., Friedmann, A., and Becker, Y. *Br. J. Cancer* 39:414,1979.

50. Klucis, E., Jackson, L., and Parsons, P.G.: *Int. J. Cancer* 18:413, 1976.

51. Kufe, D., Hehlmann, R., and Spiegelman, S.: *Proc, Natl. Acad. Sci. USA* 70:5, 1973.

52. Kufe, D., Magrath, I.T., Ziegler, J.L., and Spiegelman, S.: *Proc. Natl. Acad. Sci. USA* 70:737, 1973.

53. Miller, G.: In: *The Epstein-Barr Virus,* M.A. Epstein and B.G. Achong (eds.), Springer-Verlag, Berlin, Heidelberg, New York, 1979, p. 351.

54. Hirai, K. and Watanabe, Y.: *Biochim. Biophs. Acta* 447:328, 1976.

Giraldo and Beth (eds): The Role of Viruses in Human Cancer, Volume 1

Studies on the Epstein-Barr Virus

Vladimir Vonka, Ivan Hirsch, Alena Suchánková,
Beda Břicháček, Hana Závadová,
Lea Kuchlerová, and Otakar Šibl

Institute of Sera and Vaccines, and Bulovka Hospital, Prague, Czechoslovakia

Among all human viruses, the Epstein-Barr virus (EBV) is the one most directly associated with human cancer. This virus has been identified as the etiological agent in infectious mononucleosis (IM) and has been implicated in the pathogenesis of Burkitt lymphoma (BL) and nasopharyngeal carcinoma (NPC). This paper is concerned with two topics which are at present under investigation in our laboratory, namely the properties of the EBV-determined nuclear antigen (EBNA) and the nature of the association between EBV and tonsillar carcinoma (TC).

EBV-Related Soluble Antigen (SA) vs EBNA

EBNA or SA is one of the nonstructural polypeptides of EBV. It is present in all EBV genome-positive tumor cells, EBV genome-positive lymphoblastoid cell lines (LCL) derived from these tumors or from peripheral lymphocytes, and in cells transformed by EBV *in vitro*. Thus, the antigen seems to be a reliable indicator of the presence of EBV DNA and it is suspected that this substance plays an essential role in the process of cell transformation by EBV.

Probably the first report on the presence of a soluble antigen in LCL was published by Armstrong and his co-workers in 1965.[1] At that time, however, its relationship to EBV was not recognized. Three years later this soluble, complement-fixing antigen was identified independently in two laboratories as an EBV-associated but nonstructured antigen.[2-5] We based this conclusion on the following data (Table 1).

(a) About 50% of sera possessing antibodies against viral capsid antigen

(VCA) in the immunofluorescence test (IF) were reactive with SA in the complement-fixation (CF) test; all sera negative in the IF test were also negative in the CF test. This indicated that the presence of CF-SA antibody is conditioned by infection with EBV.

(b) The antibodies reactive with VCA and SA were clearly distinct. Some sera possessing high levels of VCA antibody were free of detectable SA antibody. The reactivity of human sera with VCA in the IF test could not be blocked by excess of SA. Moreover, SA could be separated from virus particles by physical means and there was no relationship between the virus particle content and the SA titer. In addition, the antigen was also detected in cell lines not producing EBV. The reactivity of human sera with SA from productive and nonproductive cell lines was the same, revealing an identity of the antigens or their major components.

Soon after the discovery of the SA we called attention to the late development of SA antibody in the course of EBV infection. The first indication of this was the virtual absence of SA antibody in a group of subjects aged 7–12 months, i.e., subjects most probably only recently infected with EBV (Table 2). While in older age groups 56% or more sera possessing VCA antibody contained SA antibody also, in the 7–12 months age group SA antibody was detected only exceptionally.[4]

To investigate this point more deeply, we examined sera from subjects suffering from IM, a disease considered to be the clinical manifestation of acute EBV infection.[6] As indicated in Table 3, practically all sera from 48 patients within the first month after the onset of the disease were VCA-antibody positive and SA-antibody negative. Thus, IM patients are very similar to children aged 6–12 months in this respect, and differ strikingly from older subjects with no history of IM, in whom the majority of VCA-positive sera are also reactive with SA.

Some of the IM patients were followed for a longer period of time. As indicated in Table 4, until the fifth month after the onset of disease, SA antibody was detected only rarely. Only after the seventh month did most of the subjects develop SA antibodies. These results were later confirmed by Henle and Henle[7] and some other groups. However, the

Table 1. Relationship Between EBV and the Soluble Antigen of Lymphoblastoid Cell Lines

1. The development of SA antibody is conditioned by the infection with EBV.
2. VCA and SA are different, because:
    a) some sera possessing high levels of VCA antibody are free of SA antibody;
    b) SA can be separated from virus particles by physical means;
    c) SA is present in nonproductive lymphoblastoid cell lines;
    d) VCA-IF reaction cannot be blocked by SA excess;
    e) the kinetics of VCA and SA antibody development are markedly different.

Table 2. Age Distribution of Complement-Fixing SA Antibody in Subjects
Positive for VCA Antibody in Indirect Immunofluorescence Test

Age Group	No. Sera Reactive with VCA	No. and Percentage of Sera Reactive with SA	
		No.	(%)
0- 6 m	11	6	(55)
7 12 m	45	1	(2)
13-24 m	22	17	(77)
5-10 yr	17	11	(65)
10-15 yr	39	25	(64)
22-25 yr	41	27	(65)

reasons for the late development of SA antibody remain unclear. Several
possibilities can be considered to explain this observation. It is possible
that the SA is a very weak antigen and that long-term stimulation is a
prerequisite for antibody development. It is also possible that SA-
containing (EBV-transforming) cells are rather few shortly after infection
and that their number increases later on. A further possibility is that the
SA antibody formed early in the course of infection is absorbed by the
antigen present at the cell surface or is blocked by excess antigen
released from the cells into the blood stream; the late decrease in antigen
production would then permit the achievement of detectable SA antibody.
Recently it has been shown that in ataxia teleangiectasia patients, SA
antibody is virtually absent in spite of elevated EBV VCA titers.[8] Since
these patients have a T-cell defect, it has been speculated that a late
immunological event conditioned by a normally functioning T-cell system
is responsible for this destruction of EBV genome-positive cells.

Table 3. Incidence of VCA and SA Antibodies in Sera Taken in Infectious
Mononucleosis Patients Within the First Month After Onset of Disease

Age Group (yr)	No. Patients	No. Sera Tested	No. Sera with Antibody	
			VCA	SA
2- 5	4	81	7	0
6-10	6	14	14	0
11-15	9	17	17	0
16-20	20	40	40	1
21-25	6	11	11	0
26-35	3	7	7	0
Total	48	97	96	1

Table 4. Incidence of VCA and SA Antibodies in Sera Taken in Infectious Mononucleosis Patients at Different Intervals After Onset of Disease

Interval after Onset	No. Sera	No. and Percentage of Sera with Antibody			
		VCA	(%)	SA	(%)
4- 5 m	7	7	(100)	1	(14)
7- 8 m	7	7	(100)	4	(57)
9-11 m	12	12	(100)	8	(67)
1 yr	15	15	(100)	9	(60)
2 yr	16	16	(100)	10	(62)
3 yr	12	12	(100)	7	(58)
4 yr	6	6	(100)	3	(50)
5 yr	8	8	(100)	5	(62)
6 yr	12	12	(100)	8	(67)
7 yr	7	7	(100)	7	(100)
8 yr	10	10	(100)	7	(70)
9 yr	8	8	(100)	7	(87)

In 1973, Reedman and Klein discovered the EBNA in the nuclei of EBV-transformed cells by using an anti-complement IF test (ACIF).[9] This finding is a landmark in the investigation of EBV. The antigen quickly developed into a reliable marker of EBV DNA presence in a cell. The first results suggested that this new antigen was related to the SA. In a subsequent study carried out in cooperation with Klein, we demonstrated identical reactivity of human sera with SA in the CF test and with EBNA in the ACIF test.[10]

The demonstration by Henle and Henle of late development of EBNA antibody in IM patients, which was in accord with our earlier findings on SA antibody, was another indication of the identity of SA and EBNA. A further piece of evidence supporting this conclusion was obtained by Lenoir et al.[11] They characterized SA in terms of sucrose gradient centrifugation, gel filtration and ion-exchange chromatography data. All fractions which contained CF activity also inhibited the ACIF reaction used to detect EBNA. Also the subsequent immunochemical studies that I shall mention in a while are consistent with the identity of SA and EBNA. Therefore, I shall stop speaking of SA and shall use only the term EBNA, as most people interested in the problem do today.

Characterization of EBNA

The most significant observation concerning the properties of EBNA is its recent characterization as a DNA-binding protein.[12] Simultaneously, the chromatography on calf thymus DNA-cellulose columns has been described as an efficient purification step in its isolation. It has also been reported by Ohno et al. (13) that a positive EBNA reaction can be reconstituted by adding an EBNA solution to EBNA-negative metaphase chromosomes. The latter observation was recently utilized in our laboratory for developing a microchromatography immunofluorescence test for EBNA.[14] Subsequently, the test has been utilized for investigating some EBNA properties, namely the specificity of its binding to DNA.[15] I would like to present some of these results now. The procedure used and different types of results obtained are shown in Table 5. Treatment of EBNA-positive Raji cells with a methanol-acetic acid mixture results in the removal of EBNA; an addition of an EBNA solution reconstitutes the positive reaction. However, if the fixed cells have been treated with DNAse prior to staining, the reaction is negative, indicating that EBNA links to the cell DNA. On the other hand, RNAse does not have a similar effect. Acetone treatment does not remove EBNA; but when acetone is followed by trypsin treatment, EBNA is removed and the reaction can be reconstituted. A similar effect is seen when acetone treatment is followed by 0.6 M NaCl. This treatment results in an increased brightness of the fluorescence and an increased percentage of positive nuclei, most probably owing to the elution of cell DNA-binding proteins competing with EBNA for binding sites.

When EBNA is added to the acid-fixed nuclei of any EBV-negative, i.e., EBNA-negative, cells, they are converted into an EBNA-positive state. The effect of pH on the rate of conversion is shown in Figure 1. In this, as in most subsequent experiments, the nuclei from Ramos cells, a lymphoblastoid EBV-negative cell line, have been used. It can be seen that peak conversion of Ramos nuclei to EBNA positivity was found to occur at pH 6.0. No positive reaction was observed at pH below 5.5 or above 8.5.

Table 5. EBNA Staining of Fixed Nuclei with EBV-Determined Complement-Fixing Antigen

Fixation of Raji Cells	Source of Soluble Antigens	EBNA Reaction
MEOH/HOAc	None	−
MEOH/HOAc	Raji	++
MEOH/HOAc, DNAse	Raji	−
MEOH/HOAc, RNAse	Raji	+
MEOH/HOAc	Ramos	−
Acetone	None	++
Acetone, trypsin	None	−
Acetone, trypsin	Raji	++
Acetone, 0.6 M NaCl	None	−
Acetone, 0.6 M NaCl	Raji	+++

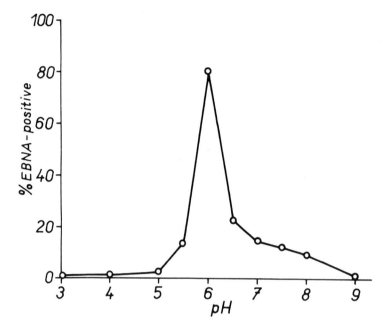

Figure 1. *In vitro* conversion of acid-fixed Ramos nuclei to EBNA positivity at different pH values.

As for ionic strength (Figure 2), Ramos cells were successfully converted to EBNA-positive forms when adsorption proceeded in the range of 0.05 to 0.15 NaCl. Negative results were obtained at a NaCl concentration level equal to or exceeding 0.2 M NaCl.

The next point of interest was whether a positive EBNA reaction of *in vitro*-converted nuclei can be abolished by treating smear preparations with increasing NaCl concentrations. Methanol-acetic acid-fixing nuclei from EBV genome-negative Ramos, EBV-positive Raji, and P3HR-1 cells were used in these experiments. Elution of EBNA was monitored by a decrease in the proportion of EBNA-positive nuclei. As can be seen in Figure 3, at NaCl concentrations equal to or lower than 0.1 M NaCl, essentially no antigen was eluted from any kind of nuclei, while complete elution of EBNA was observed in all three systems at 0.3 M NaCl. EBNA was completely eluted from Ramos nuclei with 0.2 M NaCl. However, some Raji and P3HR-1 nuclei remained positive at this concentration in all of three independent experiments.

These data suggested that: (a) The DNA-binding properties of EBNA can be studied by chromatography on fixed nuclei followed by the ACIF test. The obvious advantages of this method over chromatography on DNA-cellulose are its simplicity, the possibility of testing many samples

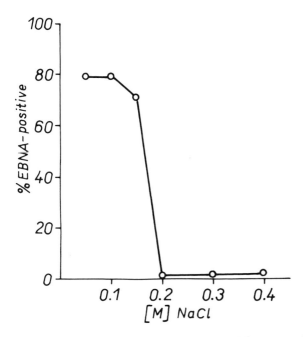

Figure 2. *In vitro* conversion of acid-fixed Ramos nuclei to EBNA positivity at different NaCl concentrations in adsorption buffer, pH 6.0.

simultaneously and, especially, the use of minimal amounts of material; (b) In analogy with the T antigen of SV40 (SV40 T), one may expect preferential binding sites to exist on homologous EBV DNA that will be missing in heterologous cellular DNA.

To investigate this point, another technique has been developed and utilized by Drs. Hirsch and Kuchlerová. The rationale of the experimental design was as follows: If there is a certain degree of specificity in the EBNA DNA reaction, some DNA species will be more capable of binding EBNA than others. Therefore, after incubation of EBNA with different DNA's, the amount of unbound EBNA would decrease proportionally to the frequency of such sequences in the particular DNA's. The amount of the unbound antigen could then be determined by its reaction with acid-fixed nuclei.

EBV DNA extracted from Raji cells superinfected with P3HR-1 virus and herpes simplex virus (HSV) DNA from human diploid cells infected with HSV-2 were purified by three cycles of CsCl gradient centrifugation. DNA's from three lymphoblastoid cell lines were extracted by phenol after SDS-pronase treatment and precipitated with ethanol. DNA dissolved in 0.1 × SSC was treated with RNAse. After further phenol-ethanol precipitation, it was dissolved in 0.1 × SSC. EBNA was partially

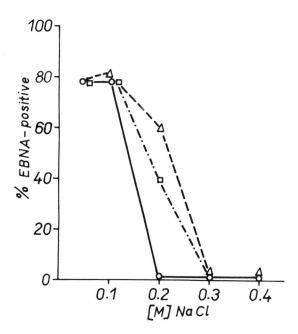

Figure 3. Elution of EBNA from *in vitro* converted nuclei. Acid-fixed Ramos (○), Raji (□) and P3HR-1 (△) nuclei were converted to an EBNA-positive state at pH 6.0 and 50 mM NaCl. The preparations were eluted with different NaCl concentration in adsorption buffer, pH 6.0.

purified on DNA-cellulose and was treated with various amounts of viral and cellular DNA at 4°C for 75 min. The reaction mixture consisted of a constant amount (20 μg) of EBNA-containing proteins and several different amounts of DNA (0.2-5.0 μg) in a total volume of 100 μl of the adsorption buffer (0.05 M NaCl, 10 mM sodium phosphate, pH 6.0, 1 mM mercaptoethanol and 5% glycerol). The amount of EBNA that failed to bind to DNA in solution was tested by the acid-fixed nuclear binding (AFNB) technique. Forty-five μl of the reaction mixture were added per fixed smear preparation of Ramos cells. After incubation at 20°C for 1 h in a humid box, the smears were washed and samples were tested for EBNA by ACIF.

Almost all Ramos nuclei were successfully converted to the EBNA-positive form by the addition of untreated EBNA. As can be seen in Figure 4, no positive reaction was observed when EBNA had been treated with more than 3 μg of EBV DNA or with approximately three times higher amounts of either Ramos or Raji or P3HR-1 cell DNA. This implies that EBV DNA was about three times more potent than any of the cellular DNA's in blocking *in vitro* conversion of Ramos nuclei to an EBNA-positive form. It can also be seen that the effect of the other viral DNA tested, HSV-2 DNA, was of an intermediate character.

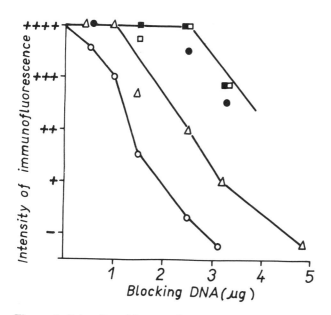

Figure 4. Intensity of immunofluorescence of the acid-fixed Ramos cell nuclei after treatment with 20 μg of DNA-cellulose purified EBNA treated with various amounts of DNAse, Symbols: O=EBV DNA, Δ=HSV DNA, ●=Ramos cell DNA, □=Raji cell DNA, ■=P3HR-1 cell DNA. The degrees of the ACIF reaction (+ to ++++) refer to the intensity of staining.

Two types of control experiments were set up. First, the DNAs were fragmented by sonication to a uniform size of 300–400 nucleotide-long chains in order to find out whether the differences in molecular weight were not responsible for the observed difference. The results indicated that the blocking potencies of EBV DNA and HSV-2 DNA were strongly decreased by the fragmentation, whereas no blocking activity at all was observed after treatment of EBNA with Raji DNA in the interval tested. Still, EBV DNA was clearly more effective, even under these conditions. In the second experiment the possibility that the presence of nicks in the herpesvirus DNA's had been associated with their elevated binding capacity was examined. Such nicks were artificially cut out in the cell DNA's by DNAse I. No visible increase in the blocking potency of DNA was observed after such treatment.

These data seem to suggest the presence of specific DNA-binding sequences for EBNA in EBV DNA. However, there is at least one reason that makes it difficult to link the observed differences entirely to the content of specific DNA-binding sequences. In the test, the EBNA preparations used were only partially purified. The impurities present could react in an unpredictable way with different DNA species and interfere with the binding of EBNA. In this series of experiments we failed to demonstrate a difference between the DNA's from EBV-positive and EBV-negative cells. However, the two observations need not necessarily be contradictory. In the present experiments, residual free EBNA was determined while in the previous tests, residual bound EBNA was monitored. It would apparently be more difficult for the free antigen, present in amounts insufficient to give an appreciable overall reaction, to find the rare specific sites (if they should really exist) than for small amounts of antigen attached to such sites to leave them.

Recently we have found that the technique is also applicable to the study of another nonstructural, DNA-binding, virus-induced polypeptide, namely the SV40 T. Immunofluorescence of Ramos nuclei treated with either SV40 T or EBNA is shown in Figure 5. It can be seen that both substances form a similar pattern of staining, including the staining of metaphase chromosomes. No fluorescence was seen either in preparations treated with DNAse prior to SV40 T or EBNA addition. These negative findings confirm the specificity of the reaction and demonstrate that both EBNA and SV40 T bind to DNA.

The results of some further experiments undertaken to specify the conditions of the reaction are summarized in Table 6. As can be seen, parallel tests with EBNA demonstrated a close similarity in the behavior of both substances. The significance of this observation is not understood at the moment. Despite this, it seems that the technique may provide a powerful means for further investigating T antigens, i.e., the DNA-binding properties of T antigens of ts mutants of SV40, the DNA-binding properties of the various T subcomponents, or the pattern of its binding to chromosomes.

EBV and Tonsillar Carcinoma (TC)

Now I shall switch to another problem which is more directly associated with the topic of this book, the nature of the association between EBV and carcinoma of the palatine tonsils. This is a continuation of a study, the initial phase of which we reported two years ago.[16]

As in NPC, tonsillar carcinoma (TC) originates in the Waldayer ring. This malignancy is much more common among Caucasians than NPC is. It accounts for 2–3% of all cancer cases and is second in frequency only to laryngeal carcinoma among neoplastic diseases of the upper respiratory tract.[17] TC is two to five times more frequent in males than females.[18,19] The disease is most common in the sixth and seventh decades. Histologically, the majority of the tumors are classified as squamous cell carcinomas, either keratinizing or nonkeratinizing. Some of them are heavily infiltrated by small lymphocytes; these used to be denoted as lymphoepitheliomas.[20]

In the past three years we examined sera from a group of 39 TC patients serologically, and some tumor biopsies were tested for the presence of EBV DNA. Table 7 summarizes the serological findings in 39 patients with TC and in 39 matched controls. It can be seen that antibodies to EBV-VCA, early antigen (EA) and EBNA were detected more frequently and in significantly higher titers in patients than in controls. Twenty serum pairs were also investigated for HSV, cytomegalovirus (CMV) and varicella-zoster virus (VZV) antibodies. No marked differences were revealed. This suggests a specificity of the EBV-TC association.

In a further analysis, antibody titers to the three EBV antigens were

Figure 5A-F. Immunofluorescence of SV40 T antigen and EBNA bound to acid-fixed nuclei of Ramos cells. **A.** T antigen from SV40 transformed hamster cells, serum pool from hamsters bearing tumors induced by SV40-transformed cells. The inset indicates metaphase chromosomes.($\times$ 1,040) **B.** The same as in A, reacted with normal hamster serum. **C.** The same as in A, but prior to T antigen addition, the acid-fixed nuclei had been treated with DNAse. **D.** EBNA, human serum containing EBNA antibody. The inset indicates metaphase chromosomes.($\times$ 1,040) **E.** The same as in D, but EBNA antibody negative human serum was used instead of EBNA antibody positive serum. **F.** The same as in D, but prior to EBNA addition, the acid-fixed nuclei had been treated with DNAse.

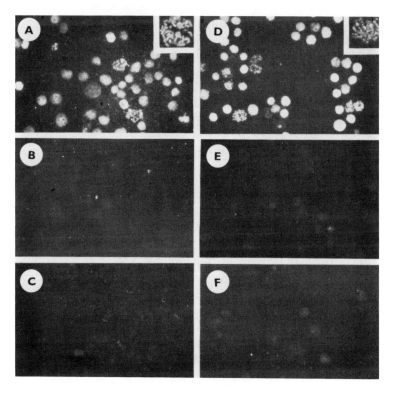

Table 6. Influence of pH and Ionic Strength on the Reactivity of SV40 T EBNA with Acid-Fixed Ramos Cell Nuclei

Ionic Strength	pH	Percentage of Cells Giving Positive Reaction After Treatment With	
		SV40 T	EBNA
0.05 M	5.5	$-$ [a]	$-$
	6.0	70-90	70-90
	6.5	>90	>90
	7.0	50	50
	7.5	$\pm$ [b]	$\pm$
0.2 M	5.5	$-$	$-$
	6.0	30-60	30-60
	6.5	$\pm$	$\pm$
	7.0	$-$	$-$
	7.5	$-$	$-$

[a] No fluorescence.
[b] Weak fluorescence in some cells.

compared between patient groups with different histological types of TC (Table 8). It is apparent that no significant differences were encountered between the groups. This is at variance with findings obtained in NPC, where the association with increased EBV antibody titers was limited to undifferentiated or poorly differentiated carcinomas.[21] Similarly, as indicated in Table 9, only moderate differences were encountered between TC patients with progressive disease and those in remission. This is also different from the findings in NPC or BL, in which a relationship between the clinical stage of the disease and the antibody status was demonstrated.[22]

Molecular hybridization tests have thus far been performed with eight biopsy specimens obtained from six patients. The results are summarized in Table 10. Of the materials tested, three specimens originating from three different patients were found positive. The results of reassociation kinetic tests with these three materials, as well as with positive and negative controls are illustrated in Figure 6. The demonstration of EBV DNA in the biopsy specimens seems to be compatible with the involvement of EBV in the pathogenesis of some TC, or may indicate, at least, that the relationship of EBV to some of these tumors is comparable to its relationship to NPC. At the moment, however, the possibility cannot be precluded that the EBV DNA detected in the three materials was present in nontumor cells and that it was unrelated to the tumor etiology. The information needed most is whether the virus genome in the EBV genome-positive TC—provided such cases are detected in the future—resides in cancer cells or in infiltrating lymphoid elements.

Table 7. Antibodies to Viral Capsid Antigen (VCA), Early Antigen (EA) and Nuclear Antigen (EBNA) of EBV in Tonsillar Carcinoma Patients and Matched Controls

Group	VCA			EA			EBNA		
	No. Test.	No. Pos.	GMT	No. Test.	No. Pos.	GMT	No. Test.	No. Pos.	GMT
Patients	39	39 (100%)	124 ($p < 0.001$)	39	30 (77%)	29 ($p < 0.001$)	38	34 (89%)	31 ($p < 0.001$)
Controls	39	36 (92%)	67	39	11 (28%)	8	34	16 (47%)	12

Table 8. EBV Antibodies in Patients with Different Histological Types of Tonsillar Carcinoma

Group	Histological Type	No. of Patients	EBV Antibodies								
			VCA			EA			EBNA		
			No. Pos.	(%)	GMT	No. Pos.	(%)	GMT	No. Pos.	(%)	GMT
1	Epidermoid carcinoma with keratinization	13	13	(100)	110	10	(77)	34	12	(92)	37
2	Epidermoid carcinoma without keratinization	10	10	(100)	85	7	(70)	20	9	(90)	30
3	Anaplastic carcinoma	8	8	(100)	160	7	(88)	37	6	(86)[a]	15
4	Transitory cell carcinoma	2	2	(100)	160	2	(100)	40	1	(50)	14
5	Unspecified	6	6	(100)	200	4	(67)	28	6	(100)	63

[a] One serum was not tested for EBNA antibodies.

Table 9. EBV Antibodies in Tonsillar Carcinoma Patients with Progressive Disease or in Remission

Group	VCA			EA			EBNA		
	No. Test.	No. Pos.	GMT	No. Test.	No. Pos.	GMT	No. Test.	No. Pos.	GMT
Progressive disease[a]	26	26 (100%)	139	26	20 (77%)	33	25	21 (84%)	27
Remission[b]	13	13 (100%)	98	13	10 (77%)	23	13	13 (100%)	40

[a] Blood taken before treatment or within one year after treatment or in patients with relapse of the disease.
[b] Blood taken one year to eight years after successful treatment.

Table 10. Serological and Molecular-Hybridization Tests in Tonsillar Carcinoma Patients

Patient No.	Sex	Age (yr)	Material (code)	Histological Diagnosis	EBV Antibodies			No. of EBV Genomes/Cell
					VCA	EA	EBNA	
1	f	64	TC9	Epidermoid Ca	160	80	160	3
2	m	25	TC11	without kerat.	160	10	40	4-5
				Anaplast. Ca				
3	f	57	TC13	Epidermoid Ca	160	20	40	15-18
				without kerat.				
4	f	53	TC14	Epidermoid Ca	320	<10	10	<2
				without kerat.				
			TC15[a]	Epidermoid Ca	NT	NT	NT	<2
				without kerat.				
5	m	81	TC16	Epidermoid Ca	NT	NT	NT	<2
				without kerat.				
6	m	77	TC17p[b]	Epidermoid Ca	80	10	10	<2
				without kerat.				
			TC17m[b]	Epidermoid Ca	80	10	10	<2
				without kerat.				

[a] Biopsy material obtained from patient No. 4, one year after the first surgery.

[b] Two materials obtained from patient No. 6; TC17p originated from the primary tumor, TC17m from a metastase localized in the ipsilateral cervical node (the surgery occurred at the same time).

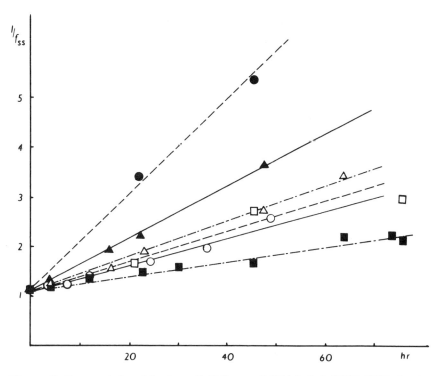

Figure 6. Reassociation kinetics of 13.7 ng of ³H-labeled EBV DNA in the presence of 0.3 mg DNA extracted from tonsillar carcinoma TC9 (○-○), TC11 (□---□) or TC13 (●-●) and 32.5 (△-△) or 65 ng (▲-▲) of Raji DNA supplemented with 267.5 μg or 235 μg of Ramos DNA, respectively. The negative control contained 13.7 ng of ³H-DNA and 0.3 ng of Ramos DNA (■---■).

Conclusion

On the whole, the hybridization results obtained from TC patients are different from those of NPC patients, suggesting in most instances of TC, a different relationship between EBV and the malignancy. Furthermore, it should also be realized that TC patients differ in that they have a high prevalence of EBV-EA antibodies compared to other diseases associated with increased EBV antibody titers (i.e., Hodgkin's disease). This may indicate that the EBV-TC association is also different from these conditions. Veltri et al.[23] demonstrated the presence of EBNA-positive cells in the tonsillar tissues of patients suffering from chronic exudative tonsillitis, and in a quite recent series of experiments, Dr. Břicháček of our laboratory demonstrated the presence of significant amounts of EBV DNA (2–3 genome equivalents per cell) in four out of 35 such materials examined. One can speculate that cells possessing markers of EBV-transformed cells are present quite frequently in tonsillar tissues, and that the proliferation of such cell clones is supported by hyperplastic changes associated with either chronic tonsillitis or tumor development. This condition may then be reflected by increased EBV antibody titers.

References

1. Armstrong, D., Henle, G., and Henle, W.: *J. Bacteriol.* 91:1257, 1966.
2. Pope, J.H., Horne, M.K., and Wetters, E.J.: *Nature* 222:186, 1969.
3. Vonka, V., Porter, D.D., McCombs, R.M., and Benyesh-Melnick, M.: *Bact. Proc.* 10:154, 1969.
4. Vonka, V., Benyesh-Melnick, M., and McCombs, R.M.: *J. Natl. Cancer Inst.* 44:865, 1970.
5. Vonka, V., Benyesh-Melnick, M., Lewis, R.T., and Wimberly, I.: *Arch. Ges. Virusforsch.* 31:113, 1970.
6. Vonka, V., Vlčková, I., Závadová, H., Kouba, K., Lazovská, J., and Duben, J.: *Int. J. Cancer* 9:529, 1972.
7. Henle, G., Henle, W., and Horwitz, C.A.: *J. Infect. Dis.* 130:231, 1974.
8. Berkel, A.I., Henle, W., Henle, G., Klein, G., Ersoy, F., and Sanai, O.: *Clin. Exp. Immunol.* 35:196, 1979.
9. Reedman, B.M. and Klein, G.: *Int. J. Cancer* 11:499, 1973.
10. Klein, G. and Vonka, V.: *J. Natl. Cancer Inst.* 53:1645, 1974.
11. Lenoir, G., Berthelon, M.C., Favre, M.C., and de-Thé, G.: *J. Virol.* 17:672, 1975.
12. Luka, J., Siegert, W., and Klein, G.: *J. Virol.* 22:1, 1977.
13. Ohno, S., Luka, J., Lindahl, T., and Klein, G.: *Proc. Natl. Acad. Sci. USA* 74:227, 1977.
14. Hirsch, I., Suchánková, A., Závadová, H., and Vonka, V.: *Int. J. Cancer* 22:535, 1978.
15. Hirsch, I., Kuchlerová, L., Břicháček, B., Suchánková, A., and Vonka, V.: *J. Gen. Virol.* 1980, (in press).
16. Vonka, V., Šibl, O., Suchánková, A., Simonová, I., and Závadová, H.: *Int. J. Cancer* 19:456, 1977.
17. Scanlon, P.W., Gee, V.R., Erich, J.B., Williams, H.L., and Woolner, L.B.: *Amer. J. Roentgenol.* 80:781, 1958.
18. Wang, C.C.: *Radiology* 104:667, 1972.
19. Fletcher, G.H. and Lindberg, R.D.: *Amer. J. Roentgenol.* 96:574, 1966.
20. Matar, J.H. and McCarten, A.B.: *Amer. J. Roentgenol.* 117:517, 1973.
21. Huang, D.P., Ho, J.H.C., Henle, W., Henle, G., Saw, D., and Lui, H.: *Int. J. Cancer* 22:266, 1978.
22. Henle, W., Ho, M.C., Henle, G., and Kwan, H.C.: *J. Natl. Cancer Inst.* 51:361, 1973.
23. Veltri, R., McClung, J., and Sprinkle, P.: *J. Gen. Virol.* 32:455, 1976.

Multifactorial Etiology of Epstein-Barr Virus-Related Malignancies

Guy de-Thé

CNRS–Faculty of Medicine Alexis Carrel, Lyon, France

Since Virchow, in the late nineteenth century, cancer has been considered a cellular disease, and therefore most of the research on cancer has been focused on trying to uncover the fundamental cause of the disease at the cellular level, that is the basic mechanism by which a normal cell becomes malignant and grows as a clinical tumor. *In vitro* as well as *in vivo*, one can obtain cellular transformation by chemical, physical and biological agents (i.e., viruses). The field of viral oncology has greatly developed in the last twenty-five years and most leukemias and sarcomas of many vertebrate species have been found associated with RNA tumor viruses. *In vitro*, not only RNA tumor viruses, but small and large DNA viruses as well, can induce transformation at the cellular level; and molecular virologists have succeeded in defining the gene and the corresponding polypeptide which causes cellular transformation. But such a polypeptide is eventually found in normal cells and therefore part of the mystery remains as to the exact origin of transformation at the cellular level and of tumor growth at the host level. In parallel, the epidemiologists in the last ten years have accumulated evidence suggesting the crucial role of the environment in the development of human cancers, which raised the theoretical possibility of preventing some cancers before understanding the basic mechanism which presides at their birth and development.

The association between the Epstein-Barr virus (EBV) and two human tumors, namely Burkitt's lymphoma (BL) and nasopharyngeal carcinoma (NPC), represents a good example of both fields, inasmuch as it may show that a virus could act not as the necessary and sufficient factor for a disease, but as an environmental risk factor. This notion is difficult to accept for virologists who feel that since Pasteur, viruses have grown to be the necessary and often sufficient factors for so many acute to slow-developing disease, that they may also be at the origin of many types of cancers. The question remains open. After discussing the multistep carcinogenesis process, we shall review the actual knowledge of the relationship between EBV in the etiology and control of both BL and NPC, concluding with a discussion of the possible means of intervention against EBV to better control these malignancies.

Multistep Carcinogenesis

Chemical oncologists have proposed different models for carcinogenesis, all implying a succession of inheritable changes at the cellular level. Recently, Richard Peto[1] proposed that all carcinomas known to be caused by environmental factors develop as the result of a multistage process involving four to six independent stages. The essence of his hypothesis was that cancer arises from the proliferation of a clone derived from a single cell which has undergone all the necessary changes and then can begin to proliferate indefinitely. Forty years before Peto, Beremblum[2] proposed the now-classical, two-stage model of initiation-promotion for skin carcinogenesis. He suggested that specific mutations at the cellular level were responsible for the "initiation" leading to a population of "dormant tumor cells." The "promotion" would represent the encouragement of such dormant tumor cells to become free malignant cells. Promotion and initiation were found to be caused by two different classes of chemicals. Cocarcinogenesis, another notion proposed even earlier by Beremblum,[3] should, according to him, be restricted to substances not directly involved in the carcinogenic process, but which have a permissive influence on any step leading to tumor growth. As an example of cocarcinogenic agents, he proposed enzymes involved in the conversion of "precarcinogens" into "ultimate" carcinogens, or hormones which act on immature glandular structures of the mammary gland modifying the response to the specific mammary tumor agent.

EBV in the Etiology of BL

Three etiological factors are believed to play a role in the pathogenesis of BL: the herpes EBV, malaria, and chromosomal anomalies. We shall discuss them in turn, showing that the multistage carcinogenesis model, which was restrictively proposed for carcinomas, seems to be well applicable to this lymphoma.

Epstein-Barr Virus

The association between EBV and BL lies in the regular presence of viral markers [EBV DNA and EBV-determined nuclear antigens (EBNA)] in the tumor cells and the high antibody profile against EBV antigens in patients with BL.[4] The Ugandan prospective study[5] conducted at the International Agency for Research on Cancer (IARC) between 1968 and 1978 has produced epidemiological evidence of a causal relationship between BL and long-standing high titers of EBV antibody directed against the viral capsid antigen (VCA) in the children who eventually develop the disease. In this seroepidemiological study, which involved 42,000 children aged zero to eight years, children with VCA titers two dilutions higher than the mean for the corresponding age and sex-matched general population were shown to have an increased relative risk of developing BL of 30-fold that of the general population. Such high VCA titers are believed to reflect a particularly severe primary infection by the virus in candidate children, related either to an infection at a very early age, or to a massive simultaneous infection by malaria. That people living in endemic BL areas suffer from particularly heavy EBV infection early in life was shown by the results of seroepidemiological surveys in the general population of Uganda and for comparison in Hong Kong, Singapore and Nancy in France.[6] During the second year of life, the geometrical mean titers of VCA antibodies in the general population of Ugandan children reached very high levels comparable to that of BL patients. As this was not observed in the Far East, or in Europe, it was postulated that very early infection by EBV was related to BL development.[7] Thus a very severe primary infection by EBV can be compared to an "initiating" process in the sense given by Beremblum, i.e., a mutational, inheritable cellular change resulting in a "transformed B lymphocyte" population. We know that *in vitro* infection of B lymphocytes by EBV results in immortalization and that such immortalized cells are not tumors, thus rendering further steps necessary to have a clone of malignant cells. BL has a monoclonal origin, whereas such a "transformed" cell population has a polyclonal origin, as in the case of infectious mononucleosis. The initiation by early EBV infection appears to occur in about 10% to 15% of the children in Uganda who were found to have VCA titers similar to those of BL candidates, and BL develops in about one out of 1,000 children born in equatorial Africa. Another critical event might relate to hyperendemic malaria as discussed in the following section.

Malaria

It was Dalldorf et al.[8] and Burkitt[9] who stressed that the peculiar geographic distribution of BL fitted best with that of holoendemic malaria. Malaria surveys, carried out by the IARC within the Ugandan prospective study and in the North Mara district of Tanzania, confirmed the association between high incidence of BL and heavy malaria burden: the BL high-risk areas exhibited higher parasitemia levels and higher antibody titers to *Plasmodium falciparum* antigens that BL-free areas close by.[10-12] There are many theoretical ways in which malaria could favor BL development. The first relates to congenital malaria, known to exist in equatorial Africa, and which may create conditions favoring transplacental EBV infection of the fetus; but no data are yet available to support such a hypothesis.[7] The second possibility refers to a simultaneous heavy malaria and primary EBV infection resulting in a very large population of EBV-transformed lymphocytes which, under an altered cell-mediated immune control mechanism, could lead to tumor growth in subsequent years, as suggested by O'Conor.[13] A third possibility raised by the work of Greenwood and Vick[14] is that malaria parasites contain a nonspecific B-cell mitogen as well as an antigen able to elicit a specific cell-mediated response to malaria. More recently, Greenwood et al.[15] observed that *Plasmodium falciparum* antigen could stimulate *in vitro* both T and B lymphocytes from malaria immune and malaria nonimmune donors, suggesting the existence of T-cell as well as B-cell mitogens. The respective role of T- or B-cell function in the hypergammaglobulinemia associated with malaria infection and the stimulation of abnormal growth of B lymphocytes remains to be determined; and the role of the natural killer (NK) cells particularly should be investigated.

Cytogenetic Abnormalities

The next critical step in BL pathogenesis might result from specific cytogenetic mutations directly responsible for the development of a malignant clone. The observations of Malonov and Malonova,[16] confirmed by Jarvis et al.[17] and Zech et al.,[18] that an 8q−; 14q+ translocation was regularly observed in BL cells, urged Klein[19] to propose that random Darwinian chromosomal alteration might result in this selective change (8-14 translocation) due to growth advantages to the cellular clone that carries it. A selection process of random, genetic alteration would be responsible for a cytogenetic convergence causing the birth of a malignant clone.

BL thus becomes an ideal model for the multistage carcinogenesis model as proposed by Peto[1] where at least three independent changes would lead to tumor growth. The first would be an initiating change brought about by a very early and massive EBV infection leading to a large population of EBV-transformed B lymphocytes, which in a second step suffers a high mitogenic activity under the constant stimulation of a malaria burden. The third and last event, according to Klein,[19] would be a chromosome alteration which would bring the final mutation necessary for the cancerous stage.

That the last step in BL carcinogenesis occurs quite suddenly is well known from the clinicians. Lachet et al.[20] analyzed all available epidemiological data related to BL incidence in the West Nile district of Uganda and concluded that a precipitating event was most probably taking place six to 18 months prior to the diagnosis of the disease. Whether such a determining event is related to sudden chromosomal changes is not yet known.

Control of BL

The ultimate aim of epidemiology is the prevention of disease; and one could speculate upon the best possible means for controlling BL. Theoretically, any successful intervention against any of the three steps leading to BL development described above should succeed in preventing the disease. The intervention by an EBV vaccine—which would have to be around the time of birth—might be efficient but very difficult, if not practically impossible, to implement. Epstein has proposed that the development of an EBV vaccine is the best means of obtaining final proof of the oncogenic potential of EBV in humans beings.[21] But it seems rather difficult to propose to vaccinate an entire population at birth against a disease which kills ''only'' one out of 1,000 children, while, at the same time, malaria kills more than 300 of those between zero and five years of age. His views, however, are much more feasible for prevention of infectious mononucleosis, known to be associated with an increased risk of developing Hodgkin's-type lymphoma.[22] On the other hand, the changes which can be expected to take place in hygienic standards during the socioeconomic development of equatorial Africa might bring some delay in the mean age of primary infection by EBV, and thus eliminate the critical conditions leading to an initiation process as discussed above.

Intervention against malaria appears to be much easier to implement than intervention against EBV. The IARC,[11] together with the Tanzanian government, has implemented a malaria intervention program in the North Mara district where 90,000 children aged zero to ten years are being given chloroquine tablets twice a month. The aim of this program is to see if BL will decrease in incidence after a few years, which would establish the causal relationship between holoendemic malaria and BL. The results of the project are being hampered, however, by an unexpected fall in the incidence of BL in that area just prior to the implementation of the chloroquine distribution and more recently by a resistance to chloroquine of the *Plasmodium falciparum*.[12]

Burkitt-Type Lymphoma Not Related to EBV

That EBV is not a necessary factor in the development of all Burkitt-type lymphoma cases is an important matter for consideration. In the Ugandan prospective study,[5] one patient, a five-year-old boy, who exhibited BL both clinically and histopathologically, had a low VCA titer 18 months prior to tumor onset, his VCA titer remaining at the same level after tumor growth. Furthermore, there were no detectable viral markers in his tumor cells (no EBNA or viral genomes). EBV-free BL cases are exceptional in equatorial areas, whereas in temperate climates it is the rule. Ziegler et al.,[23] studying 20 American BL cases, observed that in only two of them were there detectable viral markers in the tumor cells and an EBV serological profile in five, which could be compared to those of African cases. International studies are actually being implemented to evaluate the proportion of EBV-associated, BL-type lymphomas in temperate climates. These EBV-free BL lymphomas suggest that the initiation of the multistep carcinogenesis process can be caused by different agents. In equatorial Africa this appears to be due to an early EBV infection, whereas in temperate climates we do not yet have any clues as to the origin of such initiation, nor to the promoting factors involved.

Nasopharyngeal EBV in the Etiology and Control of Nasopharyngeal Carcinoma (NPC)

In contrast to the situation of BL, where only the equatorial type is regularly associated with EBV, the level of association between EBV and the undifferentiated carcinomas of the nasopharynx (NPC) is high, consistent and specific the world over. Among the high EBV-specific antibody profiles observed in patients with NPC, antibodies to early antigens (EA-D) in both the IgG and IgA classes appear to be the most critical serological markers with diagnostic and prognostic value for clinicians. It is very interesting to note that whereas the ratio between the geometrical mean titers of antibodies to VCA in patients with NPC and those of patients with other tumors are very similar, in different geographical areas the absolute level of antibodies to VCA in both groups of patients varies from one geographical area to another, possibly reflecting differences in socioeconomical environment.[24] Viral makers (EBV genomes and EBNA) are regularly found in undifferentiated carcinomas of the nasopharynx all around the world, in high, intermediate and low-risk areas for the disease.[25-27] Such a high, consistent and specific association between a virus and a cancer strongly favors, although does not prove, a causal relationship. The situation would be much further enlightened if we knew the EBV profile of the NPC candidates prior to tumor onset, as we have been able to achieve for BL. Thanks to our colleagues in the People's Republic of China, we now have new important information. They have carried out, in the autonomous region of the Guangsi province, epidemiological surveys aimed at assessing the usefulness of serum IgA VCA levels to detect NPC. In mid-1978, they were able to collect blood from and to test for IgA in more than 56,000 individuals aged 30 years or more from the Zangwu county of the Guangsi autonomous region. Selecting the highest IgA VCA titer, they were able to detect 18 new NPC cases, seven of them at a very early stage of the disease.[28] These most interesting results indicate that a high IgA VCA level can be used for an efficient and early detection, allowing a better and a more economical treatment. What such a study does not indicate is how long before clinical onset such an IgA profile is present and whether a high IgA profile could help to define individuals at highest risk for this cancer, years prior to its development. These important questions have been partially answered by the study of Ho et al.[29] on three NPC patients who emerged from a normal population survey which we carried out together in the early 1970's in Hong Kong. It was found that two of three patients had high IgA VCA titers (1:80, 1:320, respectively) three to five years prior to onset of tumors, while the third patient, who was bled five years before the diagnosis of cancer, showed a titer of 20. Ninety-five percent of sex and age-matched controls had no IgA VCA antibodies, while only 5% of the general population had low levels of IgA VCA with titers of 1:10. The ongoing population surveys in the People's Republic of China should provide most important information on large numbers of individuals, years prior to tumor onset.

On the other hand, our Chinese colleagues during these seroepidemiological population surveys were also able to detect lesions of the nasopharynx, which they consider as precancerous and which include nodular, follicular and adenoid hyperplasia of the nasopharynx, as well as leukoplasia and metaplasia. Although only some of those may represent preneoplastic lesions, it is most important to evaluate them for their relation to a chronic EBV infection, as it may well be possible that high IgA VCA secretion reflects a chronic infection of the nasopharynx by EBV and relates to one of the conditions described above. If this is the case and if NPC is accompanied by or due to reactivation of an EBV infection of the nasopharynx, the theoretical possibility of an intervention against such chronic or reactivated lesion of the nasopharynx might lead to the prevention of tumor development. The study of these precancerous lesions and the assessment of the possibility of intervention against chronic infection by EBV should become a research priority toward a better understanding and control of this cancer. The use of a vaccine to control NPC is doubtful, and specific antiviral chemotherapy might prove to be very useful to control pretumorous lesions. Once NPC has developed, proviral chemotherapy might help in bringing about tumor cell lysis, but this is still far out of reach.

Genetic and Chemical Environmental Factors in NPC Etiology

Genetic factors are most probably involved in NPC causation, and Simons et al.[30] have defined an HL-A profile associated with NPC among the Chinese. The possible impact of chemical carcinogens in the environment in NPC causation is a current subject of wide concern, with the possibility of nitrosamines present in salted fish playing an important role, as repeatedly stressed by Ho.[29,31] Intervention against an environmental factor closely linked to the life-style of the Cantonese will certainly meet strong resistance, but Ho is already engaged in a public information campaign to prevent weaning babies from being fed with salted fish in Hong Kong.

Nasopharyngeal carcinoma, as well as BL, appear multifactorial in origin. The role of EBV might take place at a late step of carcinogenesis in NPC, thus increasing the hope of successful intervention. It is obvious that only the pursuing of multidisciplinary studies on this tumor will bring to light new pieces of information regarding the genetic and environmental factors associated with this cancer. The investigation of NPC in adolescents, as observed in intermediate risk areas of North and East Africa, may well prove to be very rewarding since the latent period between the oncogenic events and tumor growth is much more reduced than in the adult case observed in the Far East.

Summary

The multifactorial and multistep carcinogenesis hypothesis which has been proposed for carcinoma fits quite well with Burkitt's lymphoma in which three causal factors are known today. It is proposed that an early EBV infection acts as an "initiating" event, whereas holoendemic malaria would "promote" the next step toward development of a tumorous cellular clone caused by specific cytogenetic changes. In temperate climates, Burkitt-type lymphomas are rarely associated with EBV, and never with malaria, but regularly with the same chromosomal translocation as observed in African BL. In nasopharyngeal carcinoma, the association with EBV is high, consistent and specific the world over. The recent results from seroepidemiological population surveys in the People's Republic of China have shown that high IgA VCA titers can be used for early and massive detection of tumors and that precancerous lesions of the nasopharynx associated with such IgA levels might exist.

The control of EBV-related malignancies should be made by different approaches. In BL, intervention against malaria is much easier, more logical and more feasible than an intervention against EBV. In NPC, if

EBV reactivation or chronic infection of the nasopharynx is directly linked to a late step in carcinogenesis, then an antiviral intervention might be successful. It is proposed that chemotherapy against herpesviruses might help to better control this cancer.

References

1. Peto, R.: In: *Origins of Human Cancer, Cold Spring Harbor Conferences on Cell Proliferation, Vol. 4,* H.H. Hiatt, J.D. Watson, and J.A. Winster (eds.), Cold Spring Harbor Laboratory, Cold Spring Harbor, New York, 1977, p. 1403.

2. Beremblum, I.: *Cancer Res.* 1:807, 1940.

3. Beremblum, I.: *J. Pathol. Bacteriol.* 32:425, 1979.

4. De-Thé, G.: *Epidemiol. Reviews* 1:32, 1979.

5. De-Thé, G., Geser, A., Day, N.E., Tukei, P.M., Williams, E.H., Beri, D.P., Smith, P.G., Dean, A.G., Bornkamm, G.W., Feorino, R., and Henle, W.: *Nature* 274:756, 1978.

6. De-Thé, G., Day, N.E., Geser, A., Lavoué, M.F., Ho, J.H.C., Simons, M.J., Sohier, R., Tukei, P.M., Vonka, V., and Zavadova, H.: In: *Oncogenesis and Herpesviruses II, Part 2,* IARC Scientific Publications No. 11, G. de-Theé, M.A. Epstein and H. zur Hausen (eds.), International Agency for Research on Cancer, Lyon, 1975, p. 3.

7. De-Thé, G.: *Lancet* 1:335, 1977.

8. Dalldorf, G., Linsell, C.A., Barnhart, F.E., and Martyn, R.: *Perspect. Biol. Med.* 7:435, 1964.

9. Burkitt, D.P.: *J. Natl. Cancer Inst.* 42:19, 1969.

10. IARC, Annual Report, International Agency for Research on Cancer, Lyon, 1976.

11. IARC, Annual Report, International Agency for Research on Cancer, Lyon, 1977.

12. IARC, Annual Report, International Agency for Research on Cancer, Lyon, 1978.

13. O'Conor, G.T.: *Am. J. Med.* 48:279, 1970.

14. Greenwood, B.M. and Vick, R.: *Nature* 257:592, 1975.

15. Greenwood, B.M., Oduloju, A.J., and Plattis-Mills, T.A.E.: *Trans. R. Soc. Trop. Med. Hyg.* 73:178, 1979.

16. Manolov, G. and Manolova, Y.: *Nature* 237:33, 1972.

17. Jarvis, J.E., Ball, G., and Rickinson, A.B.: *Int. J. Cancer* 14:716, 1974.

18. Zech, L., Haglund, H., and Nilsson, K.: *Int. J. Cancer* 17:47, 1976.

19. Klein, G.: *Proc. Natl. Acad. Sci. USA* 76:2442, 1979.

20. Lachet, B., Day, N.E., De-Thé, G., and Dufour, J.: *Med. Biol. Environ.* 5:60, 1977.

21. Epstein, M.A.: *Cancer Res.* 36:711, 1976.

22. Munoz, N., Davidson, R.J.L., Witthoff, B., Ericsson, J.E., and De-Thé, G.: *Int. J. Cancer* 22:10, 1978.

23. Ziegler, J.L., Andersson, M., Klein, G., and Henle, W.: *Int. J. Cancer* 17:701, 1976.

24. De-Thé, G., Lavoué, M.F., and Muenz, L.: In: *Nasopharyngeal Carcinoma: Etiology and Control,* IARC Scientific Publications No. 20, G. de-Thé and Y. Ito (eds.), International Agency for Research on Cancer, Lyon, 1978, p. 471.

25. Wolf, H., zur Hausen, H., and Becker, Y.: *Nature* 244:245, 1973.

26. Desgranges, C., Wolf, H., De-Thé, G., Shanmugaratnam, K., Cammoun, N., Ellouz, R., Klein, G., Lennert, K., Munoz, N., and zur Hausen, H.: *Int. J. Cancer* 16:7, 1975.

27. Andersson-Anvret, M., Forsby, N., Klein, G., Henle, W., and Biölund, A.: *Int. J. Cancer* 23:762, 1979.

28. Zeng, Y., Liu, Y., Liu, C., Chen, S., Wei, J., Zhu, J., and Zai, H.: *Intervirology,* 1980 (in press).

29. Ho, J.H.C.: *Int. J. Radiat. Oncol. Biol. Phys.* 4:181, 1978.

30. Simons, M.J., Chan, S.H., Wee, G.B., Shanmugaratnam, K., Goh, E.H., Ho, J.H.C., Chan, J.C.W., Darnalingam, S., Prasad, V., Betuel, H., Day, N.E., and De-Thé, G.: In: *Nasopharyngeal Carcinoma: Etiology and Control,* IARC Scientific Publications No. 20, G. de-Thé and Y. Ito (eds.), International Agency for Research on Cancer, Lyon, 1978, p. 271.

31. Ho, J.H.C.: *J. R. Coll. Surg. Edinb.* 20:223, 1975

Giraldo and Beth (eds): The Role of Viruses in Human Cancer, Volume 1

The Relationship of Cytomegalovirus to Certain Human Cancers, Particularly to Kaposi's Sarcoma

Gaetano Giraldo and Elke Beth

Memorial Sloan-Kettering Cancer Center, New York, New York
Present address: Tufts-New England Medical Center, Boston, Massachusetts

If complex mechanisms (latency, reactivation and possibly cellular transformation) occur *in vivo* after cytomegalovirus (CMV) infection in man, a closer review of the sites of virus infection is inevitable, as well as consideration of whether cancers deriving at those same sites would not be the most appropriate types to be studied.

A prominent site for CMV replication has been repeatedly identified in the salivary gland. It has been reported to occur in the salivary glands in 10-32% of autopsies performed on infants and young children, regardless of the causes of death.[1] The gastrointestinal tract represents another site of CMV infection[2] which has recently prompted Huang and Roche to analyze by cRNA-DNA hybridization whether a CMV association with colon carcinoma could be established[3].

CMV infections of the female genital tract are common during pregnancy and probably represent an important source of neonatal infection. Furthermore, with the recognition of CMV infections in the cervix and secretion of the virus in semen, venereal acquisition and transmission has been established.[4,5] Therefore, cancers of the male and female tract would be selected groups for a study of CMV association. Antibodies to CMV have been detected more often in sera of women with atypia than in sera of women with other cervical disorders or in sera of healthy controls.[6] Growing awareness of its potential role in human cancer also derives from the recent isolation of CMV from cell cultures of two cervical carcinoma biopsies.[7] It is known that certain human CMV strains can induce oncogenic transformation of hamster embryo fibroblast cells[8] and can stimulate the synthesis of host cell DNA and RNA.[9] These properties are commonly associated with oncogenic viruses. Furthermore, a human genital isolate of cytomegalovirus (Mj) was shown to have transformed human embryonic lung cells *in vitro*. These cells produce tumors when injected into athymic nude mice.[10,11] Geder and Rapp[12] demonstrated that intranuclear CMV-related antigens can be detected in CMV-transformed human cells by the anti-complement immunofluorescent (ACIF) test. Immune sera from patients with prostatic cancer, or from individuals in the convalescent phase of an acute CMV infection who had a CMV antibody titer greater than 1:64, demonstrated this nuclear reactivity. In another study by Sanford et al.,[13] it was reported that two cell lines which derived from tissue from human prostatic carcinoma survived more than 20 passages *in vitro* and demonstrated CMV-specific membrane antigens. Significant humoral antibody titers against CMV and cell-mediated lymphocytotoxicity against these transformed cells were demonstrated in patients with prostatic carcinoma and other urinary tract tumors. All of this evidence indicates that an association between CMV and human prostatic cancer may be more than coincidental.

The purpose of this communication will be to review data, mainly accumulated in our laboratory over the past eight years, on another malignancy, Kaposi's sarcoma (KS), and its association with CMV. This malignancy appeared to us as an interesting model to be investigated for a possible viral involvement due to various epidemiological, biological and clinical features reminiscent of Burkitt's lymphoma (BL) in Africa,[14,15] a neoplasia clearly associated with a herpesvirus, the Epstein-Barr virus (EBV).[16] Consequently, we established a world-wide collaborative effort with African Cancer Centers in Uganda, Cameroon, Senegal, Morocco, Tunisia and Algeria, which represent high and moderate KS incidence areas. Furthermore, KS patients from low-incidence areas in France and the United States were also included.

Herpesvirus-Related Serologic Analyses of KS Patients

Viral antibody profiles were determined on a total of 176 KS patients. Control sera were derived from healthy subjects matched by age, sex (± 5 years), race, geographic location and socioeconomic status. A second control group consisted of serum samples from age- and sex-matched melanoma patients. Antibodies to CMV, herpes simplex virus type 1 and type 2 (HSV-1, HSV-2) were titrated by complement fixation (CF) and indirect hemagglutination (IHA). The indirect immunofluorescence (IIF) test was applied for the titration of antibodies to viral capsid antigens (VCA) of EBV and the ACIF for EBV-determined nuclear antigen (EBNA). The prominent finding of two comprehensive analyses was the demonstration of a specific serologic association of CMV with European and American KS patients (Figures 1 and 2).[17,18] All KS sera contained CMV antibodies and had significantly higher geometric mean titers (GMT) (6-16 times by CF or IHA, respectively) than those of the matched control groups. In contrast to the serologic evidence for an association of CMV with KS, such evidence of disease-virus association was not forthcoming for HSV-1, HSV-2 and EBV. However, the situation for African KS was somewhat different; all Africans, whether KS patients, their family members, or healthy non-related adults had antibodies to CMV, HSV-1, HSV-2 and EBV with significantly higher GMT to CMV, HSV-1 and HSV-2, if one compares the African control group with the American healthy adults. Viral infection, along with reinfection and/or reactivation resulting in specific immune responses,[19] must therefore occur more frequently in equatorial Africans. Therefore, although

Figure 1. Distribution of anti-CMV (K9V) titers in 16 European Kaposi's sarcoma (EKS) patients compared to titers of 33 European healthy adult controls (EC). IHA = indirect hemagglutination; CF = complement fixation test; open bars = low titers; hatched bars = high titers.

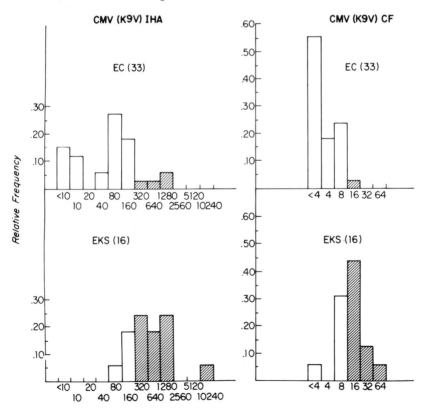

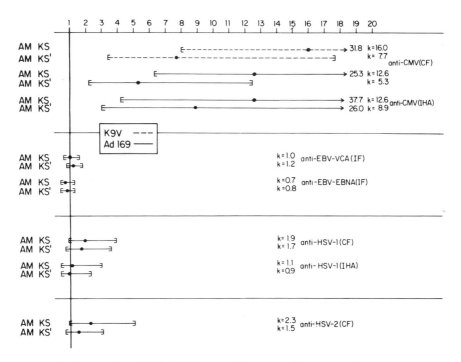

Figure 2. Comparison, by k-fold increase in geometric mean and 95% confidence limit, of anti-CMV (K9V and Ad169), anti-EBV, anti-HSV-1 and anti-HSV-2 titers of American KS over controls. AM KS = American KS vs American healthy adults; AM KS′ = American KS vs American melanomas; CF = complement fixation; IHA = indirect hemagglutination test; IF = immunofluorescence test.

the GMT to CMV of African KS patients were similar to the GMT of the American KS group, their significance cannot be demonstrated due to a high background of CMV infections in the control groups. In reference to occurrence of antibodies to HSV-2,[20] similar observations were made previously on sera from African cervical cancer patients and their controls.

Establishment of Reference HV-Antigenic Systems

Conforming to the terminology and operational criteria established for the molecular biology of phages, herpesvirus (HV)-coded proteins belonging to three main classes[21] can be classified as: (a) the *"immediate-early" gene products* [α-infectious cell polypeptides (ICP)] which are the first to be synthesized and demonstrable in the infected cells in which protein synthesis has been inhibited from the time of infection, as by cycloheximide; (b) *"early" gene products* (β ICP) which are synthesized before onset of viral DNA synthesis; and (c) *"late" gene products* (γ ICP) which are synthesized only after initiation of viral DNA synthesis and include primarily the structural proteins of the virions. Expression of these latter genes requires viral DNA replication and can be almost completely blocked in the presence of DNA synthesis inhibitors like Ara C. In papovavirus,[22] adenovirus,[23] and EBV[24,25] systems, the "late" antigens do not appear to be essential for the cell transformation process. Therefore, the search for the proteins encoded in the viral genome which trigger the transformation process must be restricted to the products of the early genes, i.e., T antigens in the papovavirus system. In HV systems, with the exception of EBV, the expression of early products in transformed cells has been difficult to detect, most likely due to the lack of specific probes.

Therefore, we initially developed new antigenic reference systems in CMV, HSV-1 and HSV-2 infected cell cultures of either human skin fibroblasts or HEp-2 cells (Table 1).[26,27] [The α and β polypeptides will be referred to from now on as immediate early antigens (IEA) and early antigens (EA), respectively, while the γ polypeptides will be referred to as late antigens (LA)]. The purpose of that study was to demonstrate the IEA, EA and LA determined by CMV, HSV-1 and HSV-2 by ACIF, and to assess their specificity by an ACIF-blocking test using $F(ab')_2$ fragments of specified antisera. ACIF was chosen since it is a more sensitive method than IIF.[28,29] Various selected sera with either high titer anti-CMV, HSV-1, HSV-2 or EBV antibodies, as determined by IHA, IIF, and ACIF, were obtained from patients with KS, recurrent gingivostomatitis, vulvo-vaginitis, cervical carcinoma and infectious mononucleosis (Table 2). Reference sera from healthy donors, selected for the absence or low reactivity of HV-determined antibodies, were used as the source of complement and as negative controls.

CMV Gene Products in KS

In order to demonstrate the presence of CMV-related antigens in KS biopsies, cryostat sections (4 microns thick) were prepared. Sections from lymph nodes and skin biopsies of KS patients served as controls. Tumor and skin biopsies were explanted into tissue culture. Reference antisera for CMV were derived from selected individuals with known anti-HV antibody profiles and a hyperimmune serum to CMV which was prepared in a baboon.[27] Seven of 31 (22%) KS biopsies showed fluorescent staining prominently localized in the nuclei when the sensitive ACIF test was applied (Figure 3). Furthermore, four tissue culture lines from tumor biopsies with an early passage history showed a similar staining pattern in 0.5-2% of the nuclei (probably CMV-early antigens). The

Table 1. Experimental Systems to Detect "Immediate Early," "Early," and "Late" Antigens of Herpesviruses in ACIF

Cell Lines[a]	Cell/ml	Virus[b]	PFU/Cell	Metabolic Inhibitor	Time of Infection (h)	Virus Induced[c] Antigen	Serologic Procedure Used
82C P.15	5×10^4	CMV	5-10	cycloheximide	12	IEA	ACIF
82C P.15	5×10^4	CMV	5-10	Ara C	48	EA	ACIF
82C P.15	5×10^4	CMV	5-10	—	72	LA	ACIF
HEp-2	7×10^4	HSV-2	5-10	cycloheximide	8	IEA	ACIF
HEp-2	7×10^4	HSV-2	5-10	Ara C	12	EA	ACIF
HEp-2	7×10^4	HSV-2	5-10	—	12	LA	ACIF

[a] 82C = human adult skin fibroblasts established in our laboratory; HEp-2 = larynx carcinoma cell line.

[b] Forty-eight hours previously seeded and cultured 82C and HEp-2 cells, using "multi spot" slides with 12 wells, are infected with CMV for 90 min and HSV-2 for 60 min at a multiplicity of 5-10 PFU/cell. For IEA induction, cycloheximide (50 μg/ml) is added immediately after infection for 12 h for CMV and 8 h for HSV-2, then removed, washed and cells are further incubated for 30 min and 15 min respectively. For EA induction, Ara C (20 μg/ml) is added immediately after infection for 48 h for CMV and 12 h for HSV-2. For CMV-LA and HSV-2-LA induction, no metabolic inhibitors are applied.

[c] IEA, EA, and LA test slides are fixed in -20°C methanol/acetone for 3 min for ACIF tests.

Table 2. Herpesvirus Antibody Profile of Reference Sera

Serum	Code	Diagnosis	Reference for:	CMV Titer[a]			HSV-1 Titer		HSV-2 Titer		EBV Titer			Uninfected Human Skin Fibroblasts[c]
				LA	EA	IEA[b]	LA	EA	LA	EA	VCA	EA	EBNA	
1	S-Achj	Hyperimmune baboon serum	Anti-CMV	1280	160	20	<10	<10	<10	<10	<10	<10	<10	<2
2	S-601	Kaposi's sarcoma	Anti-CMV	2560	320	80	160	10	80	20	40	<10	<10	<2
3	S-585	Kaposi's sarcoma	Anti-CMV	2560	320	40	160	<10	10	<10	40	<10	10	<2
4	S-1649	Infectious mononucleosis	Anti-CMV	2560	160	40	40	<10	10	<10	160	<10	40	<2
5	S-1650	Infectious mononucleosis	Anti-CMV	5120	160	80	80	<10	40	<10	40	<10	20	<2
6	S-300	Infectious mononucleosis	Anti-EBV	20	<10	<10	40	<10	10	<10	320	160	20	<2
7	S-670	Healthy subjects	Anti-EBV	<10	<10	<10	40	10	10	10	640	<10	320	<2
8	S-383	Gingivostomatitis	Anti-HSV-1	10	<10	<10	1280	80	80	20	80	10	10	<2
9	S-330	Vulvovaginitis	Anti-HSV-2	80	10	<10	320	20	1280	80	80	<10	10	<2
10	S-ACB	Cervical carcinoma	Anti-HSV-2	10	<10	<10	640	32	640	160	40	<10	10	<2
11	S-666	Healthy subject	Negative control	<10	<10	<10	10	<10	10	<10	<10	<10	<10	<2
12	S-422	Healthy subject	Negative control	<10	<10	<10	20	<10	10	<10	20	<10	<10	<2

[a] CMV = cytomegalovirus; HSV-1 = herpes simplex virus type 1; HSV-2 = herpes simplex virus type 2; EBV = Epstein-Barr virus.

[b] Antibody titers to CMV, HSV-1 and HSV-2-LA (late antigens) were determined by indirect hemagglutination; to -EA and -IEA (early and immediate early antigens) by ACIF; to EBV-VCA and -EA indirect immunofluorescence and to EBNA by ACIF.

[c] All sera were negative when tested by ACIF against uninfected skin fibroblasts.

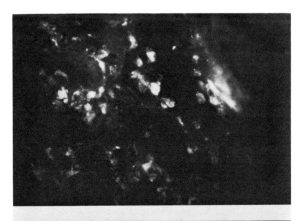

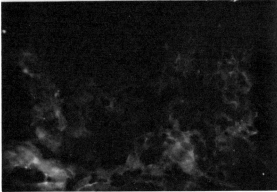

Figure 3. ACIF patterns of cryostat sections from tumor biopsy specimen of KS-80 with positive and negative reference serum. **Top:** Tumor section reacted with serum No. 2; a high number of cells show a punctated or diffuse fluorescence staining mainly at nuclear level,($\times$ 270) **Bottom:** Tumor section reacted with serum No. 12 (negative control).($\times$ 270)

specificity was further elucidated by skin fibroblast cell lines from KS patients under study, negative reference sera and by the ACIF blocking test.

The significance of the detection of CMV-related antigens was strengthened by the recent finding of nucleic acid sequence homology with CMV-DNA in three of eight KS tumor biopsies (Table 3).[30]

Oncogenicity Studies of CMV Strain K9V in Old World Monkeys

The CMV involvement in certain human cancers would be strengthened if it could be demonstrated that infection with an oncogenic strain results in malignancy, preferably in a species closely related to humans. The

CMV strain K9V (Figure 4), which we isolated previously in tissue culture from a cell line of a KS biopsy specimen,[31] was therefore injected into newborn and juvenile baboons *(Papio cynocephalus)*. Glaser et al. observed that this strain and the oncogenic Mj strain had certain peculiarities in common after infection of human fibroblasts *in vitro*.[32]

Four baby baboons (age: < 1 day to 11 days) and three juvenile baboons (age: three to six months) were injected intramuscularly with 10^7 plaque forming units (PFU) of virus. All baby baboons died within seven days to 41 weeks. Two of them, which died 21 and 41 weeks after infection showed generalized lymphoadenopathy, and had histopathologic evidence of lymphoproliferative changes of the lymph nodes, together with a mild lymphoreticular and mesothelial cell hyperplasia and histocytosis in some areas of the spleen and colon (Figure 5). Co-cultivation experiments of mesenteric lymph node fragments from one of these two animals with human skin fibroblasts revealed a CMV-related antigen demonstrable by the ACIF test after six months in tissue culture in 0.1-0.5% of the cells. Furthermore the baboon had developed complement-fixing antibodies to CMV at a titer of 1:16.

Kaposi's Sarcoma Field Study in the West Nile District of Uganda

In attempts to encompass multiple factors and events responsible for the development of cancer in man, the search for etiological agents and for cofactors, and the definition of their actual involvement has continued throughout the past years. Therefore, we initiated a collaborative field study with Drs. J. McHardy, E. H. Williams, A. Geser and G. de-Thé (IARC, WHO, Lyon) in the West Nile district during 1974-1975 with the aim of studying further the epidemiology of KS. Seventy-two patients were seen at the Kuluva Hospital during 1951-1974. The addresses and coordinates of 64 of the 72 KS patients were known (Figure 6) and 22 survivors were followed up at their home addresses. The results can be summarized as follows. Space clustering was observed: on five occasions, a new case occurred within less than 1 km of another case, and two pairs had tumors commencing in the same year. The spatial distribution of the population cannot explain the cluster-type occurrence of KS cases since people of this district are scattered throughout small villages with no obvious concentration in certain areas, and no major migrations have been registered. It is interesting to note that the KS clustering occurred in close proximity to the previously described BL time-space clusters.[33,34] Although BL has been associated with EBV[16] and seroepidemiologic studies have associated KS with high antibody titers to CMV,[17,18] it remains to be established, whether for BL or KS, which multifocal events (genetic make-up of the individual, hormones, immune compe-

Table 3. Detection of CMV-Related Antigens and CMV-DNA in Kaposi's Sarcoma Biopsies and/or Tissue Culture (TC) Cells Derived from Them

| KS Code | Geographic Location | Sex | Age (yr) | CMV-Related Antigens[a] | | CMV-DNA[b] |
				Cryostat Sections	TC Cells	Biopsies
KS-22	Uganda	M	53•	NT[c]	+	NT
KS-32	Uganda	M	40	+	+	NT
KS-38	Uganda	M	35	+	NT	NT
KS-55	Senegal	M	15	+	NT	NT
KS-71	Senegal	M	24	+	NT	NT
KS-80	Uganda	M	34	+	NT	+
KS-82	Uganda	M	25	NT	+	NT
KS-93	Uganda	M	50	+	NT	NT
KS-95	Uganda	M	60	+	NT	NT
KS-102	Uganda	M	44	NT	NT	+
KS-111	Uganda	M	34	NT	+	+

[a] 7/31 (22%) tumor biopsies and 4/12 (33%) cell lines deriving from them were positive for CMV-related antigens when tested as cryostat sections by ACIF.

[b] 3/8 (37%) tumor biopsies were positive when tested for CMV-DNA by DNA-DNA reassociation kinetics.

[c] NT = Not tested.

tence, age and/or environmental cocarcinogens) are involved that give rise to this cluster-type occurrence in the same area.

Retrospective Statistical Analysis on KS Patients with Second Primary Malignancies

In view of the fact that the development of cancer in man derives from a sequence of multifactorial events, of which the specific involvement of an oncogenic virus is just one, it appeared important to us to perform an extensive retrospective statistical analysis on patients with KS to determine the coexistence of other primary malignancies, especially of the lymphoreticular system. It has been previously observed that a second primary neoplasm, particularly Hodgkin's disease, is not rare in patients with KS, which might emphasize the persistence of a common tumor inducer.[35-37]

We found that 37% of KS patients seen at Memorial Hospital during 1949-1975 had other primary malignancies. Furthermore, there is a 20-fold increase in the incidence of lymphoreticular malignancies after the diagnosis of KS. In this series of double primaries, lymphoreticular malignancies were involved in 8% of patients (360 of 4517 cases), while for KS alone, the corresponding figure was 58% of patients (18 of 31

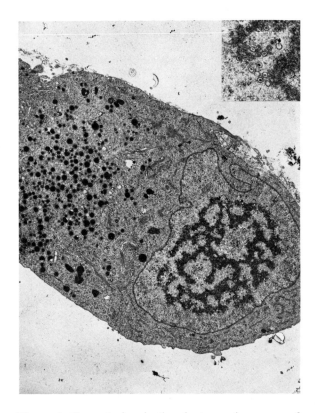

Figure 4. General view in the electron microscope of a skin fibroblast in tissue culture infected by CMV strain K9V. Note its rounded shape, typical reticulate inclusion body in the nucleus with virus particles. In the cystoplasm viruses are associated with lysosome-like bodies (the CMV-specific "dense bodies").(× 56,000) **Inset:** Higher magnification of CMV particles embedded in the nucleus.(× 17,000)

cases). Thus, this study confirmed a significant association between KS and second primary malignancies of the lymphoreticular system.[38]

Concluding Remarks

Kaposi's sarcoma, a neoplasia which probably involves different cell types, represented a potentially interesting model in the search for virus-associated human malignancies.[15,17,18] The particular geographic concentration of KS among the native population of equatorial Africans is strongly reminiscent of the distribution of African BL. The cluster-type occurrence in endemic areas is suggestive of involvement of infectious, environmental or genetic factors. The biological behavior of KS seems

68

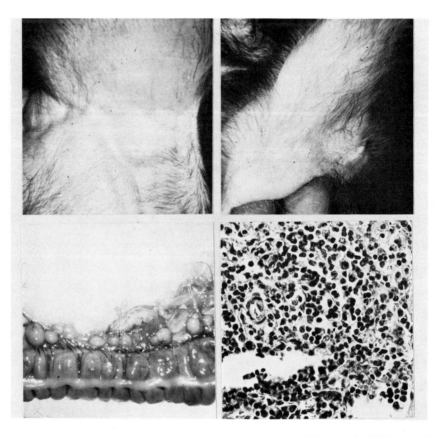

Figure 5. Baboon No. 4 inoculated as newborn with CMV strain K9V (1×10^7 PFU/i.m.) showed generalized lymphoadenopathy at the time of death (41 weeks after inoculation). **Top left and right:** Highly enlarged inguinal and axillary lymph nodes. **Bottom left:** Significantly enlarged pericolonic lymph nodes visualized at autopsy. **Bottom right:** Lymphoreticular cell infiltration in laminar propria and submucosa of the colon (hematoxylin-eosin).($\times$ 285)

to indicate a marked immunological response similar to virus-induced tumors in animals: KS in children evolves rapidly, but in adults runs a protracted course with some spontaneous regression of the tumors. Although the biologic mechanism responsible for the association of KS with a second primary tumor, particularly of the lymphoreticular system, is not clear, the latter suggests susceptibility of the host to some type of common initiator for malignant changes.[38]

The initial search for virus particles resulted in the isolation of a CMV in a KS tissue culture cell line.[14,15,31] Subsequent immunovirologic analyses have revealed a specific serologic association with CMV but not with HSV-1, HSV-2 and EBV in KS patients.[17,18] These data are

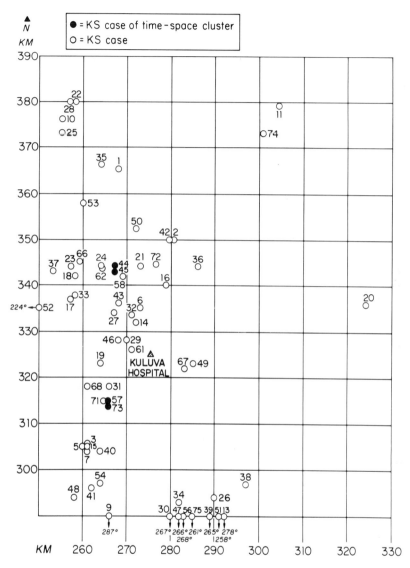

Figure 6. Geographic locations of 64 patients with KS in the West Nile district of Uganda as recorded at Kuluva Hospital during 1951-1974.

reminiscent of the serologic association of EBV with African BL.[39] However, if one compares the CMV-KS association with the EBV-BL association, CMV must have a different quantitative relationship to the transformed cells from that of EBV, the DNA and gene products of which are clearly in abundance. This hypothesis is further supported by

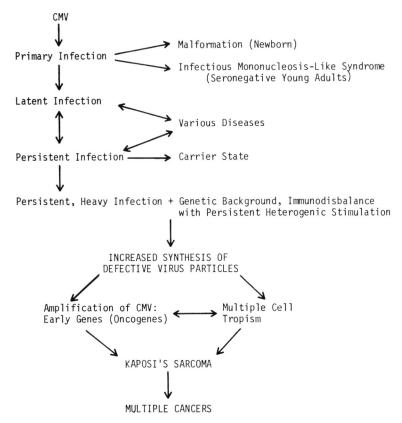

Figure 7. Hypothetical etiopathogenic mechanisms for the development of KS as well as a second primary tumor, particularly of the lymphoreticular system, in KS patients.

the recently obtained CMV-DNA hybridization data and the demonstration of CMV-related antigens in KS biopsies.[30]

At this point it may be worthwhile to look at certain similarities between CMV and EBV. Primary infection of adolescents and young adults by both viruses can cause a self-limiting lymphoproliferative disease,[40-44] and *in vitro* they have transforming capabilities.[45,46] CMV has a broader cell tropism then EBV including, in addition to lymphocytes, cells of the mononuclear phagocytic system, granulocytes, epithelial cells and fibroblasts.[47,48]

By analogy to the EBV involvement in children with long and persistent EBV infections who subsequently develop BL,[49] it might be speculated that similar events may take place in CMV-infected subjects developing KS. It was demonstrated in experimental systems in adult mice,[50,51] which have CMV infections resembling those in man,[52,53] that a primary

CMV infection leads to latency and reactivation as well as to persistent infection. Prominent factors closely linked to these events were a genetic susceptibility and immunologic responses. The relatively high incidence of KS in certain ethnic groups[54] indicates, indeed, a particular genetic susceptibility, and immunologic disorders have been observed in these patients.[55-59] Latency of ubiquitous oncogenic herpesviruses and their continuous reactivation due to foreign antigenic stimulation (e.g., malaria or onchocerciasis in Africans or various mitogens in Europeans and Americans) might be of importance. Whether this can lead to an increased synthesis of defective viruses, similar to *in vitro* systems infected at a high multiplicity of infection[60] which prominently retain and amplify their oncogenes, is purely speculative (Figure 7).

Near conclusive evidence of a strict virus-tumor association has been provided for the EBV with Burkitt's lymphoma and, almost as striking, with nasopharyngeal carcinoma. Whether CMV plays that role in the development of Kaposi's sarcoma or certain other human malignancies is worthy of consideration.

ACKNOWLEDGMENTS
This study was supported by NCI grants CA-08748 and CA-19763. The authors would like to thank Dr. F. Deinhardt for his support.

References

1. Smith, M.G. and Vellios, F.: *Archs. Path.* 50:862, 1950.
2. Levine, R.S., Warner, N.E., and Johnson, C.F.: *Ann. Surg.* 159:37, 1964.
3. Huang, E.-S. and Roche, J.K.: *Lancet* 1: 957, 1978.
4. Montogmery, R., Youngblood, L., and Medearis, D.N.: *Pediatrics* 49:524, 1972.
5. Lang, D.J. and Kummer, J.F.: *N. Engl. J. Med.* 287:756, 1972.
6. Pacsa, A.S., Kummerländer, L., Pejtsik, B., and Pali, K.: *J. Natl. Cancer Inst.* 55:775, 1975.
7. Melnick, J.L., Lewis, R., Wimberly, I., Kaufman, R.H., and Adam, E.: *Intervirology* 10:115, 1978.
8. Albrecht, T. and Rapp, F.: *Virology* 55:53, 1973.
9. St. Jeor, S.C., Albrecht, T.B., Funk, F.D., and Rapp, F.: *J. Virol.* 13:353, 1974.
10. Geder, L., Lausch, R., O'Neill, F., and Rapp, F.: *Science* 192:1134, 1976.
11. Geder, L., Kreider, J., and Rapp, F.: *J. Natl. Cancer Inst.* 58:1003, 1977.
12. Geder, L. and Rapp, F.: *Nature* 265:184, 1977.
13. Sanford, E.J., Geder, L., Laychock, A., Rohner, Jr., T.J., and Rapp, F.: *J. Urol.* 118:789, 1977.
14. Giraldo, G. and Beth, E.: *C. R. Acad. Sc. Paris* 275:289, 1972.
15. Giraldo, G., Beth, E., Coeur, P., Vogel, Ch. L., and Dhru, D.S.: *J. Natl. Cancer Inst.* 49:1495, 1972.
16. Epstein, M.A. and Achong, B.G.: In: *The Epstein-Barr Virus,* M.A. Epstein and B.G. Achong (eds.), Springer-Verlag, New York, 1979, p. 321.

17. Giraldo, G., Beth, E., Kourilsky, F.M., Henle, W., Henle, G., Miké, V., Huraux, J. M., Andersen, H.K., Gharbi, M.R., Kyalwazi, S.K., and Puissant, A.: *Int. J. Cancer* 15:839, 1975.

18. Giraldo, G., Beth, E., Henle, W., Henle, G., Miké, V., Safai, B., Huraux, J.M., McHardy, J., and de-Thé, G.: *Int. J. Cancer* 22:126, 1978.

19. Krech, U., Jung, M., and Jung, F.: In: *Cytomegalovirus Infections in Man,* U. Krech, M. Jung and F. Jung (eds.), Karger, Basel, 1971, p. 18.

20. Adam, E., Sharma, S.D., Ziegler, O., Iwamoto, K., Melnick, J.L., Levy, H., and Rawls, W.E.: *J. Natl. Cancer Inst.* 48:65, 1972.

21. Honess, R.W. and Roizman, B.: *J. Virol.* 12:1347, 1973.

22. Salzman, N.P. and Khoury, G.: In: *Comprehensive Virology, Vol. 3,* H. Fraenkel-Conrat and R.R. Wagner (eds.), Plenum Press, New York, 1974, p. 106.

23. Philipson, L. and Lindberg, U.: In: *Comprehensive Virology, Vol. 3,* H. Fraenkel-Conrat and R.R. Wagner (eds.), Plenum Press, New York, 1974, p. 178.

24. Aya, T. and Osato, T.: *Int. J. Cancer* 14:341, 1974.

25. Yata, J., Desgranges, C., Nakagawa, T., Favre, M.C., and de-Thé, G.: *Int. J. Cancer* 15:377, 1975.

26. Beth, E., Giraldo, G., and Bernhard, M.: *Biomedicine* 25:366, 1976.

27. Giraldo, G., Beth, E., Hämmerling, U., Tarro, G., and Kourilsky, F.M.: *Int. J. Cancer* 19:107, 1977.

28. Reedman, B.M. and Klein, G.: *Int. J. Cancer* 11:449, 1973.

29. Beth, E., Cikes, M., and Giraldo, G.: *Int. J. Cancer* 21:1, 1978.

30. Giraldo, G., Beth, E., and Huang, E.-S.: *Int. J. Cancer,* (1980) in press.

31. Giraldo, G., Beth, E., and Haguenau, F.: *J. Natl. Cancer Inst.* 49:1509, 1972.

32. Glaser, R., Geder, L., St. Jeor, S., Michelson-Fiske, S., and Haguenau, F.: *J. Natl. Cancer Inst.* 59:55, 1977.

33. Williams, E.H., Spit, P., and Pike, M.C.: *Br. J. Cancer* 23:235, 1969.

34. Williams, E.H., Smith, P.G., Day, N.E., Geser, A., Ellice, J., Tukei, P.M., *Br. J. Cancer* 37:109, 1978.

35. Moertel, C.G.: In: *Recent Results in Cancer Research, Vol. 7,* P. Rentchnick (ed.), Springer-Verlag, New York, 1966, p. 34.

36. Oettlé, A.G.: *Acta. Un. Int. Cancer* 18:330, 1962.

37. Taylor, J.F., Smith, P.G., Bull, D., and Pike, M.C.: *Br. J. Cancer* 26:483, 1972.

38. Safai, B., Miké, V., Giraldo, G., Beth, E., and Good, R.A.: *Cancer* 45:1472, 1980.

39. Henle, G., Henle, W., Clifford, P., Diehl, V., Kafuko, G.W., Kirya, B. G., Klein, G., Morrow, R.H., Munube, G.M.R., Pike, P., Tukei, P.M., and Ziegler, J.L.: *J. Natl. Cancer Inst.* 43:1147, 1969.

40. Henle, G., Henle, W., and Diehl, V.: *Proc. Natl. Acad. Sci. (USA)* 59:94, 1968.

41. Miller, G.: *Prog. Med. Virol.* 20:84, 1975.

42. Epstein, M.A. and Achong, B.G.: *Lancet* 2:1270, 1977.

43. Klemola, E., von Essen, R., Henle, G., and Henle, W.: *J. Infect. Dis.* 121:608, 1970.

44. Jordan, M.C., Rousseau, W.E., Stewart, J.A., Noble, G.R., Chin, T.D.Y.: *Ann. Intern. Med.* 79:153, 1973.

45. Pope, J.H., Horne, M.K., and Scott, W.: *Int. J. Cancer* 3:857, 1968.

46. Albrecht, T. and Rapp, F.: *Virology* 55:53, 1973.

47. Pagano, J.S.: *J. Infect. Dis.* 132:209, 1975.
48. Rinaldo, C.R., Jr., Black, P.H., and Hirsch, M.S.: *J. Infect. Dis.* 136:667, 1977.
49. de-Thé, G.: *Lancet* 1:335, 1977.
50. Olding, L.G., Jensen, F.C., and Oldstone, M.B.A.: *J. Exp. Med.* 141:561, 1975.
51. Olding, L.B., Kingsbury, D.T., and Oldstone, M.B.A.: *J. Gen. Virol.* 33:267, 1976.
52. Brodsky, I. and Rowe, W.P.: *Proc. Soc. Exp. Biol. (N.Y.)* 99:654, 1958.
53. Medearis, D.N.: *Am. J. Hyg.* 80:103, 1964.
54. Slavin, G., Cameron, H.M., and Singh, H.: *Br. J. Cancer* 23:349, 1969.
55. Master, S.P., Taylor, J.F., Kyalwazi, S.K., and Ziegler, J.L.: *Br. Med. J.* 1:600, 1970.
56. Taylor, J.F., Junge, U., Wolfe, L., Deinhardt, F., and Kyalwazi, S.K.: *Int. J. Cancer* 8:468, 1971.
57. Taylor, J.F.: *Lancet* 1:883, 1973.
58. Dobozy, A., Husz, S., Hunyadi, J., Berkó, G., and Simon, N.: *Lancet* 2:625, 1973.
59. Taylor, J.F. and Ziegler, J.L.: *Br. J. Cancer* 30:312, 1974.
60. Huang, A.S. and Baltimore, D.: In: *Comprehensive Virology, Vol. 10,* H. Fraenkel-Conrat and R.R. Wagner (eds.), Plenum Press, New York, 1977, p. 73.

Herpes Simplex Virus Type 2 and Cervix Cancer: Perspectives on the Possibility of a Causal Relationship

Laure Aurelian, Raxit J. Jariwalla, Albert D. Donnenberg, and John F. Sheridan

The Johns Hopkins Medical Institutions, Baltimore, Maryland

The Problem

Herpesviruses are large DNA viruses that infect man and most animal species. In recent years one of the herpesviruses infecting man, designated herpes simplex virus type 2 (HSV-2), has received special attention as the cause of sexually transmitted genital lesions, the incidence of which is reaching epidemic proportions, and since it is suspected as the agent responsible for squamous carcinoma of the cervix. In this presentation we will focus on the association of HSV-2 with cervix cancer particularly as it pertains to the question of causation.

Cancer may be viewed as resulting from the development of modified cells that are capable of cloning in an otherwise hostile environment, because the organism has somehow become incapable of responding in a proper fashion. Thus, the disease is multifactorial. It involves extraneous factors that can cause the modification of the cell (such as chemical carcinogens and/or viruses), other cofactors that facilitate the cloning of the modified cell(s), and the host that is to support the establishment of the clone of modified cells. This classic concept of carcinogenesis[1] visualizes two factors that are operative at a cellular level in a sequentially ordered fashion designated "inducer" and "promoter" (Figure 1). Although the third component of the puzzle, i.e., the host itself, has not been clearly delineated, it is quite evident that at least immunologically, it must play a significant role. Finally, the study of carcinogenesis in humans is further complicated by the limitations of human experimentation. Accordingly, virologists have historically chosen to study virus-

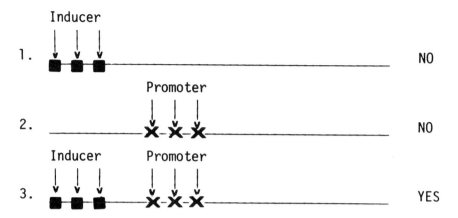

Figure 1. Schematic representation of the classic concept of carcinogens.[1] It posits tumor induction as resulting from the sequential exposure of cells to two carcinogenic factors, the first of which acts as an inducer, whereas the second one acts as a promoter. The number of exposures to either one of the two factors is insignificant.

induced transformation of cells *in vitro* as the means of inquiring into the mechanisms of viral carcinogenesis. Their failure to establish the viral causation of most human cancers should serve as a reminder of the limitations of this approach.

Studies performed in our laboratory on HSV-2 and cervix cancer are based on the premise that consideration of the viral causation of human cancer must come to grips with the following basic problems: (a) the philosophical limitations associated with the question of causality, (b) the limitations imposed by the biology of the specific virus under consideration, in this case HSV-2, and (c) the limitations imposed by the biology of the host and the specific organ that is affected, in this case the human uterine cervix. Our working hypothesis argues that HSV-2 acts as an inducer in the classic concept of carcinogenesis (Figure 1). It visualizes the virus as being capable of transforming cervical cells from normal to neoplastic via a mechanism akin (though not necessarily identical) to that whereby it induces the transformation of mammalian cells in culture. Thus, it posits HSV-2 as the inducer of the transforming event that will result in atypical lesions (Figure 2). Since there seems to be no evolutionary advantage to the virus resulting from its ability to transform cells, our working hypothesis further argues that transformation must be the consequence of a function that is normally expressed and required in the course of productive viral multiplication but the regulation of which has somehow failed. This failure could result from the loss of the regulatory genes and their modification. Although virus-

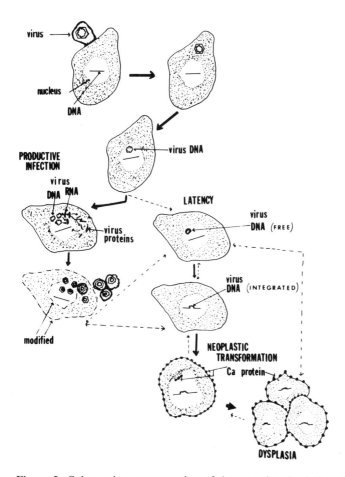

virus

nucleus

DNA

PRODUCTIVE
INFECTION

virus DNA

virus
DNA RNA

virus
proteins

LATENCY

virus
DNA (FREE)

virus
DNA (INTEGRATED)

modified

NEOPLASTIC
TRANSFORMATION

Ca protein

DYSPLASIA

Figure 2. Schematic representation of the postulated relationship of HSV-2 with cervical cells. The hypothesis is based on the assumption that during latency HSV-2 persists in cervical cells according to the dynamic state hypothesis (free virus DNA). It argues the possible fragmentation of viral DNA and its integration into the host cell genome (integrated virus DNA) resulting in a modified cell that expressed transformation-specific (Ca protein) virus-coded function(s). Such function(s) would be located in the nucleus or the surface of the cell, although presently available evidence favors the cell surface. It is further postulated that multiplication of the modified cell results in the earliest preneoplastic lesion designated dysplasia or atypia.

modified cells have an evolutionary advantage based on their increased rate of DNA synthesis, we are cognizant of the difficulties associated with their ability to clone and overcome the organism's defense mechanisms. We, therefore, postulate that for the transformed cells to successfully establish nonregressive tumors, further alterations must occur both at the cellular (promoter) and the organism levels. Indeed, in the case of cervical carcinogenesis, it is well established that frank neoplasia is generally preceded by atypia and/or carcinoma *in situ* lesions, the great majority of which (35 and 65%, respectively) have been shown to regress.[2]

Causation and Disease

For nearly 100 years, the Koch postulate has served as a reference point in evaluating the causal relationship of an agent to the disease with which it is associated. It is based on three concepts: (a) the agent occurs in every case of the disease under circumstances that account for pathological changes and clinical course, (b) the agent never occurs in any other disease as a fortuitous parasite, and (c) after isolation and growth in pure culture, the agent can induce the disease anew.[3] While many diseases fulfill these criteria, a number of infectious agents (viz., leprosy, cholera, typhoid) do not meet them all. The major limitations of the Koch postulate are: (a) the inability to produce the disease anew, (b) the inability to grow many human pathogens in pure culture in the laboratory, and (c) the ability of at least some organisms to cause asymptomatic infections. These limitations are particularly significant in the consideration of the viral causation of disease. Accordingly, Rivers,[4] suggested that in order to establish a viral etiology of disease the specific virus must be associated with the disease with a certain degree of regularity and it should not occur in the sick individual as an accidental finding as determined by seroconversion. Another dimension was added by Huebner,[5] who emphasized the epidemiologic concept: (a) retrospective and prospective studies of population groups in order to identify patterns of infection and disease, (b) inoculation of human volunteers with the newly recognized agent in double-blind studies in order to reproduce the clinical syndrome, and (c) prevention of the disease by a specific vaccine.

The problem of virus causation of human cancer is complicated by the nature of the host, the infectious identity of the putative agent and the chronic nature of the disease. Difficulties stem from: (a) the long incubation period between exposure to the suspected agent and cancer development, (b) the relatively low incidence of most cancers in contradistinction with the widespread ubiquitous nature of the viruses suspected of being oncogenic in humans, (c) the possibility that cancer may result as a consequence of reactivated virus, rather than as the direct consequence of a primary infection, (d) the probable role of environmental and/or genetic cofactors, (e) the difficulty in reproducing the disease in animal models, and (f) the impossibility of human experimentation.

In an attempt to overcome these difficulties, Evans[6] has recently synthesized the epidemiologic, seroepidemiologic, immunologic, and virologic criteria of disease causation in a unified concept (Table 1). It is based on the assumption that in humans, not unlike animals, virus-induced carcinogenesis depends on the persistence and expression of transforming viral genes.

Causation and the Biology of HSV-2 Infections

Exposure of human and most mammalian cells to infectious HSV-2 *in vitro* virtually always results in viral replication and cell death, phenomena that are also believed to occur *in vivo*. Since for the cell, cancer represents immortality, it seems reasonable to conclude that if HSV-2 causes human cancer it must do so as the consequency of an *in vivo* condition analogous to abortive infection in which no (or very little)

Table 1. Koch Postulate Revised[a]

1. Exposure to putative cause should be more common in cases than controls. Virus-specific antibody or cell-mediated immune response present more often in patients with cancer than in healthy age/sex matched controls living in the same area.

2. Cancer-associated immune response must have characteristics indicative of virus expression, viz., anti-"early" antigen or IgM antibody and effector-cell response.

3. Immunologic specificity means that response is virus-specific and that a similar response is not observed with other viruses or in other cancers.

4. Temporally, the disease should follow exposure to the putative agent.

5. Incidence of disease should be higher in those exposed to putative agent than in those not so exposed as shown in prospective studies. Prospective sero-epidemiological studies must show virus-specific antibody is present prior to onset or to recurrence of disease.

6. A spectrum of host responses should follow exposure to the putative agent along a biological gradient from mild to severe. Virus-specific antibody should demonstrate equal prevalence in hosts with all aspects of this spectrum.

7. Presence of virus and/or viral genetic material in affected tissues.

8. Expression of virus information should be detected in affected tissues.

9. Demonstration of the ability of the virus and/or its genetic information to induce neoplastic transformation of cells *in vitro*.

10. Reproduction of disease in animal model.

11. Elimination or modification of the putative cause should decrease incidence of disease.

12. The whole thing should make biologic and epidemiologic sense.

13. If association between virus and cancer is seen in some populations but not in others, then the presence of cofactor(s) should be sought.

[a] Adapted from Evans, A.S.: *Yale J. Biol. Med.* 49:175, 1976.

virus is produced. Pertinent to an understanding of these interpretations are the following documented facts about productive and abortive infections *in vitro* and *in vivo*.

Virus Reproductive Cycle in Culture

(a) Enveloped virus adsorbs to the surface of the cell. The capsid penetrates the cell and is disaggregated in the cytoplasm. The viral DNA is transported to the cell nucleus.[7]

(b) In the nucleus, the viral DNA is transcribed and processed. It is translocated to the cytoplasm where viral polypeptides are made and where some of them become modified by various processes (viz., glycosylation, phosphorylation). Specific sets of proteins (functional and structural) are transported to the cell nucleus. Other sets of viral proteins become incorporated into the cellular membranes, thus altering their antigenicity. Viral DNA is synthesized in the nucleus beginning at four hours postinfection.[7]

(c) Capsids are assembled in the nucleus. They acquire an envelope as they bud through the nuclear membrane that had previously been modified by the incorporation of viral proteins.[8] Purified virions contain at least 24 polypeptides. The infected cell contains at least 20 more viral proteins.[9]

(d) As a result of virus replication, several modifications occur in the structure and metabolism of the infected cell. Chromatin margination and the disaggregation of nucleoli and of host polyribosomes coincide with the inhibition of host DNA and protein synthesis. At approximately 6 hours postinfection, infected cells demonstrate morphologic alterations consistent with cell death.[7]

Abortive Infections In Vitro

Two types of abortive infections have been described for HSV. The first type consists of nonpermissive cells that fail to support the replication of virus that is, under similar experimental conditions, infectious for permissive cells. The second type of abortive infection consists of permissive cells that are infected with damaged (noninfectious) virus, or with infectious virus but under nonphysiological conditions. An example of an abortive infection of the first type is our study of a strain of HSV-1 (HSV-1 MPdk⁻) that multiplies in HEp-2 but not in dog kidney (DK) cells.[10] Mutants derived from this strain multiply in both cell lines.[11] In this system the outcome of infection is dependent on the multiplicity of infection. At high multiplicities, the DK cells make viral DNA and capsids but not enveloped particles. At low multiplicities, abortively infected DK cells make only interferon.[12] Abortive infection of the second type has invariably led to transformation. Thus cells infected with inactivated virus,[13,14] or with infectious virus at suboptimal or supraoptimal temperatures,[15] displayed *in vitro* properties characteristic of neoplasia and at least some of them were tumorigenic to newborn animals. The transformed cells expressed viral antigens and maintained DNA sequence corresponding to 8-32% of the viral genome.[16]

Productive Replication In Vivo: Herpetic Disease

The obvious objective of *in vitro* studies is to examine the behavior of the virus in multicellular organisms from the vantage points of the studies on infected tissue culture systems. *A priori,* it should be stressed that the two situations are not identical. Thus, cells in culture are generally infected at high multiplicities, whereas it is very likely that the multiplicity of infection in a multicellular organism under natural conditions is low and, at best, averages one infectious unit per cell. Furthermore, the multicellular organism probably consists of both permissive and nonpermissive cells, and as we have previously shown,[12] the multiplicity of infection plays a significant role in the outcome of infection of nonpermissive cells. Finally, high multiplicity of infection has been reported to generate particles containing defective DNA.[17] Additional levels of complexity are provided by the immune system and the various mechanical defense mechanisms operative in the multicellular organism. Nevertheless, it seems legitimate to assume that events taking place in infected permissive cells that produce virus in the multicellular organism and in tissue culture are similar.

Latency

A significant property of the herpesviruses is their ability to persist in infected hosts, causing periodic recurrent disease. This phenomenon is designated latency. The pertinent facts concerning it may be summarized as follows: (a) Primary exposure to HSV-2 follows puberty and results from sexual transmission. (b) Following recovery from primary infection, approximately 40% of the infected individuals suffer from recurrent self-limiting lesions appearing at or near the site of the primary infection. (c) Recurrent lesions can be predicted and are induced by a variety of stress provocations such as sun, strong wind, fever, hormone therapy or menstruation.[18] The predictable character of the recurrences and their occurrence always at the same site on the body suggests that they are not due to reinfection, but, rather, are derived from an endogenous virus residing in the body in the interim between recrudescences. This conclusion is corroborated by the observation that people suffering from recurrences have high levels of circulating neutralizing antibody.

The key problems of latency are: (a) the mechanism of virus persistence, and (b) the mechanism of recurrent disease. Several lines of evidence suggest that HSV-1 is maintained in sensory neurons. Thus, in rabbits and mice latently infected with HSV-1, virus could be induced to multiply by explanting the surgically removed ganglia and maintaining them for some time *in vitro,* or by implanting them in virgin animals.[19] Similar results were obtained for HSV-1 from trigeminal ganglia removed from randomly picked human cadavers.[20] HSV-2 also persists in the ganglia; however, the relatively high frequency of its isolation from male genitourinary samples in absence of clinical lesions.[21] and the relatively low frequency of its isolation from sacral ganglia of randomly picked cadavers,[22] suggest that this virus also persists at the site of infection. In support of this conclusion is our observation that in the guinea pig model of recurrent HSV-2 disease originally described by Scriba[23] and recently established in our laboratory in the inbred NIH 13 strain, virus is preferentially isolated from the site of infection (Table 2).

Two hypotheses have been advanced by Roizman[24] to explain the mechanisms of virus persistence. The first hypothesis, designated "dynamic state," suggests that persistence results from low grade multiplication of the virus in confined pockets of chronically infected tissue. This intrepretation posits recurrent disease as resulting from an increased replication of the virus following stress and predicts successful virus isolation in the interim between recrudescences. According to the alternative hypothesis, designated "static state," the viral genome is maintained in a nonproductive state and resumes a productive infection when induced as a consequence of stress provocation.

In support of the dynamic state hypothesis, HSV-1 was isolated from human tears[25,26] and saliva,[27] and HSV-2 was isolated from genital secretions[21] in absence of overt lesions. HSV-1 was also isolated from homogenates of the ganglia of latently infected mice[19] in the absence of overt lesions[28] and HSV-2 was successfully isolated from the footpad of HSV-2 seropositive strain 13 guinea pigs without a history of recurrent disease or studied during quiescence (Table 3). The data support the concept of virus persistence according to the dynamic state hypothesis and argues in favor of preferential persistence at the site of infection.

Table 2. HSV-2 Isolation from Latently-Infected Guinea Pigs[a]

	Positive Isolation from Animals			
Organ	Quiescence	Active Recurrence	No History of Recurrence	Total (%)
Foot	6/14	9/10	6/19	21/43 (49%)
Sciatic nerve	1/8	0/5	0/8	1/21 (5%)
Sacral ganglia (L_3-S_3)	4/8	0/5	2/8	6/21 (29%)

[a] Primary guinea pig kidney cells were used for virus isolation. Cultures were considered negative if virus was not isolated after 6 weeks of incubation.

Recurrent disease occurs only in a fraction (40%) of those individuals previously infected with HSV-2. Since all HSV-2 infected individuals remain seropositive, a key aspect of the latency problem is the mechanism of recurrent disease in this subgroup of the infected population. Our recent data support the interpretation that recurrent disease results from the defective conversion of virus-specific immune memory to effector functions thus allowing virus replication to proceed unimpeded and reach levels critical to the development of symptomatic disease. Significantly, the defect is transient. It is overcome by the high levels of antigen achieved during symptomatic disease resulting in the containment of the symptoms. Unlike those individuals suffering from recurrent disease, seropositive controls display an efficient conversion of immune memory to effector functions thus maintaining virus replication at subclinical levels (Donnenberg, Sheridan and Aurelian, in press) (Figure 3).

HSV-2 and Cervix Cancer

Based on our present knowledge, it seems reasonable to suggest that if HSV-2 transforms cervical cells *in vivo:* (a) this transformation must result from the conversion of the replicative cycle of the virus that is operative during latency to an abortive one, and (b) since cervical cells

Table 3. Koch Postulate Revised: HSV-2 and Cervix Cancer

1. Exposure: Virus-specific antibody and cell-mediated immunity (CMI) response more prevalent in cancer than in matched control groups.
2. Cancer-associated immune response has characteristics indicative of virus expression:
   a. Antibody to AG-4 is against an "early antigen" and is IgM. It reflects tumor progression.
   b. CMI response directed against AG-e reflects lymphoid effector function driven by continuous expression of AG-e exfoliated cervical tumor cells.
3. Immunologic specificity:
   a. Humoral and CMI response is virus-specific.
   b. Similar response not seen with other viruses (CMV, VZ, HSV-1).
   c. Similar response not seen in other cancers (breast, vulva, ovary, vagina).
4. Incidence: Women with HSV-2 infections are at higher risk of developing cervix cancer than uninfected ones as shown by prospective studies.
5. A spectrum: Atypia and carcinoma *in situ* follow exposure to HSV-2 and precede cancer. Prevalence of virus-specific antibody is identical in all 3.
6. Presence of virus and viral DNA in tumor cells.
7. Expression: Viral mRNA and antigens/proteins in tumor cells (AG-4, AG-e, VP 134, others).
8. Virus and viral DNA cause neoplastic transformation.
9. Reproduction of disease: Cervically infected Cebus monkeys develop atypia.
10. Elimination or modification: Unstudied.
11. Biologic and epidemiologic sense: Human virus; persists in infected host without causing cell death (latency) and is sexually transmitted, as in cervix cancer.

84

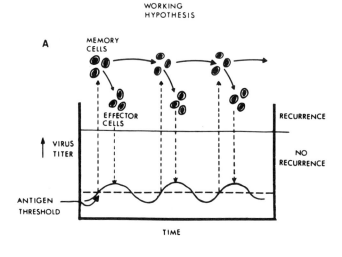

WORKING
HYPOTHESIS

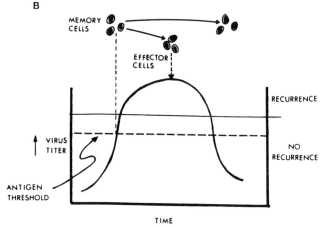

Figure 3A, B. Schematic representation of our postulate for the recurrent HSV-2 disease (Donnenberg, Sheridan and Aurelian, in press). **Panel A** describes the condition operative in seropositive individuals without a history of recurrent disease. It indicates the relatively low antigen threshold and short time interval necessary to convert immune memory to effector functions resulting in the maintenance of the antigen level below that necessary to cause symptomatic disease. **Panel B** represents the structure that is operative in patients with recurrent disease. It posits high antigen threshold and long time effector functions. Under these conditions virus replication proceeds unimpeded reacting levels that surpass those necessary for the causation of symptomatic disease. These antigen levels and the prolonged time interval are finally sufficient to convert the immune memory cells into effectors, thus terminating the recurrent disease.

are permissive, abortive infection must result from loss of virus infectivity. The successful cloning of the transformed cells depends on their further alteration (Figure 1) and their ability to overcome the host's general and virus-specific immunity. In the context of the loss of virus infectivity, it should be pointed out that the structure of the viral DNA[29] is highly conducive to its fragmentation and the generation of sequences specifically enriched in some viral genes. The continuous replication of the virus, suggested by the dynamic state hypothesis and supported by the available evidence, also favors fragmentation. Cells that contain only those viral DNA sequences possessing transforming activity will convert from a normal to a neoplastic phenotype (Figure 2). This interpretation mechanistically posits the virus at the level of induction of carcinogenesis (Figure 1). The role and identity of the promoter, and the factors relating to the establishment of a clone of neoplastically transformed cells in an immunologically restrictive host, remain largely unknown.

Based on the interpretations discussed above, Table 3 summarizes presently available evidence on HSV-2 and cervix cancer in the context of the unified concept of causation described by Evans.[6] Briefly, HSV-2-infected women are at a significantly higher risk of developing cervix cancer than uninfected ones.[30] Infection with HSV-2 precedes neoplasia. It is followed by a spectrum of disease starting with the mildest (cervical atypia or carcinoma *in situ*) to the most severe (invasive cancer).[31] Exposure to the virus is more prevalent in anaplastic patients than in control subjects matched to the cancer group for variables (viz., promiscuity) associated with the disease.[32] The immune response observed in cancer patients is virus- and cancer-specific and it is indicative of continuous virus expression. Thus, patients have antibody to at least one "early" viral antigen (AG-4) (Table 4), and it is a 19S immunoglobulin.[33] Another "early" viral antigen associated with cervix cancer is VP 134.[34] Furthermore, patients respond to another viral antigen (AG-e), in an effector-type CMI response,[35] that is driven by the continuous expression of the antigen in cervical atypia, but not normal, cells.[36] Consistent with these observations, viral mRNA[37] was found in cervical atypical cells. Viral DNA sequences corresponding to 30% of the viral genome were also described in one cervical tumor;[38] however, these results were not confirmed. Since only some viral DNA sequences persist in transformed cells,[16] and since a relatively small number of the cells in the tumor mass are neoplastic, the resolution of this apparent contradiction must await further developments in hybridization techniques. Infectious virus, designated HSV-2 (S-1), was isolated from cervical atypia cells grown in culture[53] but not from similarly grown invasive cancer cells, suggesting that progression from mild (atypia) to severe (cancer) disease involves the loss of viral DNA sequences that express lytic functions associated with cell death.[39] In this context, the recent isolation, after 19 months, of

86

Table 4. Frequency of AG-4 Seropositivity in Cancer Patients[a] and Matched Controls

Patient Groups	Number Tested	AG-4 Positive[b]	
		No.	(%)
Atypia	84	40	47.6
In situ (CIS)	75	43	54.5
Invasive	107	81	75.7
Controls	165	20	12.1
Treated	41	0	0
Recurrent	13	13	100.0

[a] Sera from patients in this series were collected prior to therapy (atypia, CIS, invasive), once after therapy (treated) or at the time of diagnosis of recurrent cancer (recurrent). Patients were not followed-up.

[b] Reaction is considered positive if at least 10% of the complement is fixed in presence of AG-4 antigen. Complement is not fixed in presence of control antigen prepared from mock-infected HEp-2 cells. (Data from Aurelian, et al., 1973.)

infectious virus from tumors caused by HSV-2 transformed rat cells (Macnab, personal communication) supports the concept that the complete viral genome can persist in tumor cells.

Cancer Associated Viral Antigens

The rationale for the postulated expression of viral DNA sequences in human carcinogenesis was discussed above. It posits this expression as an "early" function occurring during productive infection before onset of viral DNA synthesis. AG-4 is a good candidate for this role. Thus, it is a virus-specific antigen normally made during the reproductive cycle of the virus between 4–9 hours post infection.[40] It is immunologically identical to a virus-specific infected cell protein designated ICP 10[41] that is made in cells sequentially treated with cycloheximide and actinomycin D ("immediate early" protein).[42] ICP 10 comigrates on SDS-acrylamide gel electrophoresis with a virion envelope protein and antibody to ICP 10 neutralizes virus infectivity in the presence of complement or anti-globulin.[41,42]

Antibody to AG-4 is cervix cancer-specific. It is virtually absent in control women without cancer or in patients with cancer at other sites, but is present in 70–80% of cervix cancer patients.[40,43–47] Moreover, AG-4 reflects tumor progression. Thus, in a group of 444 subjects studied prior to therapy, AG-4 seropositivity was found to reflect the percentage of lesions (atypia: 47.6%; CIS: 54.5%) that progress[2] to invasive cancer. This compares to 12% of the normal control women and 100% of recurrent cancers (Table 4). Consistent with a cancer-associated role, AG-4 seropositivity appears to be predictive of increased risk of recurrent disease. Thus, 15 of 19 (79%) patients with invasive cancer studied prospectively were AG-4 seropositive prior to therapy. Of these, eight (54.3%) converted to seronegativity following therapy, whereas seven (46.6%) remained AG-4 seropositive. Four of the AG-4 seropositive patients (57.1%) had recurrent neoplastic disease during follow-up, whereas all 12 seronegative patients remained free of disease. Similarily, 16 of 34 asymptomatic patients treated for cervix cancer or CIS prior to entry into the study were AG-4 seropositive. Fourteen of these (87.5%) developed recurrent neoplastic disease, whereas all of the 18 AG-4 seronegative patients remained free of neoplastic disease (Figure 4).

Another viral antigen originally described by our laboratory appears to be consistently expressed in cervix cancer and has been designated AG-e. It is a virus-specific antigen consisting of two infected cell proteins designated ICP 12 and ICP 14, that comigrate on SDS-acrylamide gel electrophoresis with virion envelope proteins.[48] ICP 12 is an "immediate early" protein.[42] AG-e is expressed in approximately 28% of the exfoliated cervical tumor cells from 80% of patients in all stages of disease (atypia, carcinoma *in situ,* or invasive cancer).[36] Consistent with the expression of the AG-e antigen in cervical tumor cells, patients with cervical atypia, carcinoma *in situ* or invasive cancer, are positive in an *in vitro* assay of cell-mediated immunity in which reactivity depends on the continuous *in vivo* exposure of lymphoid cells to the specific antigen under consideration.[35] Unlike the cancer patients, individuals suffering from herpetic disease are positive in this assay only while suffering from recurrent HSV-2 lesions.

Neoplastic Transformation Induced by a Specific Viral DNA Fragment

We have previously shown[49] that Syrian hamster embryo (SHE) cells are transformed to a neoplastic phenotype with native noninactivated HSV-2 DNA at concentrations at which it fails to induce productive infection.[49] Several lines of evidence are compatible with the interpretation that this transformation is mediated by fragment(s) of the HSV-2 genome: (a) mechanically sheared HSV-2 DNA of approximately one-eleventh the size of the viral genome (average molecular weight 9×10^6 daltons) induces neoplastic transformation at a frequency (one out of 10^5 cells per 0.01 μg DNA) identical to that observed with native, intact viral DNA,[50] (b) hamster cells transformed by UV irradiated HSV-2 retain only a variable fraction (8–32%) of the viral DNA sequences,[16] and (c) transforming activity of the virus is more resistant to damage by

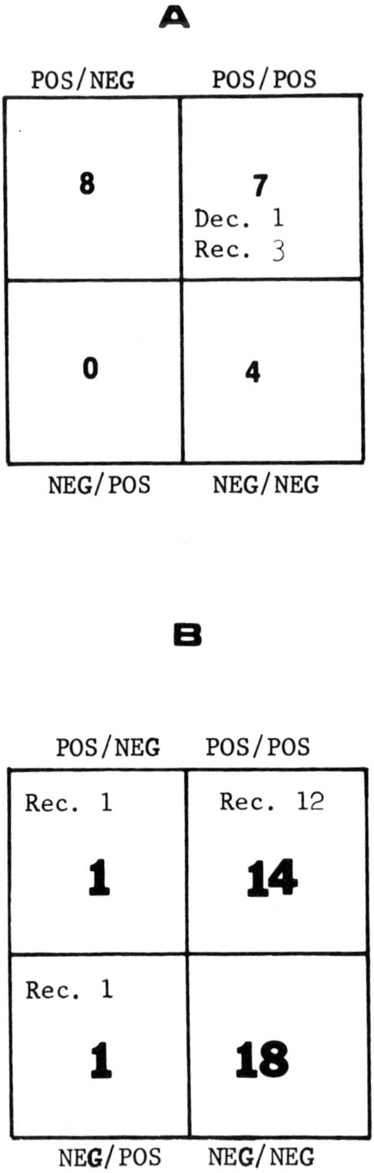

A

POS/NEG	POS/POS
8	7 Dec. 1 Rec. 3
0	4
NEG/POS	NEG/NEG

B

POS/NEG	POS/POS
Rec. 1 **1**	Rec. 12 **14**
Rec. 1 **1**	**18**
NEG/POS	NEG/NEG

Figure 4A, B. AG-4 seropositivity in: **(A)** Patients diagnosed as invasive cancer studied prior to therapy and followed up at three- to six-month intervals for three years. **(B)** Patients entered into the study at various intervals following therapy for invasive cancer (20 patients), CIS (10 patients), and atypia (4 patients). Follow-up, including AG-4 assay, was performed at three- to six-month intervals for three years. POS/NEG = AG-4 sera positive at entry into study converted to seronegative. POS/POS = AG-4 seropositive throughout study. NEG/POS = AG-4 seronegative at entry into study converted to seropositive. NEG/NEG = AG-4 seronegative throughout study. REC = Recurrent disease. DEC = deceased.

radiation than is its infectivity.[14] Consistent with this interpretation, Camacho and Spear[51] described hamster cell transformation to a morphologically altered phenotype by a restriction endonuclease fragment of HSV-1 DNA located at 0.3–0.45 map units on the viral genome, but transformation, albeit at lower frequency, was also observed with other fragments of the viral DNA. Morphologic transformation was also reported with Bgl II N fragment of HSV-2 DNA located at 0.58–0.62 map units on the viral genome.[52] However, the oncogenic potential of these transformants was not established.

We proposed that neoplastic transformation should be demonstrable with an isolated fragment generated by cleavage of viral DNA with appropriate restriction endonucleases, provided that oncogenic activity does not depend on several noncontiguous genes, and that suitable restriction endonucleases can yield appropriate fragments of viral DNA that do not express lytic functions. The S-1 strain of HSV-2 was used since, having been isolated from a case of intraepithelial cervical carcinoma,[53] the possibility was considered that it may have increased transforming potential. The results of these studies were originally reported by Jariwalla et al.[55] Viral DNA was purified by buoyant centrifugation in NaI gradients as previously described.[49] It was digested with Bgl II and/or Hpa I and DNA fragments were separated by electrophoresis on 0.3% agarose gels.[54] Bgl II and Hpa I cleavage maps of the DNA of the G[29,54] and 333 (Third Herpesvirus Workshop, CSH, September, 1976) strains of HSV-2 are established. Consistent with our previous observations[53,56] indicating that S-1 is a *bona fide* isolate from the cervical tumor cells biologically different from established laboratory HSV-2 strains,[56] we observed minor differences in the Bgl II digestion pattern of S-1 DNA.[55] Most obvious among these was the absence of a band corresponding to the fragment G of 333. Previous reports[29] had indicated that DNA digests of variois HSV strains display the addition or absence of a cleavage site resulting in the replacement of one larger by two smaller fragments or vice versa. Consistent with these data, there were three bands in S-1 DNA that together had a sum of relative molecular weights (10.7×10^6 daltons) that approximates the molecular weight (11.7×10^6 daltons) of the missing G fragment.[55] It should be pointed out that the transforming region of S-1 DNA displayed sequence homology with the corresponding 333 DNA fragment.[55]

SHE cells transfected with unfractionated digests of Bgl II cleaved HSV-2 (S-1) DNA ($0.01-10\mu g$) displayed, within two to four passages following transfection, morphologically transformed cells that overgrew the cultures. The frequency of transformation was approximately one transformant/5×10^5 cells/0.01 μg DNA. Under identical conditions, transformation was also observed with unfractionated Hpa I limit digests ($0.1-0.01$ μg), and with total double digests of Bgl II/Hpa I cleaved HSV-2 (S-1) DNA ($0.001-1.0$ μg). It was not observed with salmon sperm

DNA. The frequency of transformation by the Bgl II/Hpa I digests was one transformant/5 × 10^5 cells/0.001 μg DNA.[55]

Within the concentration range (0.002–1.14 μg) studied in our laboratory, transformation of SHE cells was observed only with band 3 of size class II Bgl II fragments. SHE cells transfected with 0.012–0.18 μg of the double digest Bgl II/Hpa I CD_{S-1} fragment (16.5 × 10^6 daltons) also displayed morphologically altered epithelial-like cells that within six to eight further passages overgrew the cultures and produced rapidly growing lines.

Transformed lines established with unfractionated total digests of Bgl II-cleaved HSV-2 (S-1) DNA (SDNA-1B and SDNA-0.1B), or with Bgl II/Hpa I fragment CD_{S-1} (SDNA-CD) were examined for phenotypic alterations associated with the neoplastic state and for the presence of viral antigens. They exhibited increased cloning efficiency in 10% (26–43.5% CE) and 2% (5.2–19.8% CE) serum when seeded at 100–500 cells/60 mm dish and produced visible colonies in agarose and agar with colony-forming efficiencies ranging between 0.16–24%. Normal SHE cells did not grow under these conditions. Furthermore, the lines were tumorigenic for newborn Syrian hamsters. Tumors (fibrosarcomas and tumors of epithelial origin) were obtained in 100% of the animals inoculated with 2 × 10^6 SDNA-1B or SDNA-CD cells and in 20% of those inoculated with SDNA-0.1B cells.

Extracts of SDNA-1B and SDNA-CD cells fixed complement with IgG from antisera to total viral antigens (Ra-2) and to ICP 10. The reaction was virus-specific, as indicated by the observations that: (a) preimmune rabbit IgG was nonreactive; (b) anti-ICP 10 and Ra-2 IgG did not fix complement with extracts of SHE cells; (c) anti-ICP 10 IgG fixed complement with HSV-2 (G) virions pelleted by centrifugation at 82,500 × g for one hour but not with mock virus prepared identically from uninfected cells, and (d) anti-ICP 10 IgG reactivity was specifically adsorbed by pelleted HSV-2 virions but not by mock-virus antigen (Table 5).

Conclusions and Perspectives

It seems profitable, for the sake of this discussion, to assume that HSV-2 is the etiological agent of human cervical cancer and that it acts as the inducer (Figure 1) of cervical transformation. If this be the case, two pertinent questions arise: First, is the virus ever latent in the cells that it transforms? Second, when the latently infected cervical cell is induced to multiply (i.e., at transformation), what prevents the induction of the latent virus with concomitant cell death? Although direct evidence for HSV-2 persistence in normal cervical cells is not presently available,

Table 5. Complement Fixing Potential of 7S Immunoglobulin from Anti-ICP10 Sera

IgG from Antiserum	Percentage of Complement Fixed by Extract[a]							
	SHE	SDNA-1B PTP 9	SDNA-CD[b] PTP 13	SDNA-CD-1[b] PTP 39	SDNA-CD-2[b] PTP 14	AG-4	AG-H	HSV-2[c]
Preimmune	0	5.2	2.6	7.6	1.3	0	0	0
Preimmune adsorbed with HSV-2 (G)	0	ND[f]	0	ND	ND	0	0	0
Anti-ICP-10	0	42.4	19.4	25.0	29.2	55.6	0	21.6
Anti-ICP-10 adsorbed with HSV-2 (G)[d]	5.9	8.2	2	ND	ND	0	0	7
Anti-ICP-10 adsorbed with mock virus preparations[e]	ND	35.4	ND	ND	ND	54	0	24.3
Ra-2	0	ND	55.1	49.2	61.5	ND	ND	86.8
Preimmune	7	ND	0	0	1.2	ND	ND	2.1

[a] Extracts of SHE and SDNA cells were prepared as previously described.[4,6] AG-4 and control AG-H antigens were prepared from HEp-2 cells infected with HSV-2(G) or mock-infected with PBS for 4 h respectively as described.[15] They were all assayed at 20 μg of protein. Sera were used at ¼ dilution. Reaction is considered positive if more than 10% of the complement is fixed.

[b] Cell lines established by transfection with 0.012 μg (SDNA-CD), 0.12 μg SDNA-CD-1), and 0.17 μg (SDNA-CD-2) of Bg1 II/Hpa I fragment CD_{s-1}.

[c] HSV-2(G) pelleted by centrifugation at 82,500 g for 60 min and resuspended in Veronal buffer. Antigen is 20 μg of protein.

[d] Virions pelleted by centrifugation at 82,500 g for 60 min. 2600 μg of protein or dextran gradient purified (710 μg of protein) are fixed in 0.1 M sodium acetate, pH 5.0, containing 1% glutaraldehyde for 3 h at room temperature, and washed twice in 0.2 M potassium phosphate buffer, pH 7.2. The last pellet is used to adsorb 0.1 ml of IgG.[15]

[e] Pellets obtained from soluble extracts of mock-infected HEp-2 cells prepared as in d and used at concentrations of 2600 μg of protein/0.1 ml of IgG.

[f] ND = Not done.

it is becoming increasingly evident that cells other than neurons are capable of maintaining the virus in a latent state. In this context, the relatively low (10%) rate of HSV-2 isolation from sacral ganglia obtained from human cadavers[22] is particularly significant. The observation that a specific HSV-2 DNA fragment can transform cells *in vitro* is consistent with the detection in cervical tumor cells of viral DNA sequences corresponding to only 30% of the viral genome.[38] It argues that transformation does not necessitate the complete viral genome but rather results from the expression of specific viral gene(s). Accordingly, whatever the stress, infectious virus can not be induced, at least in most of the transformed cells. Questions that still remain unresolved include: (a) the mechanism(s) involved in the generation of viral DNA fragments, and (b) the fate of adjacent untransformed cells that remain latently infected with the complete viral genome. Indeed, such cells could potentially serve as a reservoir of infectious virus capable of destroying the transformed cells—a possible factor in the regression[2] of the preinvasive cervical lesions. Alternatively, they may be those cells that maintain intact virus such as isolated by us from cervical intraepithelial lesions[53] or by Macnab (personal communication) from rat tumors.

Within the concentration range (0.1–0.001 μg) used in our laboratory, transforming activity was displayed only by band 3 of size class II Bgl II fragments. Since all other DNA fragments were used within the same concentration range, failure to establish transformation with DNA fragments other than band 3 cannot be due to DNA insufficiency. However, the possibility cannot be excluded that the absence of transformation with other DNA fragments merely reflects a "specific transforming activity," that is, below current detection levels, and therefore probably represents a phenomenon biologically different from the one described in our laboratory.[49,50]

Our studies[55] have localized the neoplastic potential of HSV-2 in the 16.5×10^6 dalton fragment CD_{S-1} generated by double digestion of S-1 DNA with Bgl II and Hpa I. Although final conclusions pertaining to the colinearity of S-1 and 333 DNA maps must await the results of further mapping studies, three observations support the interpretation that transforming activity maps within map units 0.43–0.58 on the viral genome (Figure 5). These are: (a) the CD_{S-1} fragment displays sequence homology to the similarly generated fragment of 333 DNA,[55] (b) the similarly prepared fragment from 333 DNA is also capable of transforming SHE cells,[55] and (c) presently available evidence suggests that modification in one gene occurs to the exclusion of all others, thus supporting the concept of colinearity.[29,54]

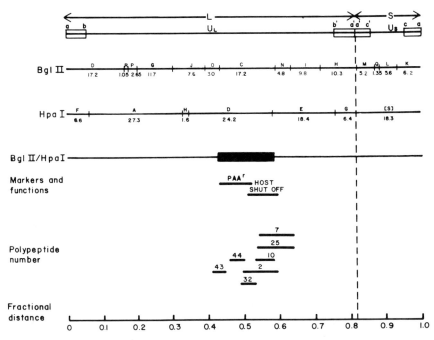

Figure 5. Location of Bgl II and Hpa I fragments in the prototype arrangement of HSV-2 333 DNA based on published maps for these sites.[54] HSV-DNA contains four populations differing in the relative orientation of the L and S components.[29] Consequently, a restriction endonuclease digest of HSV DNA contains, in addition to the one-molar fragments (found in all species of viral DNA), four 0.5 M terminal ones (two each from the L and S termini found in half of the population) and four 0.25 M ones arising from the joining of the L and S terminal fragments (found in 25% of the population). The 0.25 M fragments contain, in various permutations, the sequences present in the 0.5 M terminal fragments.[20] Accordingly, sixteen Bgl II fragments designated DK, DM, C, D, HK, HM, G, H, I, J, K, L, M, N, O, and P were reported in Bgl II digests of HSV-2 DNA.[54] Those designated with double letters describing component parts represent the 0.25 M fragments (Third Herpesvirus Workshop, CSH, Sept., 1976). We have confirmed these results for the 333 strain of HSV-2.[55] Despite strain-related minor differences Bgl II fragments of S-1 DNA were essentially similar. The location of the transforming fragment obtained by double digestion with Bgl II and Hpa I is indicated by the solid Bgl II/Hpa I block. Sequence homology is observed between this fragment from S-1 and 333 DNA.[55] Genetic markers and polypeptides that have been mapped in the Bgl II, C fragment include: (a) numbered polypeptides of unknown functions mapped by analysis of HSV-1 × HSV-2 recombinants,[60] (b) PAA resistance locus,[60] and (c) host shut-off mapped by analyses of HSV-1 × HSV-2 recombinants.[62] Fine mapping of PAA^r locus using HSV-1 marker transfer methods showed that it maps at either 0.46 or 0.49 map unit.[61]

Our findings differ from those of Camacho and Spear[51] who reported that the transforming activity of HSV-1 is contained within sequences located between coordinates 0.3 and 0.45 on the physical map of the genome, but agree with those of Cameron and Macnab (personal communication) who found that transforming potential of HSV-2 for rat cells resides within sequences located between 0.43–0.64 map units on the HSV-2 genome. The interpretation of these apparently contradictory observations should include the possibility that at least some functions may differ in their map location in the two (HSV-1 vs HSV-2) virus serotypes. Alternatively, the possibility cannot be excluded that the difference is a function of the specific nature—biochemical,[59] morphologic or neoplastic—of the transforming event under investigation.

Six polypeptides of unknown function,[60] PAA resistance[61] and host shut-off genes,[62] have been mapped in the CD_{S-1} fragment. Our finding that ICP 10 is expressed in SDNA-CD cells suggests that it also maps in this region. The latter is a likely candidate for transformation-specific protein since it is an "immediate early" protein, immunologically identical to the cervical cancer specific AG-4 antigen. Consistent with these interpretations, immediate early transcripts have been mapped in the 0.55–0.60 region of the HSV-2 genome and shown to code for the synthesis *in vitro* of at least one vital protein that appears to correspond to ICP 10 in terms of its migration pattern on SDS-acrylamide gels (Clements, personal communication).

By analogy to animal DNA tumor viruses, it seems attractive to postulate that the maintenance of a transformed state requires the persistence and expression of at least those viral gene(s) involved in transformation. Indeed, SDNA-CD cells express viral antigens during all the *in vitro* passages (PTP) studied in these series. However contradictory reports pertaining to maintenance of viral DNA sequences having been made, final conclusions pertaining to this problem will depend on further studies at increasing PTP, on the demonstration that abortive transformation involves the loss of viral gene expression and that mutants in this gene fragment do not transform under nonpermissive conditions. It should be pointed out that the hypothesis that HSV-2 acts as an inducer of atypia (Figure 1) does not require that viral DNA sequences persist in the transformed cells in order for these to progress (or be selected) to invasive cancer. Successful virus isolation from a cervical intraepithelial lesion,[53] but not from invasive cancer cells grown in culture[64] may be interpreted to support this argument. However, presently available evidence from human studies supports the concept of persistence, since viral DNA sequences were found in a cervical tumor[38] and cervical cancer patients express viral antigens that, whenever compared, are at a frequency similar to that observed in atypia.[33–36,39,40,43–47,65]

Summary

Consideration of the problem of viral causality of human cancer must come to grips with the limitations of the criteria for causation. Since cancer is a multifactorial disease, insistence on the fulfillment of the Koch postulate and of the one-to-one relationship of a specific virus to a human neoplasm is naive and should be abandoned. On the other hand, selection of one specific criterion of causation as superior to all others is scientifically invalid. The problem should be considered in the context of a series of attributes that must be fulfilled by the association of a virus with a specific human cancer before it can be accepted as causally plausible. These are: (a) consistency, (b) strength, (c) temporal relationship, (d) specificity, and (e) coherence of the association.[63] In the case of HSV-2 and cervix cancer, this approach will identify the virus as the most common carcinogenic factor in the promiscuous population at high risk of cervix cancer[32] and thus establish the relationship of the virus to squamous cancer of the human cervix by virtue of their natural relationship. The strength, consistency and coherence of the association (Table 3) are underscored by the studies described in this report. They correlate the transforming potential of the viral genetic material with cervix cancer by demonstrating that cells transformed by specific DNA sequences of a virus isolated from cervical tumor cells, express AG-4, a viral protein that reflects the progression of human cervical cancer.

ACKNOWLEDGMENTS
The work done in our laboratory was supported by Public Health Service Grants CA-16043 and CA-25019 from the National Cancer Institute. R.J.J. was supported by a National Research Service Award from the National Cancer Institute. Thanks are due Drs. Mark Manak, Cynthia C. Smith, Irving I. Kessler and Paul P.O.P. Ts'o for helpful discussions. We also thank Mrs. Gene Barbour for the AG-4 assay and Mrs. Jean Roberson for help with the manuscript.

References

1. Barenblum, J.: In: *Frontiers of Biology,* A. Neuberger and E.L. Tatum (eds.), North Holland Publishing Co., Amsterdam, 1975, p. 115.

2. Koss, L.G.: *Obstet. Gynecol. Surv.* 24:850, 1969.

3. Koch, R.: In: *Verh X. Int. Med. Congr. Berlin, 1890,* p. 35, 1892.

4. Rivers, T.M.: *J. Bateriol.* 33:1, 1937.

5. Huebner, R.J.: *Ann. N.Y. Acad. Sci.* 67:430, 1957.

6. Evans, A.S.: *Yale J. Biol. Med.* 49:175, 1976.

7. Roizman, B.: *Curr. Top. Microbiol. Immunol.* 49:1, 1969.

8. Strandberg, J.D. and Aurelian, L.: *J. Virol.* 4:480, 1969.

9. Strnad, B. and Aurelian, L.: *Virology* 69:438, 1976.

10. Aurelian, L. and Roizman, B.: *Virology* 22:452, 1964.

11. Roizman, B. and Aurelian, L.: *J. Mol. Biol.* 11:528, 1965.

12. Aurelian, L. and Roizman, B.: *J. Mol. Biol.* 11:539, 1965.

13. Rapp, D. and Duff, R.: *Fed. Proc.* 31:1660, 1972.

14. Kucera, L.A., Gusdon, J.P., Edwards, I., and Herbst, G.: *J. Gen. Virol.* 35:473, 1977.

15. Darai, G., Brain, R., Flügel, R.M., and Munk, K.: *Nature* 265:744, 1977.

16. Frenkel, N., Locker, H., Cox, B., Roizman, B., and Rapp, F.: *J. Virol.* 18:885, 1976.

17. Bronson, D.L., Dreasman, G.R., Biswel, N., and Benyesh-Melnick, M.: *Intervirology* 1:141, 1973.

18. Nahmias, A.J. and Roizman, B.: *N. Engl. J. Med.* 289:667, 1973.

19. Stevens, J.G. and Cook, M.L.: In: *Perspectives in Virology, Vol. 8,* M. Pollard (ed.), Academic Press, New York, 1973, p. 171.

20. Baringer, J.R. and Swoveland, P.: *N. Engl. J. Med.* 288:648, 1973.

21. Centifanto, J.M., Drylie, D.M., Deardourff, S.L., and Kaufman, H.L.: *Science* 178:318, 1972.

22. Baringer, J.R.: In: *Oncogenesis and Herpesvirus II,* IARC Scientific Publication No. 11, G. de-Thé, M.A. Epstein and H. zur Hausen (eds.), International Agency for Research on Cancer, Lyon, 1975, p. 73.

23. Scriba, M.: *Infect. Immun.* 12:161, 1975.

24. Roizman, B.: In: *Perspectives in Virology, Vol. 4,* M. Pollard (ed.), Harper and Row, New York, 1965, p. 283.

25. Kaufman, H.E., Brown, D.C., and Ellison, E.D.: *Science* 156:1628, 1967.

26. Kaufman, H.E., Brown, D.C., and Ellison, E.D.: *Am. J. Opthalmol.* 65:32, 1968.

27. Douglas, R.G. and Couch, R.B.: *J. Immunol.* 104:289, 1970.

28. Schwartz, J., Whetsell, W.O., Jr., and Elizan, T.S.: *J. Nueropathol. Exp. Neurol.* 37:45, 1978.

29. Roizman, B.: *Cell* 16:481, 1979.

30. Naib, Z.M., Nahmias, A.J., Josey, W.E., and Zolis, S.A.: *Cancer Res.* 33:1452, 1973.

31. Naib, M., Nahmias, A.J., Josey, W.E., and Kramer, J.H.: *Cancer* 23:940, 1969.

32. Kessler, I.I.: *Cancer Res.* 34:1091, 1974.

33. Aurelian, L., Smith, M.F., and Cornish, J.D.: *J. Natl. Cancer Inst.* 56:471, 1976.

34. Anzai, T., Dreasman, G.R., Courtney, R.J., Adam, E., Rawls, W.E., and Benyesh-Melnick, M.: *J. Natl. Cancer Inst.* 54:1051, 1975.

35. Bell, R.B., Aurelian, L., and Cohen, G.H.: *Cell. Immunol.* 41:86, 1978.

36. Aurelian, L., Gupta, P.K., Frost, J.K, Rosenshein, N.B., Smith, C.C., Tyrer, H.W., Mantione, J.M., and Albright, C.D.: *Anal. Quant. Cytol.* 1:89, 1979.

37. Jones, K.W., Fenoglio, C.M., Maitland, N.J., and McDougall, J.K.: In: *Oncogenesis and Herpesvirus III,* IARC Scientific Publications No. 24, G. de-Thé, W. Henle and F. Rapp (eds.), International Agency for Research on Cancer, Lyon, 1978, p. 917.

38. Frenkel, N., Roizman, B., Cassai, E., and Nahmias, A.J.: *Proc. Natl. Acad. Sci. USA* 69:3784, 1972.

39. Aurelian, L.: *Cancer Res.* 33:1539, 1973.

40. Aurelian, L., Strandberg, J.D., and Marcus, R.L.: *Prog. Exp. Tumor Res.* 19:165, 1974.

41. Strnad, B.C. and Aurelian, L.: *Virology* 87:401, 1978.

42. Strnad, B.C. and Aurelian, L.: *Virology* 73:244, 1976.

43. Aurelian, L., Schumann, B., and Marcus, R.L.: *Science* 181:161, 1973.

44. Heise, E.R. and Kucera, L.S.: *Proc. Am. Soc. Microbiol.*, p. 217, 1976.

45. Notter, M.F.D. and Docherty, J.J.: *J. Natl. Cancer Inst.* 57:483, 1976.

46. Kawana, T., Cornish, J.D., Smith, M.F., and Aurelian, L.: *Cancer Res.* 36:810, 1976.

47. Kawana, T., Yoshino, K., and Yasamatsui, T.: *Gan.* 65:439, 1974.

48. Smith, C.C. and Aurelian, L.: *Virology* 98:255, 1979.

49. Jariwalla, R., Aurelian, L., and Ts'o, P.O.P.: *J. Virol.* 30:404, 1979.

50. Jariwalla, R., Aurelian, L., and Ts'o, P.O.P.: *Cancer Res.* 1980 (in press).

51. Camacho, A. and Spear, P.G.: *Cell* 15:993, 1978.

52. Reyes, G.R. and Hayward, G.S.: In: *Abstracts of the Fourth Cold Spring Harbor Meeting on the Herpesvirus*, Cold Spring Harbor Laboratory, Cold Spring Harbor, New York, 1979, p. 182.

53. Aurelian, L., Strandberg, J.D., Melendez, L.V., and Johnson, L.A.: *Science* 174:485, 1971.

54. Morse, L.S., Buchman, T.G., Roizman, B., and Schaffer, P.A.: *J. Virol* 24:231, 1977.

55. Jariwalla, R., Aurelian, L., and Ts'o, P.O.P.: *Proc. Natl. Acad. Sci. USA*, 1980 (in press).

56. Aurelian, L. and Strandberg, J.D.: *Arch. Gesamte Virusforsch.* 45:27, 1974.

57. Maniatis, T., Jeffrey, A., and Kleid, D.G.: *Proc. Natl. Acad. Sci. USA* 72:1184, 1975.

58. Southern, E.M.: *J. Mol. Biol.* 98:503, 1975.

59. Wigler, M., Silverstein, S., Lee, S.-S., Pellicer, A., Cheng, Y.-C., and Axel, R.: *Cell* 11:223, 1977.

60. Morse, L.S., Pereira, L., Roizman, B., and Schaffer, P.A.: *J. Virol.* 26:389, 1978.

61. Knipe, D.N., Ruyechan, W.T., and Roizman, B.: *J. Virol.* 29:698, 1979.

62. Fenwick, M., Morse, L.S., and Roizman, B.: *J. Virol.* 29:825, 1979.

63. Surgeon General Advisory Committee of the USPHS, "Smoking and Health," PHS Pub. No. 1103, Supt. of Doc., Washington, D.C., 1974.

64. Aurelian, L.: *Cancer Res.* 34:1126, 1974.

65. Melnick, J.L., Adam. E., Lewis, R., and Kaufman, R.H.: *Intervirology* 12:111, 1979.

On the Latency and Oncogenicity of Herpes Simplex Virus

Klaus Munk

Institut für Virusforschung, Deutsches Krebsforschungszentrum, Heidelberg, Federal Republic of Germany

The question of the oncogenicity of the human pathogenic herpes simplex virus (HSV) is of paramount interest. In some of its prominent properties, HSV resembles other members of the herpesvirus group known to be oncogenic even for their natural host. The stage of latency belongs to one of these outstanding properties. In the case of HSV infection, latency can be correlated with the clinical appearance of the recurrence of herpes lesions (Figure 1). It is well established from various oncogenic DNA viruses that the nonproductive host-virus relationship is the biological basis for latency and that it is a prerequisite for the oncogenic function of a DNA virus.

Therefore, studies on the latency of HSV infection in experimental systems could be one of the approaches toward understanding the oncogenic functions of HSV, particularly because it has not yet been possible to induce tumors by HSV infection *in vivo* whereas experimental *in vivo* models for the study of the processes of latency already exist.[1,2]

Latency

In our laboratory, we studied the pathogenesis of HSV in the animal host system of the primitive prosimian tupaia (tree shrews) (Figure 2).[3,4] This animal has been used only recently as a laboratory animal in virology. It shares a number of properties with subhuman primates and is highly susceptible to HSV infection in particular. The clinical appearance of an acute infection after intraperitoneal inoculation with HSV is expressed predominantly in an acute necrotic hepatitis, while the symp-

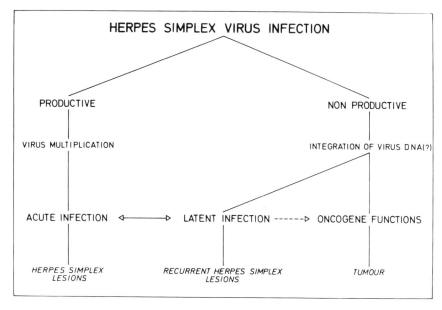

Figure 1. Recurrence of herpes lesions.

Figure 2. Primitive prosimian tupaia (tree shrews).

toms of the central nervous system are secondary.[5,6] This is in contrast to the pathogenesis of HSV infection in rodents.

In a series of experiments, however, a number of animals infected with the HSV-2 strain HG-52 survived the acute infection. These animals were infected at the age of 150 days with this HSV strain. When the animals were sacrificed several months after infection, we were able to recover infectious HSV from their spinal cords after cocultivation of spinal cord material with African green monkey kidney (RC 37) cells (Table 1). This indicates that HSV resides in a latent state in tupaia as previously shown for various other animals. The genome of the recovered viruses was compared with the viral DNA of the inoculated virus using restriction endonuclease cleavage (Eco RI and Hind III) and subsequent separation of the resulting DNA fragments in agarose gels. Changes in the DNA fragment patterns were not detected. Therefore, the experiments demonstrate that the recovered virus is actually the inoculated herpes simplex virus and not one of the three known members of the tupaia herpesvirus.[7]

In another series of experiments aimed at inducing a higher survival rate or even establishing a complete latent infection system in these animals, we used temperature-sensitive (ts) HSV mutants developed and characterized by Subak-Sharpe et al.[8] The temperature optimum of these ts-mutants is 32°C. It should be noted that the physiological body temperature of the tupaia varies from 36°C at night to more than 41°C in the daytime. It was found that even juvenile tupaia survived an infection with these temperature mutants.

In the course of these experiments, we challenged the latent infected tupaias with high inocula of HSV strains known to induce lethal infections in adult tupaias in various intervals of time after the first ts-mutant infection. As a result of these experiments we found that the animals were resistant to lethal doses of highly pathogenic HSV strains (Table 2). This leads to the conclusion that the originally inoculated mutant of HSV maintains a latent infection which prevents a secondary infection with another HSV strain. This observation is in accordance with results of Roizman.[9] He reported that he was able to isolate the same HSV strains from patients with recurrent herpes lesions after a great number of years. However, one can reasonably assume that these patients had been exposed to secondary HSV infection. In addition, experiments are in progress in our laboratory to isolate the latent virus from these doubly-infected tupaias and to investigate the DNA restriction pattern of the recovered virus. It would be of interest to demonstrate whether, according to the restriction pattern, the recovered HSV, is in fact the originally inoculated virus, the secondary strain, or a genetic mixture of both strains. The results of such experiments could contribute to consideration of booster vaccinations with viral antigen containing HSV genome material in cases of recurrent herpes simplex lesions.

Table 1. Recovery of HSV-1 and 2 During Chronic Latent Infection of Adult Tupaia[a]

| No. of Animals | Age of Animals[b] (days) | Infection State | | Time When Animals Were Sacrificed After Infection (mo) | Virus Recovered from[c] | | | | |
| | | Strain of HSV Inoculated | pfu of Virus/Animal | | Whole Blood | Leukocytes | Spinal Cord Segments | | |
							Sacral	Lumbothoracic	Cervical
1	50	HSV-2 HG-52	1.0×10^5	4 1/2	0/1	0/1	0/1	1/1	0/2
2	50	HSV-2 HG-52	1.0×10^5	8	0/2	0/2	0/2	1/2	0/2
2	60	HSV-2 HG-52	4.0×10^5	6 3/4	0/2	0/2	1/2	0/2	0/2
4	60	HSV-2 HG-52	4.0×10^5	4	0/4	0/4	0/4	1/4	0/4
4	80	HSV-2 HG-52	4.0×10^5	3 1/2	0/4	0/4	0/4	0/4	0/4
1	50	HSV-1 Thea	1.0×10^5	2 3/4	0/1	0/1	1/1	1/1	0/1
1	60	HSV-1 Thea	1.0×10^5	2 1/4	0/1	0/1	0/1	1/1	0/1
1	60	HSV-1 Thea	1.0×10^5	3 1/3	0/1	0/1	1/1	1/1	1/1
1	100	HSV-1 Thea	1.0×10^5	2 1/3	0/1	0/1	0/1	0/1	0/1

[a] The animals were inoculated intraperitoneally.
[b] Average values of age.
[c] Number of animals from which virus was isolated/number of animals infected.

Table 2. Sensitivity of Tupaia Infected with HSV-1 and 2 or Temperature-Sensitive Mutants of HSV-2 HG-52 to Superinfection with Killing Dose of Wild Type of HSV-1 or -2

No. of Animals	State of First Infection				State of Second Infection (1.0 x 10⁷ pfu/Animal)		
	Weight/Age of Animals[a] (g/days)	Strain of HSV Inoculated	Route of Infection	pfu of Virus/Animal	Weight/Age of Animals[a] (g/mon)	Strain of HSV Inoculated	No. of Animals Dead/No. of Animals
4	153/100	HSV-1 Thea	ip	4.5×10^3	182/14	HSV-2 Müller	0/4
4	201/100	HSV-2 HG-52	ip	1.0×10^6	207/ 8	HSV-1 Thea	0/4
2	111/ 52	HSV-2 HG-52, tsm No. 1	iv	1.0×10^7	180/ 4	HSV-1 Thea	0/1
						HSV-2 Müller	0/1
2	120/ 53	HSV-2 HG-52, tsm No. 2	iv	1.0×10^7	172/ 4	HSV-1 Thea	0/1
						HSV-2 Müller	0/1
2	123/ 52	HSV-2 HG-52, tsm No. 5	iv	1.0×10^7	169/ 4	HSV-1 Thea	0/1
						HSV-2 Müller	0/1
2	129/ 52	HSV-2 HG-52, tsm No. 9	iv	1.0×10^7	177/ 4	HSV-1 Thea	0/1
						HSV-2 Müller	0/1
2	135/ 51	HSV-2 HG-52, tsm No. 10	iv	1.0×10^7	176/ 4	HSV-1 Thea	0/1
						HSV-2 Müller	0/1
2	149/ 58	HSV-2 HG-52, tsm No. 12	iv	1.0×10^7	168/ 4	HSV-1 Thea	0/1
						HSV-2 Müller	0/1
2	165/ 55	Mock			212/ 4	HSV-1 Thea	2/2
1	153/ 61	Mock			185/ 4	HSV-2 Müller	1/1

[a] Average values of weight and/or age.

Table 3.   Cell Transformation with Altered Herpes Simplex Virus

Method	Cells	Transformation In Vitro	Out-growth of Tumor in Vivo
UV-inactivation	Hamster	+	+
Temperature-sensitive mutants	Rat	+	+
	Hamster	+	+
Photodynamic inactivation	Hamster	+	+
Inactivation by high-energy radiation	Human	+	ND[a]
	Tupaia	+	ND

[a] ND = Not done.

Oncogenicity

Studies to demonstrate the oncogenic potential of HSV *in vitro* have been performed by a number of laboratories. In all attempts, however, in order to transform cells *in vitro* by HSV, it was first necessary to find and to work out conditions under which the lytic functions of the HSV are inhibited. The prerequisite for all transformation experiments was the establishment of a nonpermissive or a nonproductive virus-host cell system. Such conditions were obtained by various laboratories in two different ways. One group of investigators inhibited the lytic function of the HSV by altering the inoculated virus (Table 3), while another group changed the cell conditions of permissive to those of nonpermissive cells (Table 4).[10] In our laboratory, for HSV-induced neoplastic cell transfor-

Table 4.   Transformation of Nonpermissive Cells by Herpes Simplex Virus

Method	Cells	Transformation In Vitro	Out-growth of Tumor in Vivo
RSV Pretransformed Cells	XC-cells	+	–
Supraoptimal incubation temperature (42°)	Human	+	ND[a]
	Rat	+	+
Suboptimal incubation temperature (20°)	Rat	+	+
Photodynamic inactivation and supraoptimal incubation temperature (42°)	Rat	+	+
	Human	+	ND

[a] ND = Not done.

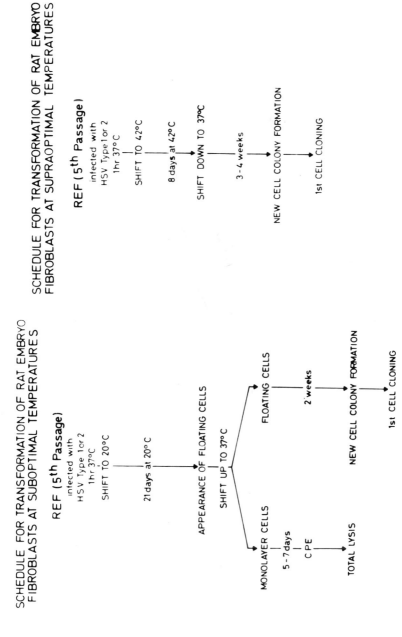

Figure 3. Schedules for transformation of rat embryo fibroblasts.

Table 5. Characterization of Normal and HSV-Transformed Rat Embryo Fibroblast Cells

Cell Type[a]	Morphology of Cells[b]	Plating Efficiency of Cells (%)	Modal Number Chromosomes	Growth in Soft Agar	Immunofluorescence	
					Cytoplasmic	Nuclear
REF normal	F	(20)	42	–	–	–
REF-T (HSV-1)-20[a]	sp	(58)	89	+	+	–
REF-T (HSV-2)-20	sp	(52)	99	+	+	–
REF-T (HSV-2)-20	ep	(40)	66	–	(+)	–
REF-T (HSV-1)-42	sp	(56)	86	+	–	–
REF-T (HSV-2)-42	sp	(52)	72	+	+	–
REF-T (HSV-2)-42						
Clone 1	ep	(36)	56	–	(+)	–
Clone 2	sp	(55)	93	+	+	–

[a] HSV-1 (Thea), HSV-2 (Müller), HSV-2 (HG-52).

[b] F = fibroblast; sp = spindle-like; ep = epithelial-like.

mation, we used the technique of establishing a nonpermissive host cell system which allows the application of wild-type HSV. Principally, we performed two series of experiments. On one hand, we applied the supraoptimal incubation temperature of 42°C for limited periods of incubation time[11] and, on the other hand, we used the suboptimal temperature of 20°C for a certain period of time (Figure 3).[12]

The transformed cells were morphologically different from each other and different from the control cultures. The new cells were either epithelial-like or spindle-like, as reported for HSV-transformed rat embryo fibroblast (REF) cells. Some clones were isolated by being picked from foci of colonies which had originated from floating cells and which became established in tissue culture. The plating efficiency of transformed cell clones, determined by standard procedures, was two or three times greater than that of the original, normal REF cells. We also found that the modal chromosome number of the transformed cell clones was greater than 42, which is the modal number of primary rat cells. When the extent of colony formation in soft agar was measured, the spindle-like transformed cell clones grew in soft agar, but the epithelial-like clone did not (Table 5). Independent of the method of transformation, when the transformed rat cells were injected into isogenic rats, metastasizing tumors were induced (Table 6). Thus, these results clearly show that HSV has oncogenic potential under these conditions.

Table 6. Efficiency of Tumor Induction of Different Cell Lines as a Function of the Number of Cells

Cell Type[a]	Morphology of Cells[b]	Number of Tumors/Number of Animals Different Number of Cells Transplanted				
		1×10^8	2×10^7	1×10^7	1×10^6	5×10^7
REF normal	F	0/9		0/9		
REF-T (HSV-1)-20	sp				10/10	
REF-T (HSV-2)-20	sp				6/6	
REF-T (HSV-2)-20	ep			0/8	0/10	0/10
REF-T (HSV-1)-42	sp					14/18
REF-T (HSV-2)-42	sp					17/17
REF-T (HSV-2)-42						
Clone 1	ep		0/10		0/9	0/19
Clone 2	ep				8/8	

[a] HSV-1 (Thea), HSV-2 (Müller), HSV-2 (HG-52).

[b] F = fibroblast; sp = spindle-like; ep = epithelial-like.

Conclusion

The question of an HSV etiology of human tumors should be considered. Because latency, as the expression of a nonproductive virus-host cell system, is one of the prerequisites of virus-induced carcinogenesis, it should be further investigated. Latency is regularly observed in human beings. Therefore extensive studies and the development of new approaches and experimental models may lead to a resolution of the question of HSV etiology in human tumors.

References

1. Nahmias, A.J., Naib, Z.N., Josey, W.E., Luce, C.F., and Guest, B.A.: *Amer. J. Epidemiol.* 91:547, 1970.
2. Stevens, J.G. and Cook, M.L.: In: *Perspectives in Virology Vol. 8,* M. Pollard (ed.), Academic Press, New York, 1972, p. 171.
3. Campbell, C.B.G.: *Science* 153:436, 1966.
4. Goodman, M.: *Science* 153:1550, 1966.
5. Munk, K., Schwaier, A., and Darai, G.: In: *Oncogenesis and Herpesviruses III,* IARC Scientific Publications No. 24, G. de-Thé, W. Henle and F. Rapp (eds.), International Agency for Research on Cancer, Lyon, 1978, p. 789.
6. Darai, G., Schwaier, A., Komitowski, D., and Munk, K.: *J. Infect. Dis.* 137:221, 1978.
7. Darai, G., Gramlich, U., Zöller, L., Matz, B., Schwaier, A., Flügel, R.M., and Munk, K.: In: *Abstracts of the Fourth Cold Spring Harbor Meeting on Herpesviruses,* Cold Spring Harbor Laboratory, Cold Spring Harbor, New York, 1979, p. 124.
8. Subak-Sharpe, J.H., Brown, S.M., Ritchie, D.A., Tilbury, M.C., Macnab, J.C.M., Marsen, H.S., and Hay, J.: *Cold Spring Harb. Symp. Quant. Biol.* 39:717, 1974.
9. Roizman, B.: *Cell* 16:481, 1979.
10. Munk, K.: In: *Advances in Medical Oncology, Research and Education, Vol. 1,* P.G. Margison (ed.), Pergamon Press, Oxford and New York, 1979.
11. Darai, G. and Munk, K.: *Int. J. Cancer* 18:469, 1976.
12. Darai, G., Braun, R., Flügel, R.M., and Munk, K.: *Nature* 265:744, 1977.

Giraldo and Beth (eds): The Role of Viruses in Human Cancer, Volume 1

Herpes Simplex Virus-Tumor-Associated Antigen (HSV-TAA) Detected by the Enzyme-Linked Immunosorbent Assay (ELISA)

Giulio Tarro, Giovanni Flaminio,
Roberta Cocchiara, Giuseppe D'Alessandro,
Alfonso Mascolo, Giuliana Papa, Mario Di Gioia,
and Domenico Geraci

Oncological Virology of the First Faculty of Medicine and Surgery, University of Naples, D. Cotugno Hospital, Naples, Italy

An early antigen was obtained from guinea pig kidney (GPK) cells after three hours of infection with herpes simplex virus (HSV) type 1 or type 2.[1] The antigen was induced by HSV, as shown by the protein A antibody adsorbent (PAA) technique, and subsequent purification and characterization resulted in a 70,000 dalton glycoprotein.[2,3] It reacted in the complement fixation (CF) test with an absorbed specific anti-HSV antiserum prepared in hyperimmunized guinea pigs and appeared to be a nonvirion antigen.[4] Patients with various head andck tumors and patients with carcinomas of the urogenital tract had a high incidence of antibodies to this antigen, as demonstrated by the enzyme-linked immunosorbent assay (ELISA).[5,6] Since there was crossreactivity between the antigen deriving from HSV-1 or HSV-2 infected cells, it was designated as HSV-tumor associated antigen (HSV-TAA).

Materials and Methods

Preparation and Purification of HSV-TAA

Capsulary and medullary parts were removed from sterily obtained guinea pig kidneys. The cortex was finely minced into fragments of 1 mm³, and cell suspensions were prepared by incubation at 37°C for 60–90 min with 0.25% trypsin in Eagle's minimum essential medium (MEM). The cells were washed in lactalbumin hydrolysate and resuspended in growth medium consisting of MEM plus 10% fetal calf serum and 0.04% NaHCO$_3$. Spinner flasks were applied for cell propagation with a revolution rate of 100 rpm. After two days of incubation of 37°C, it was found that the number of cells had significantly increased as compared to cells grown in stationary Roux bottles. Three days after initiation of GPK spinner cultures the cells were infected by HSV-1 or HSV-2 (strains Schooler and E-304, respectively) at a multiplicity of ten plaque-forming units/cell. They were simultaneously radiolabeled with 30 μCi/ml of ^{35}S-methionine. Mock-infected GPK cells were used under the same conditions. After a 1-h, 2-h and 3-h exposure to the radioactive amino acid, cells were harvested, washed once in cold phosphate buffered saline (PBS) and the protein was extracted by three cycles of freezing and thawing in a solution of 20 mM Tris-HCl, pH 8, 80 mM NaCl, 20mM EDTA, 1 mM dithiothereitol and 1 mM phenylmethylsulfonyl fluoride. Cellular debris was removed by centrifugation (12,000 rpm for 30 min).

The supernatant containing the antigen was used in the PAA technique.[7,8] Precipitations were obtained with the anti-HSV antiserum, selected human cancer sera which had been previously associated with HSV,[9,10] and sera from healthy donors.

Further purification of the antigen was achieved on columns by Sephadex G-100 gel filtration, ion exchange chromatography with DEAE-Sephadex A-50, and by affinity chromatography using concanavalin A-Sepharose.

Protein A-Antibody Adsorbent (PAA) Technique

The PAA technique[7,8] was used to immunoprecipitate the antigen under investigation. Briefly, antigens were precipitated with normal, pooled guinea pig serum to reduce nonspecific background. Therefore, antigens were first treated with normal guinea pig serum for 12–16 h at 4°C, then fixed *Staphylococcus aureus* protein A (kindly supplied by Dr. G. Giraldo, Sloan-Kettering Cancer Center, New York, N.Y.) (1:1, 10% [vol/vol]) was added and incubation continued for 30 min at room temperature. After pelleting the bacterial adsorbent, the supernatant was mixed with the anti-HSV antibody and various human sera from HSV-associated carcinomas.[9,10] Thirty microliters of serum were sufficient for this step. After overnight incubation at 4°C, bacteria suspension (4 volumes) was added for 30 min at room temperature. The bacteria were then pelleted, resuspended in electrophoresis buffer containing 2% sodium dodecylsulfate (SDS), 10% (vol/vol) glycerol, 80 mM Tris-HCl, pH 6.8, and 2mM phenylmethylsulfonyl fluoride and the antigens were eluted for 15 min at room termperature. The eluted samples were then subjected to SDS-polyacrylamide gel electrophoresis (PAGE) and processed for autoradiography using the X-Omat R film.[11] The following molecular weight standards were added to calibrate the gels: bovine serum albumin (69,000), ovalbumin (43,000), and myoglobin (17,200).

Results

Biochemical Analysis[2,3]

Immunoprecipitation and SDS-PAGE analysis of antigens, derviving from 1-h, 2-h and 3-h HSV-infected and labeled cells with specific anti-HSV antibodies or HSV-associated cancer sera, resulted in a single band

Figure 1. ^{35}S-methionine-labeled immunoreactive protein separated by SDS-polyacrylamide gel electrophoresis (7.5% acrylamide running gel). N = GPK cells infected with HSV-2 strain E-304; S = GPK cells infected with HSV-1 strain Schooler; C = Mock-infected GPK cells. The molecular weights on the right refer to molecular weight standards.

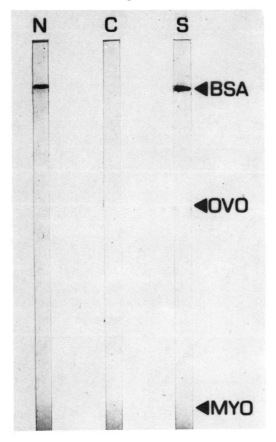

with an apparent molecular weight of 70,000 daltons (Figure 1). Optimal expression of the antigen load was found three hours after infection, whereas control samples (antigen from mock-infected cultures) did not yield a detectable band. The result of this finding leads to the conclusion that this protein is a specific antigen which is synthesized during early infection of cells by HSV. Further purification by filtration on Sephadex G-100 and ion exchange chromatography resulted in active peaks detected by the CF tests (Figures 2 and 3). The eluted protein was further characterized as a glycoprotein by affinity chromatography (Figure 4). The presence of a glycoside group was confirmed after staining with Schiff periodic acid.

Seriologic Analysis by ELISA[5,6]

Purified antigen, deriving from the eluted, CF-active fractions of the concanavalin A-Sepharose column, was used in an ELISA test system,

Figure 2. HSV-TAA (HSV-1) gel filtration on Sephadex G-100; the dark area shows the CF active fractions.

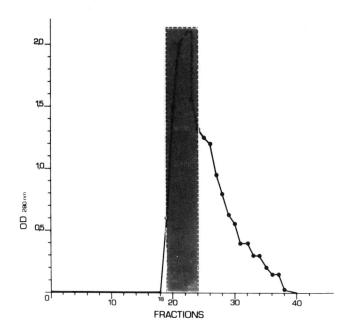

DEAE SEPHADEX A 50

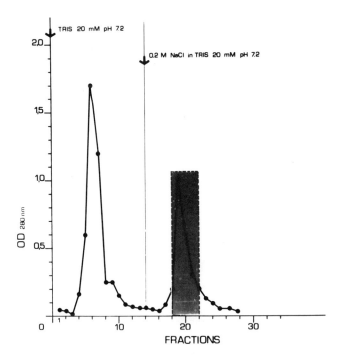

Figure 3. Chromatography on DEAE-Sephadex G-100 of CF-active fractions from the Sephadex G-100 column. The protein eluted with 0.2 M NaCl in 20 mM Tris-HCl, pH 7.2.

following similar procedures described by Voller et al.,[12] in order to detect specific HSV-associated antibodies in sera from control subjects, from patients with primary or recurrent HSV infections, and from patients with head and neck tumors, as well as from patients with urogenital cancers (Table 1). Some key results can be summarized as follows: 36 of 581 (6%) control sera were positive, while four of 23 (17%) patients with HSV infections had antibodies. However, sera from patients with cancer of the head and neck, as well as those with urogenital tract cancers, had anti-HSV-TAA reactivity in a high percentage (122 of 193 sera, or 63%). When these patients were divided into groups of (a) treated and (b) untreated patients, it was found that 20 of them (16%) were undergoing chemotherapy at the time of serum collection.

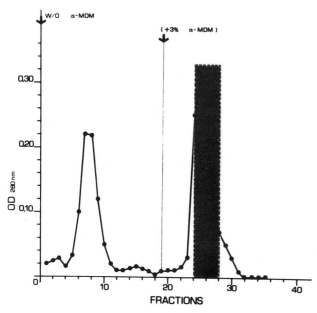

Figure 4. Chromatography on conconavalin A-Sepharose of CF-active fractions from the DEAE-Sephadex A-50 column. Proteins were eluted by 3% alfa-methyl-D-mannopyranoside.

Table 1. Antibody to HSV-TAA in Human Sera Detected by ELISA

Diagnosis	No. of Patients	Positive	(%)
Controls[a]	581	36	(6)
Primary and recurrent HSV infections	23	4	(17)
Head and neck tumors[b]	7	0	(0)
Urogenital tract tumors[b]			
Kidney, bladder	6	1	(17)
Cervix	6	1	(17)
Testis	2	1	(−)
Head and neck tumors[c]	80	62	(78)
Urogenital tract tumors			
Kidney	8	5	(63)
Bladder	11	7	(64)
Cervix	33	24	(73)
Testis	2	1	(−)
Prostate	36	19	(53)
Penis	2	1	(−)

[a] Controls consisted mainly of healthy subjects along with patients with other infections than HSV (e.g., chronic hepatitis and rubella).

[b] These patients had long-term clinical histories and were mainly undergoing chemotherapy.

[c] Progressive tumors.

Conclusion

In summary, the data presented here confirm an association of certain human cancers (head and neck region, and urogenital tract) with the HSV-TAA.[13] Furthermore, ELISA appears to be a sensitive, rapid and simple method for the detection of specific anti-HSV-TAA antibodies in cancer patients.

References

1. Tarro, G.: In: *Oncogenesis and Herpesviruses II,* IARC Scientific Publications No. 11, G. de-Thé, M.A. Epstein and H. zur Hausen (eds.), International Agency for Research on Cancer, Lyon, 1975, p. 291.

2. Cocchiara, R., Tarro, G., Flaminio, G., Di Gioia, M., Smeraglia, R., and Geraci, D: *Cancer* 45:938, 198, 1980.

3. Tarro, G., Cocchiara, R., Di Gioia, M., Flaminio, G., and Geraci, D.: In: *Int. Symp. on the Role of Immunotherapy in Cancer Treatment,* A. Pedersini (ed.), Minerva Medica, Turin, 1980 (in press), p. 8.

4. Tarro, G. and Sabin, A.B.: *Proc. Natl. Acad. Sci. USA* 65:753, 1970.

5. Tarro, G., Flaminio, G., Cocchiara, R., Di Gioia, M., and Geraci, D.: *Cell. Mol. Biol.,* 1980 (in press).

6. Cocchiara, R., Flaminio, G., Di Gioia, M., Geraci, D., Scala, C., and Tarro, G.: In: *Int. Meet. on the Application of RIA in Diagnosis, Prognosis and Therapy of Tumors,* C. Pandolfi (ed.), Arti Grafiche Lonardi, Naples, 1980 (in press), p. 96.

7. Kessler, S.W.: *J. Immunol.* 115:1617, 1975.

8. Ito, Y., Spurr, N., and Dulbecco, R.: *Proc. Natl. Acad. Sci. USA* 74:1259, 1977.

9. Tarro, G., Di Gioia, M., Cocchiara, R., Smeraglia, R., Giordano, G.G., and Tripodi, A.: *Tumori* 62:615, 1976.

10. Hollinshead, A.C., Chretien, P., Lee, O., Tarpley, J., Kerney, S., Silverman, N., and Alexander, J.: *Cancer Res.* 36:821, 1976.

11. Bonner, W.M. and Laskey, R.A.: *Eur. J. Biochem.* 46:83, 1974.

12. Voller, A., Bidwell, D.E., and Bartlett, A.: *Bull. WHO* 53:55, 1976.

13. Hollinshead, A.C. and Tarro, G.: *Science* 179:698, 1973.

Investigations into the Possible Role of the Human Polyomaviruses in Human Cancer

Billie L. Padgett

University of Wisconsin, Madison, Wisconsin

The polyomaviruses are small, 40–45 nm DNA viruses. Each virion contains a single molecule of double-stranded DNA with a molecular weight of about 3×10^6 daltons arranged as a covalently closed circle. Two members of the genus, mouse polyoma virus and simian virus 40, because of their oncogenicity in laboratory animals and ability to transform various cells in culture, have been studied exhaustively as model oncogenic DNA viruses. Therefore, the discovery in 1971 that man is the natural host for two distinct species of polyomaviruses, aroused speculation that these agents might be the cause of some cancer(s) in man. As more became known of the human polyomaviruses, such speculation acquired a firmer basis, and several investigations have been performed to try to disclose a connection between infection with these agents and cancer.

The two human polyomaviruses, BK virus (BKV)[1] and JV virus (JCV)[2] are known as such because the prototype strain of each species was designated by the initials of the person from whom the virus was isolated. Both viruses have all the physical-chemical characteristics of the polyomavirus genus.[3] Although BKV and JCV are distinct species, there are certain antigenic relationships between them. Both have the internal group antigen[4] common to all polyomaviruses. In addition, there is a weak antigenic relationship, demonstrable with hyperimmune antisera, between the external virion proteins of BKV, JCV, and the simian polyomavirus, SV40.[1,5-7] Furthermore, there is a strong antigenic relationship, demonstrated by immunofluorescent staining techniques, between the T antigens of these same three viruses.[8,9] This T antigen is a nonstructural antigen found in the nuclei of cells transformed by poly-omaviruses. These antigenic relationships reflect the fact that homology exists between certain specific regions, regions coding for particular proteins, on the DNA molecules extracted from BKV, JCV, and SV40.[10,11]

Serologic Surveys

Soon after the successful isolation of BKV and JCV, serologic surveys for antibodies against them by Gardner,[12] Padgett and Walker,[13] and Brown et al.,[14] among others, established that both viruses are distributed worldwide and that infection by each is a common event that generally occurs during childhood. Infection with BKV usually occurs at an earlier age than with JCV. The two viruses circulate independently but 70–80% of adults have antibodies against BKV and 70–80% have antibodies against JCV. Although it is not yet an established fact, there are reasons to believe that the primary infection is followed by a persistent, latent infection that may last for the lifetime of the individual.[15] Certainly, active infection in adults, recognized by urinary excretion and, for JCV, by the rare disease, progressive multifocal leukoencephalopathy, occurs primarily in individuals with impaired immunocompetency suggesting a reactivation of latent virus subsequent to a weakening of the immune system.[3,16]

Oncogenicity *in Vivo* and Transformation *in Vitro*

The oncogenicity of both human polyomaviruses has been demonstrated in laboratory animals, particularly in Syrian hamsters. BKV has produced tumors in neonatal hamsters following subcutaneous or intracerebral inoculation and in weanling hamsters after intravenous inoculation. Näse et al.[17] and Shah et al.[18] reported the appearance of fibrosarcomas in a very low percentage of hamsters inoculated subcutaneously with BKV. In contrast, there have been several reports[19–21] that a high percentage of animals develop papillary ependymomas following intracerebral in-oculation, and Uchida et al.[20] found that some of the animals developed insulinomas in the pancreas. Greenlee et al.[22] reported the production of choroid plexus papillomas by BKV after intracerebral inoculation. The greatest variety of tumors was found by Corallini et al.[23] after intravenous inoculation of weanling hamsters. The most numerous tumors were papillary ependymomas, insulinomas and osteosarcomas, but a variety of other tumors were also found. The same group reported that BKV could produce papillary ependymomas in newborn mice after intracere-bral inoculation.[21]

JCV will produce tumors in neonatal hamsters after inoculation intracerebrally, intraocularly, or intraperitoneally and subcutaneously. JCV is highly neurooncogenic and after intracerebral inoculation it induces a variety of malignant gliomas (medulloblastomas, glioblastomas, undifferentiated primitive gliomas, papillary ependymomas and pineocytomas) as well as an occasional meningioma.[9,24,25] After intraocular inoculation the major tumors produced are neuroblastomas[26] and retinoblastomas.[27] Although JCV exhibits a predilection for cells of neuroectodermal origin, it can induce sarcomas, particularly hemangiosarcomas and leiomyosarcomas, after combined intraperitoneal and subcutaneous inoculation (zu Rhein et al., personal communication). Moreover, of particular interest is the finding that JCV can induce malignant gliomas in adult nonimmunosuppressed owl monkeys.[28] This is the only instance of a human polyomavirus inducing tumors of any kind in a primate.

In addition to being oncogenic in animals, both BKV and JCV can transform certain cells in culture. Of particular pertinence are two recent reports that BKV can transform human cells in culture. Purchio and Fareed[29] transformed human embryonic kidney cells with BKV, and Takemoto et al.[30] transformed human fetal brain cultures. Certain clones of BKV-transformed fetal brain cells had especially interesting and novel characteristics. The clones did not contain detectable amounts of BKV T antigen and the only BKV DNA detected was that present in a nonintegrated or episomal state. This is the exact opposite of the findings for other kinds of cells transformed by BKV. JCV has only produced an abortive transformation of human fetal glial cells.[31]

So far, then, we know that the human polyomaviruses infect a majority of the world's population, that primary infection occurs in childhood and is probably followed by a lifelong latent infection, and that either or both viruses may be reactivated whenever immunity is impaired. The viruses are capable of inducing tumors in certain animals and of transforming some cells in culture.

Oncogenicity in Man

The above facts form the basis for speculation that BKV and/or JCV might be oncogenic in man. Investigations of this possiblility have taken one of two general approaches. The first is epidemiological. Sera from persons with cancer are tested for antiviral antibodies to determine whether there is a correlation between infection with a polyomavirus and the occurrence of particular kinds of cancer. Corallini et al.[32] tested sera from 952 patients with various tumors and Shah et al.[33] examined sera from 114 patients with tumors of the urogenital tract for antibodies against BKV. Neither study detected a correlation between prior infection with BKV and the occurrence of cancer, and anti-BKV antibodies were not found in every serum obtained from a group of patients with a given kind of tumor. Rziha et al.[34] tested sera from 185 five- to fifteen-year-old children with tumors. They did find a higher percentage of anti-BKV antibodies in the patient group than in the matched control group. Also, all children with certain kinds of tumors had antibodies. However, the number of patients in these groups was small so the significance of these findings cannot be assessed at the present time. In general, the epidemiological approach has not disclosed a causal connection between infection by the human polyomaviruses and cancer.

The second approach has been to look for viral genome(s) or genome products in tumor tissues and to test sera from persons with tumors for antibody against polyomavirus T (tumor) antigen. The rationale for the latter test is that most animals bearing tumors induced by a polyomavirus have anti-T antibodies in their serum, whereas nontumor-bearing animals do not.

The search for anti-T antibodies has generally given negative results (Table 1). Corallini et al.[32] found anti-BKV T antibody in 11 of 952 sera from cancer patients but four of 501 sera from persons without cancer were also positive. In four other studies of cancer patients[33,35–37] no positive sera were detected in a total of 268 tested. It would appear that if the human polyomaviruses do induce tumors in man, there is little or no accompanying production of anti-T antibody.

Searches for polyomavirus T antigen in human tumors and tumor cells in culture have also had almost uniformly negative results (Table 2). The exception is the report of Weiss et al.[38] that cells cultured from two of seven meningiomas gave a positive reaction when stained immunofluorescently with antiserum against SV40 T antigen. However, in subsequent investigations[35,37,39] T antigen was not detected in a total of 39 human meningiomas tested. In addition, human polyomavirus T antigen was not detected in 84 tumors of the urogenital tract,[33] in 21 brain tumors,[39] or in 47 miscellaneous tumors.[37] If any of the human tumors examined were indeed induced by a human polyomavirus, T antigen was

Table 1. Attempts to Detect and Correlate Antibodies Against Human Polyomavirus T Antigen in Sera from Patients with Tumors

No. of Sera Tested	No. with T Antibodies	Reference
952	11	(32)
16	0	(35)
71	0	(36)
114	0	(33)
67	0	(37)

Table 2. Attempts to Detect Polyomavirus Genome Products (T Antigen) in Human Tumors

No. of Tumors or Cell Lines Tested	Results	Reference
7[a]	2 positive	(38)
29[b]	negative	(39)
24[a]	negative	(35)
84	negative	(33)
55[c]	negative	(37)

[a] All meningiomas.

[b] Included 7 meningiomas.

[c] Included 8 meningiomas.

absent or present in amounts below the level of detection by immunofluorescent staining.

Finally, searches for integrated polyomavirus genome(s) in DNA extracted from human tumors and tumor cell lines have had conflicting but generally negative results (Table 3). Fiori and Di Mayorca[40] reported finding BKV DNA sequences in eight of 16 human tumors and tumor cell lines tested by DNA:DNA reassociation kinetics. However, three other investigations[35,37,41] did not find any evidence of the presence of BKV DNA sequences in any of a total of 197 human tumors and cell lines tested. Two of the tumor cell lines reported to contain BKV DNA sequences by Fiori and Di Mayorca[40] have been tested and reported as negative by two other groups.[37,41] In addition, two tumors have been reported as positive for BKV DNA sequences by one group and as negative by another. The discrepant results may derive from the nature of the probe used or the type of hybridization technique employed, but this is not known.

Table 3. Attempts to Detect Human Polyomavirus Genome(s) in Human Tumors by Hybridization

No. of Tumors or Cultures Tested	Technique	Results
16	DNA:DNA reassociation kinetics	8 positive[(40)]
6	DNA:RNA	negative[(35)]
25	DNA:DNA reassociation kinetics	negative[(37)]
166	DNA:DNA saturation hybridization	negative[(41)]

Conclusion

It would be worthwhile to look for JCV DNA sequences in tumor DNA, make a thorough test of tumors from young children, and, because of the novel papovavirus-transformed cell relationship reported by Takemoto et al.,[30] to also look for polyomavirus episomal DNA. On the basis of the investigations reviewed above, however, it can only be concluded that there is little evidence at present that the human polyomaviruses are a frequent or major cause of cancer in man.

References

1. Gardner, S.D., Field, A.M., Coleman, D.V., and Hulme, B.: *Lancet* 1:1253, 1971.
2. Padgett, B.L., Walker, D.L., zu Rhein, G.M., Eckroade, R.J., and Dessel, B.H.: *Lancet* 1:1257, 1971.
3. Padgett, B.L. and Walker, D.L.: *Prog. Med. Virol.* 22:1, 1976.
4. Shah, K.V., Ozer, H.L., Ghazey, H.N., and Kelley, T.J., Jr.: *J. Virol.* 21:179, 1977.
5. Penney, J.B., Jr. and Narayan, O.: *Infect. Immun.* 8:299, 1973.
6. Field, A.M., Gardner, S.D., Goodbody, R.A., and Woodhouse, M.A.: *J. Clin. Pathol.* 27:341, 1974.
7. Padgett, B.L., Rogers, C.M., and Walker, D.L.: *Infect. Immun.* 15:656, 1977.
8. Takemoto, K.K. and Mullarkey, M.F.: *J. Virol.* 12:625, 1973.
9. Walker, D.L., Padgett, B.L., zu Rhein, G.M., Albert, A.E., and Marsh, R.F.: *Science* 181:674, 1973.
10. Howley, P.M., Israel, M.A., Law, M.F., and Martin, M.A.: *J. Biol. Chem.* 254:4876, 1979.
11. Law, M.F., Martin, J.D., Takemoto, K.K., and Howley, P.M.: *Virology* 96:576, 1979.
12. Gardner, S.D.: *Br. Med. J.* 1:77, 1973.
13. Padgett, B.L. and Walker, D.L.: *J. Infect. Dis.* 127:467, 1973.
14. Brown, P., Tsai, T., and Gajdusek, D.C.: *Am. J. Epidemiol.* 102:331, 1975.
15. Padgett, B.L. and Walker, D.L.: In: *Persistent Viruses, ICN-UCLA Symposia on Molecular and Cellular Biology, Vol. 11,* J.G. Stevens et al. (eds.), Academic Press, New York, 1978, p. 751.
16. Gardner, S.D.: *Recent Adv. Clin. Virol.* 1:93, 1977.
17. Näse, L.M., Kärkkäinen, M., and Mäntyjärvi, R.A.: *Acta. Pathol. Microbiol. Scand. (B)* 83:347, 1975.
18. Shah, K.V., Daniel, R.W., and Strandberg, J.D.: *J. Natl. Cancer Inst.* 54:945, 1975.
19. Costa, J., Yee, C., Tralka, T.S., and Rabson, A.S.: *J. Natl. Cancer Inst.* 56:863, 1976.
20. Uchida, S., Watanabe, S., Aizawa, T., Kato, K., Furuno, A., and Muto, T.: *Gan.* 67:857, 1976.
21. Corallini, A., Barbanti-Brodano, G., Bortoloni, W., Nenci, I., Cassai, E., Tampieri, M., Portolani, M., and Borgatti, M.: *J. Natl. Cancer Inst.* 59:1561, 1977.
22. Greenlee, J.E., Narayan, O., Johnson, R.T., and Herndon, R.M.: *Lab. Invest.* 36:636, 1977.

23. Corallini, A., Altavilla, G., Cecchetti, M.G., Fabris, G., Grossi, M.P., Balboni, P. G., Lanza, G., and Barbanti-Brodano, G.: *J. Natl. Cancer Inst.* 61:875, 1978.

24. zu Rhein, G.M., and Varakis, J.: In: *Proceedings of the VIIth International Congress of Neuropathology, Vol. 1,* S.T. Környey et al. (ed.), Excerpta Medica, Amsterdam, 1975, p. 479.

25. Padgett, B.L., Walker, D.L., zu Rhein, G.M., and Varakis, J.N.: *Cancer Res.* 37:718, 1977.

26. Varakis, J., zu Rhein, G.M., Padgett, B.L., and Walker, D.L.: *Cancer Res.* 38:1718, 1978.

27. Ohashi, T., zu Rhein, G.M., Varakis, J.N., Padgett, B.L., and Walker, D.L.: *J. Neuropathol. Exp. Neurol.* 37:667, 1978.

28. London, W.T., Houff, S.A., Madden, D.L., Fuccillo, D.A., Gravel, M., Wallen, W.C., Palmer, A.E., Sever, J.L., Padgett, B.L., Walker, D.L., zu Rhein, G.M., and Ohashi, T.: *Science* 201:1246, 1978.

29. Purchio, A.F. and Fareed, G.C.: *J. Virol.* 29:763, 1979.

30. Takemoto, K.K., Linke, H., Miyamura, T., and Fareed, G.C.: *J. Virol.* 29:1177, 1979.

31. Padgett, B.L. and Walker, D.L.: Submitted for publication.

32. Corallini, A., Barbanti-Brodano, G., Portolani, M., Balboni, P.G., Grossi, M.P., Possati, L., Honorati, C., La Placa, M., Mazzoni, A., Caputo, A., Veronesi, U., Orefice, S., and Cardinali, G.: *Infect. Immun.* 13:1684, 1976.

33. Shah, K.V., Daniel, R.W., Stone, K.R., and Elliott, A.Y.: *J. Natl. Cancer Inst.* 60:579, 1978.

34. Rziha, H.J., Belohradsky, B.H., Schneider, U., Schwenk, H.U., Bornkamm, G.W., and zur Hausen, H.: *Med. Microbiol. Immunol.* 165:83, 1978.

35. Cikes, M., Beth, E., Giraldo, G., Acheson, N., and Hirt, B.: In: *Origin of Human Cancer, Vol. 4,* H.H. Hiatt, J.D. Watson and J.A. Winster (eds.), Cold Spring Harbor Laboratory, Cold Spring Harbor, New York, 1977, p. 1009.

36. Costa, J., Yee, C., and Rabson, A.S.: *Lancet* 2:709, 1977.

37. Israel, M.A., Martin, M.A., Takemoto, K.K., Howley, P.M., Aaronson, S.A., Solomon, D., and Khoury, G.: *Virology* 90:187, 1978.

38. Weiss, A.F., Portmann, R., Fischer, H., Simon, J., and Zang, K.D.: *Proc. Natl. Acad. Sci. USA* 72:609, 1975.

39. Becker, L.E., Narayan, O., and Johnson, R.T.: *J. Can. Sci. Neurol.* 3:105, 1976.

40. Fiori, M. and Di Mayorca, G.: *Proc. Natl. Acad. Sci. USA* 73:4662, 1976.

41. Wold, W.S.M., Mackey, J.K., Brackmann, K.H., Takemori, N., Rigden, P., and Green, M.: *Proc. Natl. Acad. Sci. USA* 75:454, 1978.

Papovavirus-Specific Surface Membrane Antigens of Cells Transformed by Simian Virus 40 and BK Virus

Rupert Schmidt-Ullrich and Donald F.H. Wallach

Tufts-New England Medical Center, Boston, Massachusetts

Immunological evidence indicates that neoplastic cells possess new surface membrane components designated as tumor-specific transplantation antigens (TSTA) and tumor-specific surface antigens (TSSA).[1,2] They are inferred to be plasma membrane components because the immune reactions known to produce tumor rejection or cytotoxic tumor cell lysis take place at the cell surface. For all tumors caused by a given virus, the antigenic properties of their TSTA and TSSA exhibit virus specificity. This commonality does not occur with spontaneous tumors or with neoplasms caused by chemical or physical carcinogens. All available evidence indicates that TSTA and TSSA are protein in nature.

The purpose of this short overview is to present the information on the molecular nature of TSTA/TSSA induced in cells neoplastically transformed by simian virus 40 (SV40) and other small oncogenic papovaviruses. SV40-transformation has been extremely valuable as a model for the complex problem of membrane anomalies in neoplasia. A restricted number of virus-specific alterations can be expected in SV40-transformed cells because the early region of the SV40 genome, required for maintenance of the transformed state,[3-5] can only encode for ~100,000 D of polypeptide. As SV40-transformed cells express nuclear large 90,000-100,000 D tumor (T) antigen,[6,7] and 17,000 D small T antigen,[8,9] nuclear/perinuclear U-antigen,[10,11] and TSTA/TSSA,[12-16] these proteins must share polypeptide sequences, or else they cannot all be encoded by the SV40 A gene.

SV40 can induce neoplastic transformation of human fibroblasts *in vitro* and in a variety of cultured rodent cells which produce tumors when injected into susceptible rodents. Recently, two human papovaviruses, BK virus (BKV)[17] and JC virus (JCV),[18–19] have been described which exhibit a similar transformation potential as SV40 for rodent[20] and possibly human cells.[21,22]. The substantial homology between the DNA of these viruses[22] and the crossreactivity between their nonstructural virus-specific T antigens[23,24] link studies on SV40 to papovaviruses possibly associated with certain human tumors.

Papovavirus-Specific Membrane Antigens

SV40-Specific Membrane Antigens

SV40-specific TSTA[12–14] and TSSA[15,16] are expressed on all cells transformed by or infected with this virus. TSTA is characterized as an antigen that represents the target for a specific cell mediated *in vivo* rejection of SV40-transformed cells in hosts immunized with SV40, SV40-transformed cells, membranes thereof or their solubilized membrane antigens.[26–28] A lymphocyte mediated cytotoxicity assay for TSTA *in vitro* has recently been reported.[29] TSSA mediates antibody-dependent cytolytic reactions against SV40-transformed cells.[15,16] There is some evidence that TSTA and TSSA are identical antigens monitored by different test systems.[15,16,29,30] However, while the two antigens copurify from SVAL/N cells upon $(NH_4)_2SO_4$ precipitation and DEAE-cellulose chromatography, their activities can be dissociated at least in part after an additional phosphocellulose chromatograph.[29] This suggests microheterogeneity of the molecules (See later section on Interspecies Papovavirus Antigens).[28,30,32,33]

Although the molecular nature of TSTA has not been defined, a close molecular relationship to T antigen, the SV40 A gene product, is suggested by a variety of data. Studies on the subcellular distribution of TSTA indicate that it largely follows that of T antigen. Most of the TSTA activity of SV40-transformed cells is therefore associated with the nuclear fraction.[34] Moreover, immunization with T antigen, purified to homogeneity by dodecylsulfate polyacrylamide gel electrophoresis (DS-PAGE),[35] can protect hosts against tumor grafts *in vivo* to a similar extent as TSTA.[36] Furthermore, TSTA appears to be encoded by the early region of the SV40 genome because there is a concurrent expression of T antigen and TSTA in cells initially infected with SV40 and in cells transformed by SV40 tsA-mutants when these cells are grown at permissive and nonpermissive temperatures.[37] The adenovirus 2-SV40 hybrids infective for HeLa cells have proven most useful in defining what segments of the SV40 genome are involved in various aspects of SV40-induced neoplastic transformation. Studies on various non-defective adenovirus 2-SV40 hybrid viruses show that the synthesis of SV40 TSTA is associated with the DNA sequence within the distal (3′-terminal) portion of the early region of the SV40 genome.[38,39] The mRNA of Ad2 ND_2 mediates the synthesis of a 56,000 D (daltons) and a 42,000 D SV40-specific protein.[40] Expression of these proteins, suggestively residing in the surface membrane of HeLa cells, coincides with expression of TSTA.[40] In contrast, Ad2 ND_4 containing the entire early region of the SV40 genome and encoding for an ∼ 92,000 D protein is required for expression of T antigen.[41] Therefore, TSTA and T antigen must share amino acid sequences of the ∼ 100,000 D polypeptide coded for by the SV40 genome. However, it is not known whether TSTA activity is exclusively conferred by one SV40-encoded protein in the plasma membrane of transformed or infected cells or whether there are additional host cell-specific components as is suggested by data of Drapkin et al.[32]

Biochemical Characterization of TSTA/TSSA

Two approaches have been applied to elucidate the molecular character-istics of SV40-specific membrane proteins which, by definition, must at least in part represent TSTA. In one, a rather indiscriminating purification procedure for TSTA/TSSA was chosen in which whole SV40-transformed cells were lysed in Triton X-100 in presence of protease inhibitors.[30,31] SV40-specific proteins were first enriched by $(NH_4)_2SO_4$ precipitation and further fractionated using ion exchange chromatography.[30] The protein fractions were then tested for T antigen using immune fluores-cence and complement fixation and for TSTA employing a tumor rejec-tion assay in immunized BALB/c mice by challenge with mKSA-ASC cells or using a cytotoxicity assay.[30,31] With this approach the molecular mass of TSTA/TSSA was estimated to lie between 45,000 and 55,000 D.[31] These results are consistent with data by Anderson et al.[34] who found a prominent 56,000 D protein when chromatographically purified T antigen, which also exhibited TSTA activity, was analyzed by DS-PAGE. The first biochemical evidence for the expression of TSTA in the plasma membrane of SV40 transformed mKSA-ASC mouse fibroblasts has been presented by Drapkin et al.[32] who could show that immuniza-tions of BALB/c mice with isolated membranes of SV40-transformed cells or papain-solubilized proteins thereof conferred a similar TSTA-specific rejection response as intact cells.

Schmidt-Ullrich et al.[42−45] have used an alternative approach to char-acterize SV40-specific membrane proteins. As a first step, plasma mem-branes of SV40-transformed cells, the subcellular fraction carrying the antigen(s) of interest, were purified to a high degree. For this, cells in suspension were disrupted by nitrogen decompression followed by the isolation of plasma membranes using differential and density gradient centrifugations.[42,46] The great advantage of purified membranes in the search for a defined group of cell surface antigens is that other cellular proteins are eliminated allowing application of sensitive high resolution protein fractionation techniques.[43-45,47] SV40-specific membrane components were first identified by comparative analyses of plasma membrane proteins from hamster GD248 lymphoid cells,[48] SV40-transformed hamster phagocytes (T19),[49] hamster embryonic fibroblasts, and SV40-transformed mouse (SV3T3) and human (SV80) fibroblasts. The techniques employed were bidimensional isoelectric focusing-immune electrophoresis (IEF-IE) using heterologous immune sera from guinea pigs against purified plasma membranes of GD248 cells (anti-GD248-membrane serum) and bidimensional isoelectric focusing-dodecylsulfate polyacrylamide gel electrophoresis (IEF-DS-PAGE). Two groups of proteins apparently specific for membranes of SV40-transformed cells were defined by these immunochemical and biochemical techniques as pI $\sim 4.7/\sim 100,000$ D and as pI $\sim 4.5/\sim 60,000$ D components (Figures 1, 2). The molecular relationship of the pI $\sim 4.7/\sim 100,000$ D and the pI $\sim 4.5/\sim 60,000$ D proteins to SV40 T antigen was investigated by IEF-IE using high titered sera from SV40 tumor (SK, line B)[50] bearing hamsters (anti-T serum). A selective reactivity of the pI $\sim 4.7/\sim 100,000$ D protein could be documented (Figure 3A).[51] Reactivity of this protein with hamster anti-T and anti-GD248-membrane serum was shown by IEF-IE in which mixing of the two sera selectively suppressed the height of the pI $\sim 4.7/\sim 100,000$ D to less than 50% in comparison to anti-GD248-membrane serum alone (Figures 3B, C). The fact that mixing of the two sera yields only one immune precipitate at pI ~ 4.7, indicates that the different antibodies recognize two antigenic sites on the same molecule. As the pI $\sim 4.7/\sim 100,000$ D protein exhibits SV40 T antigen reactivity, it must represent a host cell modified T antigen associated with the plasma membrane. Host cell modification of SV40 T antigen is further supported by the observation that the pI $\sim 4.7/\sim 100,000$ D protein is glycosylated, as defined by metabolic labeling with ^{14}C-glucosamine,[52] and that the T antigen isolated from the nucleus does not focus at pI ~ 4.7 but at three major peaks between pH 5.8 and 5.2 (Schmidt-Ullrich et al., to be published). Differences between the membrane-associated and nuclear T antigens are further proven by ^{125}I tryptic peptide analyses. These two SV40-specific proteins exhibit only an 80% homology as T antigen isolated by immune precipitation from purified plasma membranes and nuclei of GD248 cells differ in four out of 20 ^{125}I peptides (Figure 4). In contrast, there is no homology between the pI $\sim 4.7/\sim 100,000$ D membrane T antigen and the pI $\sim 4.5/\sim 60,000$ D protein (Figure 5). Treatment of sealed GD248 plasma membrane vesicles with TPCK-trypsin or neuraminidase, analyzed by IEF-IE, eliminates the reactivity of the pI $\sim 4.7/\sim 100,000$ D and the pI $\sim 4.5/\sim 60,000$ D proteins with anti-GD248-membrane serum indicating that both proteins are exposed on the outer surface of the membrane and that both carry carbohydrate

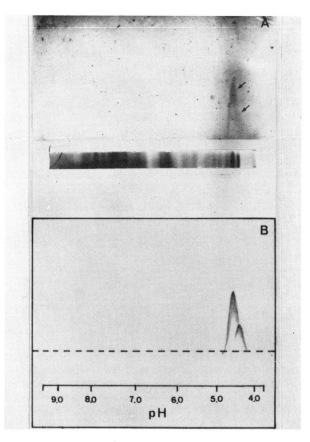

Figure 1A,B. Bidimensional isoelectric focusing-immune electrophoresis of BALB/c SV3T3 membrane proteins. Triton X-100-solubilized membranes were focused in the first dimension (horizontal) and electrophoresed in the second dimension (vertical). Focusing was performed using slab gels formed with 4% acrylamide, cross-linked with 2.5% bisacrylamide, containing 2% ampholytes (pH 3.5-10.0), 8 M urea, 1% Triton X-100 and 10% sucrose. About 0.4 mg of membrane protein was focused at 250 V for 16 hr at 4°C with 1.0 M NaOH and 1.0 M H_3PO_4 as catholytes and anolytes, respectively. For the second dimension a 5 × 50 mm gel strip, containing ~ 0.2 mg of focused protein was washed three times in 20 ml Tris/glycine (0.038 M/0.1 M), pH 8.7, 1% in Triton X-100, 10 min each time. For immune electrophoresis 50 × 50 mm immunoplates were cast in two sections: (a) a cathodal 20 × 50 × 1.5 mm agarose strip without antibody and (b) a 30 × 50 × 1.5 mm area containing guinea pig antiserum (0.045 ml/ml agarose) against membranes of GD248 hamster lymphoid cells. **A.** Immune precipitation (**top**) and focusing pattern (**bottom**). Arrows point to the overlapping immune precipitates at pH 4.7 and 4.5. **B.** Schematic of the immunoplate (A), including the pH-gradient.[45] Coomassie blue staining of the focusing gel and the immunoplate.[45]

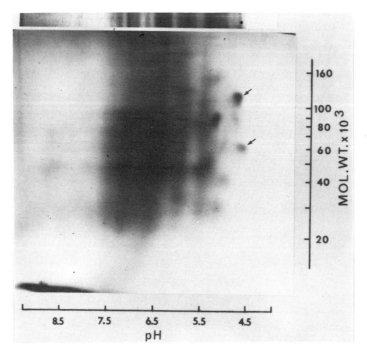

Figure 2. Bidimensional isoelectric focusing-dodecylsulfate polyacrylamide gel electrophoresis of BALB/c SV3T3-membrane proteins. First dimension (horizontal): Isoelectric focusing of 0.4 mg of protein in 4% cylindrical (3 × 65 mm) polyacrylamide gels, cross-linked with 2.5% bisacrylamide, containing 2% ampholytes (pH 3.5-10.0), 8 M urea, 1% Triton X-100 and 10% sucrose. Focusing was at 150 V for 16 hr at 4°C with 0.03 M NaOH and 0.05 M H_2SO_4 as catholytes and anolytes, respectively. Second dimension (vertical): dodecylsulfate polyacrylamide gel electrophoresis, using gel slabs (75 × 75 × 2.75 mm: 7.5% acrylamide, cross-linked with 2.5% bisacrylamide) was employed. Prior to electrophoresis, the focusing gels were equilibrated with electrophoresis buffer, 3% in dodecyl sulfate, and 0.12 M in dithiothreitol, using 10 ml of buffer per gel and changing buffer every 10 min for 50 min. The focusing gel was positioned atop the pre-electrophoresed gel slab with the focusing axis perpendicular to the direction of dodecyl sulfate polyacrylamide gel electrophoresis. Electrophoresis was for 16 hr at 8 mA/slab. Coomassie blue protein staining of the focusing and the slab gel.[45]

residues which contribute to the antigenic sites recognized by the heterologous serum.[51]

In agreement with our results, similar findings by Soule and Butel[53] show the presence of T antigen in subcellular fractions of SV40-transformed and infected mouse fibroblasts enriched in plasma membranes.

When Triton X-100-solubilized membrane proteins are reacted with anti-T serum and then deposited by goat anti-hamster IgG, both pro-

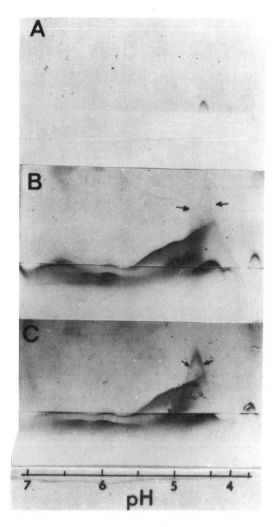

Figure 3A-C. Bidimensional isoelectric focusing-immune electrophoresis of plasma membrane proteins from GD248 lymphoid cells. About 0.4 mg of Triton-solubilized membrane proteins were fractionated by isoelectric focusing in a polyacrylamide gel strip (10 × 70 × 2 mm) in the first dimension (horizontal). The focused material, in a strip of 5 × 50 × 2 mm, was then electrophoresed in the second dimension into antibody-containing agarose (vertical). (For experimental details see Figure 1.) *A:* Serum of hamsters bearing tumors of SV40-transformed SK (line B) cells (anti T serum; 0.12 ml/ml of agarose); *B:* Anti-GD248-membrane serum (0.06 ml/ml of agarose); *C:* Anti-GD248-membrane serum (0.06 ml/ml of agarose) plus anti-T serum (0.12 ml/ml of agarose). Coomassie blue staining of the immunoplates. The pH-gradient, as measured in the first-dimension focusing gel, is depicted in Plate C.

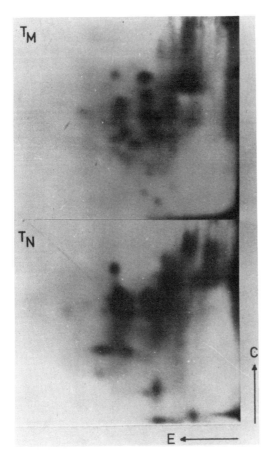

Figure 4. Autoradiograms of bidimensional ^{125}I tryptic peptide maps of SV40 T antigens from nuclei (T_N) and plasma membranes (T_M) of GD248 hamster lymphoid cells metabolically labeled with ^{35}S-methionine (Schmidt-Ullrich et al., to be published). The Triton X-100-solubilized T antigens were reacted with hamster anti-T serum and precipitated with goat anti-hamster immunoglobulin. T antigens (T_N and T_M) were separated in dodecylsulfate polyacrylamide gel electrophoresis identified by autoradiography (Kodak, X-Omat R film) in dried gels and after rehydration, subjected to proteolytic cleavage using TPCK-trypsin. For peptide mapping, the first-dimension electrophoresis of ^{125}I-labeled peptides (2.0-5.0×10^5 cpm) was performed on 10×10 cm thin layer chromatography plates (Polygram Cel 300; Brinkmann, Westbury, N.Y.) in acetic acid/formic acid/water ($15/5/80$; v/v) at 1000 V for 30 min at 4°C. After drying the plates, the second dimension chromatography was run in butanol/pyridine/acetic acid/water ($32.5/25/5/20$; v/v) with the thin-layer plate placed in the solvents parallel to the line of electrophoretically separated peptides. Autoradiograms were obtained exposing a Kodak No Screen NS-2T X-ray film.

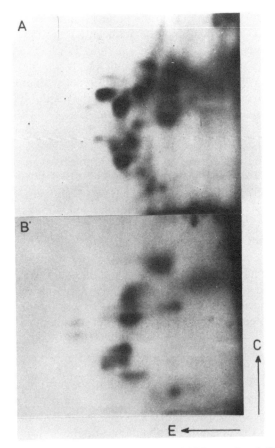

Figure 5A, B. Autoradiograms of bidimensional ^{125}I tryptic peptide maps of the SV40-specific pl ~ 4.7/~ 100,000 D (**Plate A**) and pI ~ 4.5/~ 60,000 D (**Plate B**) plasma membrane proteins from GD248 hamster lymphoid cells. The peptides were obtained by treatment of the proteins in polyacrylamide gels using TPCK-trypsin. For technical details of peptide mapping see Figure 4. The arrows in the lower right portion of Plate B indicate the direction of electrophoresis (E) and chromatography (C).

teins,[51] the ~ 100,00 D and ~ 60,000 D component, are precipitated. These results indicate that the pI ~ 4.5/~ 60,000 D protein is associated with the pI ~ 4.7/~ 100,00 D protein exhibiting T antigen reactivity. However, the pI ~ 4.5/~ 60,000 D protein does not react with anti-T serum by itself because it does not yield an immune precipitate in IEF-IE (Figure 3). Under these conditions the two proteins are dissociated by IEF prior to reaction with anti-T serum as the first dimension IEF is performed in the presence of 8 M urea.

These results are in agreement with those reported by several other groups who described a category of proteins in the molecular mass range between 44,000 and 60,000 D which precipitate with anti-T serum (in apparent analogy to the polyoma virus encoded "middle T").[53] These proteins may correspond to our pI $\sim$ 4.5/$\sim$ 60,000 D glycoprotein. However, these seemingly SV40-specific proteins do not react with anti-T serum when dissociated from T antigen,[51,55] nor do they exhibit a substantial homology in tryptic peptides with SV40 T antigen.[56-60] This, and the fact that their molecular masses vary with the host cell type, suggests that these SV40-related proteins are of host cell origin. Still another group of SV40-specific proteins of $\sim$ 130,000 D molecular mass has been found in certain SV40-transformed BALB/c cell lines.[60] They exhibit a high degree of tryptic peptide homology to SV40 T antigen.

The host cell proteins of 44,000–60,000 D molecular mass may be derepressed host cell antigens. There is no evidence by other groups that they represent embryonic antigens, as may be suggested by data of Kato.[61] Hybridoma cells produce antibodies against SV40 T antigen which precipitate a 54,000 D nonviral SV40-specific protein which is not present in two embryonal carcinoma cell lines.[57] Also, in our own studies[44,45] we were unable to identify either the pI $\sim$ 4.7/$\sim$ 100,000 D or pI $\sim$ 4.5/$\sim$ 60,000 D proteins in membranes of embryonic hamster fibroblasts.

Interspecies Papovavirus Antigens

The detection of SV40 or SV40-like T antigens in certain human tumors by indirect immune fluorescence (IIF) or complement fixation (CF)[62-64] and the presence of BK virus DNA established by DNA hybridization[65] have created great interest in the possible involvement of papovaviruses in human cancer. In these studies sera of animals bearing SV40- or BKV-induced tumors have been tested on fresh human tumor tissue or tumor cells thereof cultured for several cell cycles.[63,66] However, any interpretation of these findings is complicated for the following reasons: (a) Both papovavirus infected and transformed cells express papovavirus-induced T antigens; (b) there is a substantial immunological crossreactivity between SV40, BKV, and JCV T antigens, and (c) the sera of many human individuals exhibit high titers against human papovaviruses, i.e., BKV and JCV, due to infections in early childhood.[19] It is, therefore, difficult to define whether expression of nonstructural papovavirus-specific antigens reflects neoplastic transformation or permissive infection and to determine which of the three papovaviruses is involved. Although human cells are permissive for BKV and JCV, there is evidence that BKV can neoplastically transform human fibroblasts *in vitro*.[21,22] All three papovaviruses are clearly oncogenic in rodents.[19,48]

Crossreactivity between nonstructural SV40 and BKV encoded T antigens was demonstrated by IIF in WI38 human fibroblasts infected with BKV, using anti-T serum from SV40 tumor-bearing hamsters.[67] This crossreactivity between the T antigens induced by different papovaviruses has been investigated in much more detail by Beth et al.[24] They determined the degree of crossreactivity between T antigens of SV40, BKV, JCV and mouse polyoma virus by immune fluorescence and ^{51}Cr microcomplement fixation. Antisera against T antigen of all four viruses were obtained from hamsters carrying tumors induced by the respective viruses. Also, using IF absorption with JCV T antigen and BKV T antigen, both antigens show about 20% interspecies crossreactivity with SV40 T antigen from H-50 hamster cell extracts. In addition, there are species-specific antigenic determinants common to BKV and JCV and type-specific antigenic sites characteristic for T antigens in different cells transformed by the homologous virus. It is significant that none of the tests revealed crossreactivity with mouse polyoma T antigen. The recognition of a mosaic of T antigenic determinants with interspecies, species, and type specificity has great implications in the search for nonstructural viral antigens in human tumor cells.

The antigenic crossreactivity is in good agreement with the high homology of ^{35}S-methionine T antigen tryptic peptide maps; five peptides out of seven, from CV-1 and human embryonic kidney cells infected with SV40 and BKV,[25] respectively. In a similar study, Simmons et al.[68] showed that BKV T antigen in transformed hamster cells has a larger molecular mass of 113,000 D as compared to SV40 or BKV T antigens of lytically infected cells which exhibit T antigens of molecular masses of 97,000 D. Their homology on the basis of tryptic peptide mapping, using ion exchange chromatography, amounted to about 30%,[68] which is in good agreement with estimates reported by Beth et al.[24] The substantial similarity of papovavirus T antigens is reflected in extensive structural homology between JCV, BKV and SV40 DNA.[23] Functional homology between SV40 and BKV is further indicated because BKV T antigen (or DNA) can maintain the transformed state in cells transformed by defective SV40 mutants.[69]

Based on the close molecular relationship between SV40 T antigen and TSTA and T antigens of different strains of papovaviruses, the antigenic crossreactivity between TSTA induced by SV40 and BKV has been explored. Isolated membranes and papain-solubilized membrane proteins from JCV and BKV-transformed hamster cells were used for immunization of BALB/c mice and Syrian hamsters. The animals were then challenged with syngeneic SV40-transformed mKSA mouse fibroblasts and SV34 hamster cells.[28] Mice are equally well protected against challenges with tumor cells transformed by the homologous and heterologous virus. In contrast, hamsters are only protected when immunized with the homologous, nonstructural, virally-induced antigens. Immunization with isolated virus, i.e. SV40 or BKV, in no case conferred a tumor rejection response to cells transformed by a heterologous papo-virus.[19,62,70,71] However, Seehafer et al.[71] found that immunization of BALB/c mice with irradiated BKV-transformed mouse, rat and hamster fibroblasts yielded equally good protection against challenges with syngeneic SV40-transformed mKSA-ASC cells as immunization with SV40-transformed syngeneic cells. There is no cross-protection between polyoma virus-transformed mouse or rat fibroblasts and mKSA-ASC cells, reflecting the lack of crossreactivity between polyoma T antigen and T antigens induced by SV40 and BKV.[24]

In a limited study, we have investigated the crossreactivity between TSTA of SV40 and BKV-transformed cells on a molecular level. Anti-GD248 membrane-serum recognized a pI $\sim$ 4.7/$\sim$ 100,00 D protein in plasma membranes of BKV-transformed LSH hamster glial cells possibly equivalent to a membrane associated BKV T antigen. Precipitation of an $\sim$ 55,000 D protein from Triton X-100-solubilized BKV-transformed LSH cells using anti-GD248-membrane and anti-T serum suggested an association between a virus-specific $\sim$ 100,000 D protein and $\sim$ 55,000 D polypeptide not encoded by the virus (Beth, Giraldo and Schmidt-Ullrich, to be published).

Conclusions

Current evidence indicates that cells transformed by or infected with SV40 express two categories of seemingly SV40-specific proteins on their plasma membranes. One group of antigens represents the 90,000–100,000 D T antigen, encoded by the SV40 genome, which appears in the plasma membrane of transformed cells as a host cell-modified glycosylated,[51,52] possibly phosphorylated,[53] pI $\sim$ 4.7/$\sim$ 100,000 D protein.

As T antigen and TSTA exhibit a high degree of molecular homology, it is conceivable that the membrane-associated T antigen functions as TSTA. The glycosylation of T antigen, mediated by the host cell, could explain a host cell-specific component of TSTA described by Law and collaborators.[28,32] However, it is unknown whether the host-specific component of TSTA lies only in the microheterogeneity of the carbohy-drate[52] and/or polypeptide[5] moiety of SV40 T antigen.

As a further complication in the molecular identification of SV40 TSTA, there is a second group of 44,000–60,000 D molecular mass host cell-specific proteins represented in membranes and the interior of transformed and lytically infected cells which appear to be intimately associated with T antigen. Despite their specificity for SV40-transformed cells, these proteins are not encoded by the SV40 genome. The proposal that they represent, on the basis of $\geqslant$ 20% peptide homology to SV40 T antigen, host cell-virus hybrid proteins[60] is unwarranted until further proof is provided. The biological role of these proteins is undefined, in particular their contribution to the antigenicity and host cell specificity of TSTA/TSSA. From our own limited molecular data on virus-specific plasma membrane proteins of BKV-transformed hamster LSH cells, there appears to be a similar molecular arrangement between the virus-specific pl $\sim 4.7/\sim 100,000$ D protein, crossreacting with SV40 and BKV T antigens, and a $\sim 55,000$ D host cell-specific protein in both SV40 and BKV-transformed cells.

The crossreactivity of the modified T antigen in purified plasma membranes of cells transformed by SV40 or BKV and their analogous association with a smaller nonvirally encoded protein may have implications in the search for papovavirus-specific proteins in human tumors. It is suggested that, in the search for papovavirus-specific markers in human tumor cells, the most appropriate immunological probes should be derived from cells transformed by JCV, BKV and SV40. Further, for screening in human tumors, high titered heterologous antisera specific for SV40, JCV and BKV T antigens will more likely yield an unambiguous answer to the viral involvement in tumors than will testing of patient sera for antibodies against nonstructural virus-specific proteins. Further, if the expression of a host-cell modified SV40 T antigen with TSTA activity can be proven for cells infected with or transformed by BKV or JCV, new sensitive screening tests may be developed using a TSTA-mediated cytotoxicity assay.

ACKNOWLEDGMENT

Supported by Grant CA-12178 and CA-23642 from the National Institutes of Health. The excellent technical assistance of W. S. Thompson and S. J. Kahn is gratefully acknowledged.

References

1. Oettgen, H.F. and Hellström, K.E.: In: *Cancer Medicine,* J. Holland and E. Frei (eds.), Lea and Febinger, Philadelphia, 1973, p. 951.

2. Baldwin, R.W.: *Adv. Cancer Res.* 18:1, 1975.

3. Martin, R.G. and Chou, J.Y.: *J. Virol.* 15:599, 1975.

4. Osborn, M. and Weber, K.: *J. Virol.* 15:636, 1975.

5. Bouck, N., Beales, N., Shenk, T., Berg, P., and Di Mayorca, G.: *Proc. Natl. Acad. Sci. USA* 75:2473, 1978.

6. Rundell, K., Collins, J.K., Tegtmeyer, P., Ozer, H.L., Lai, C.J., and Nathans, D.: *J. Virol.* 21:636, 1977.

7. Tijan, R., Fey, G., and Graessmann, A.: *Proc. Natl. Acad. Sci. USA* 75:1279, 1978.

8. Smith, A.E., Smith, R., and Paucha, E.: *J. Virol.* 28:140, 1978.

9. Mellor, A. and Smith, A.E.: *J. Virol.* 28:140, 1978.

10. Lewis, A.M. and Rowe, W.P.: *J. Virol.* 7:189, 1971.

11. Robb, J.A.: *Proc. Natl. Acad. Sci. USA* 74:447, 1977.

12. Tevethia, S.S., Katz, M., and Rapp, F.: *Proc. Soc. Exp. Biol. Med.* 119:896, 1975.

13. Anderson, J.L., Martin, R.G., Chang, C., and Mora, P.J.: *Virology* 76:254, 1977.

14. Law, L.W., Takemoto, K.K., Rogers, M.J., and Ting, R.C.: *J. Natl. Cancer Inst.* 59:1523, 1977.

15. Pancake, S.J. and Mora, P.T.: *Virology* 59:323, 1974.

16. Pancake, S.J. and Mora, P.T.: *Cancer Res.* 36:88, 1976.

17. Gardner, S.D., Field, A.M., Coleman, D.V., and Hulme, B.: *Lancet* 1:1253, 1971.

18. Padgett, B.L., Walker, D.L., zu Rhein, G.M., Eckroade, R.J., and Dessel, B.H.: *Lancet* 1:1257, 1971.

19. Padgett, B.L. and Walker, D.L.: *Prog. Med. Virol.* 22:1, 1976.

20. Mayor, E.O. and Di Mayorca, G.: *Proc. Natl. Acad. Sci. USA* 70:3210, 1973.

21. Purchio, A.F. and Fareed, G.C.: *J. Virol.* 29:763, 1979.

22. Takemoto, K.K., Linke, H., Miyamura, T., and Fareed, G.C.: *J. Virol.* 29:1177, 1979.

23. Law, M.-F., Martin, J.D., Takemoto, K.K., and Howley, P.M.,: *Virology* 96:576, 1979.

24. Beth, E., Cikes, M., Schloen, L., Di Mayorca, G., and Giraldo, G.: *Int. J. Cancer* 20:551, 1977.

25. Rundell, K., Tegtmeyer, P., Wright, P.J., and Di Mayorca, G.: *Virology* 82:206, 1977.

26. Dean, J.H., Lewis, D.D., Paderathsingh, M.L., McCoy, J.L., Northing, J.W., Natori, T., and Law, L.W.: *Int. J. Cancer* 20:951, 1977.

27. Law, L.W., Takemoto, K.K., Rogers, M.J., and Ting, R.C.: *J. Natl. Cancer Inst.* 59:1523, 1977.

28. Law, L.W., Takemoto, K.K., Rogers, M.J., Hendriksen, O., and Ting, R.C.: *Int. J. Cancer* 22:315, 1978.

29. Pretell, J., Greenfield, R.S., and Tevethia, S.S.: *Virology* 97:32, 1979.

30. Luborsky, S.W., Chang, C., Pancake, S.J., and Mora, P.T.: *Cancer Res.* 38:2367, 1978.

31. Luborksy, S.W., Chang, C., Pancake, S.J., and Mora, P.T.: *Biochem. Biophys. Res. Commun.* 71:990, 1976.

32. Drapkin, M.S., Apella, E., and Law, L.W.: *J. Natl. Cancer Inst.* 52:259, 1974.

33. Lanford, R.E. and Butel, J.S.: *Virology* 97:295, 1979.

34. Anderson, J.L., Martin, R.G., Chang, C., Mora, P.T., and Livingston, D.M.: *Virology* 76:420, 1977.

35. Tenen, D., Garewal, H., Haines, L., Hudson, V., Woodward, V., Light, S., and Livingston, D.M.: *Proc. Natl. Acad. Sci. USA* 74:3745, 1977.

36. Chang, C., Martin, R.G., Livingston, D.M., Luborsky, S.W., Hu, C.-P., and Mora, P.T.: *J. Virol.* 29:69, 1979.

37. Tenen, D.G., Martin, R.G., Anderson, J., and Livingston, D.M.,: *J. Virol.* 22:210, 1977.

38. Lewis, A.M. and Rowe, W.P.: *J. Virol.* 12:836, 1973.

39. Lebowitz, P., Kelly, T.J., Nathans, D., Lee, T.N., and Lewis, A.M.: *Proc. Natl. Acad. Sci. USA* 71:441, 1974.

40. Deppert, W. and Walter, G.: *Proc. Natl. Acad. Sci. USA* 73:2505, 1976.

41. Anderson, G.W., Lewis, J.B., Baum, P.R., and Gestland, R.F.: *J. Virol.* 18:685, 1976.

42. Schmidt-Ullrich, R., Wallach, D.F.H., and Davis, F.D.G.: *J. Natl. Cancer Inst.* 57:1107, 1976.

43. Schmidt-Ullrich, R., Wallach, D.F.H., and Davis, F.D.G.: *J. Natl. Cancer Inst.* 57:1117, 1976.
44. Schmidt-Ullrich, R., Thompson, W.S., and Wallach, D.F.H.: *Proc. Natl. Acad. Sci. USA 74:643, 1977.*
45. Schmidt-Ullrich, R., Lin, P.S., Thompson, W.S., and Wallach, D.F.H.: *Proc. Natl. Acad. Sci. USA* 74:5069, 1977.
46. Wallach, D.F.H and Schmidt-Ullrich, R.: *Meth. Cell Biol.* 15:235, 1977.
47. Schmidt-Ullrich, R., Verma, S.P., and Wallach, D.F.H.: *Biochem. Biophys. Res. Commun.* 67:1062, 1975.
48. Diamandopoulos, G.T., *J. Natl. Cancer Inst.* 50:1347, 1973.
49. Lin, P.S., Butterfield, C., and Wallach, D.F.H.: *Cell Biol. Intern. Rep.* 1:57, 1978.
50. Diamandopoulos, G.T. and Dalton-Tucker, M.F.: *Am. J. Pathol.* 56:59, 1969.
51. Schmidt-Ullrich, R., Thompson, W.S., Kahn, S.J., and Wallach, D.F.H.: *J. Natl. Cancer Inst.,* 1980 (in press).
52. Schmidt-Ullrich, R., Thompson, W.S., and Wallach, D.F.H.: *Biochem. Biophys. Res. Commun.* 88:887, 1979.
53. Soule, H.R. and Butel, J.S.: *J. Virol.* 30:523, 1979.
54. Ito, Y.: *Virology* 98:261, 1979.
55. Lane, D.P. and Crawford, L.V.: *Nature* 278:261, 1979.
56. Melero, J.A., Stiff, D.T., Mangel, W.F., and Carroll, R.B.: *Virology* 93:466, 1979.
57. Linzor, D.I.H. and Levine, A.J.: *Cell* 17:43, 1979.
58. Linzor, D.I.H., Maltzman, W., and Levine, A.J.: *Virology* 78:308, 1979.
59. Kress, M., May, E., Cassingena, R., and May, R.: *J. Virol.* 31:472, 1979.
60. Chang, C., Simmons, D.T., Martin, M.A., and Mora, P.T.: *J. Virol.* 31:463, 1979.
61. Kato, K.: *J. Natl. Cancer Inst.* 58:259, 1977.
62. Tabuchi, K., Kirsch, W.M., Low, M., Gaskin, D., VanBuskirk, J., and Maa, S.: *Int. J. Cancer* 21:12, 1978.
63. Weiss, A.F., Postmann, R., Fischer, H., Simon, J., and Zang, K.D.: *Proc. Natl. Acad. Sci. USA* 72:609, 1975.
64. May, G., Fischer, H., and Zang, K.D.: *J. Gen. Virol.* 43:697, 1979.
65. Fiori, M. and Di Mayorca, G.: *Proc. Natl. Acad. Sci. USA* 73:4662, 1976.
66. Cikes, M., Beth, E., Giraldo, G., Acheson, N., and Hirt, B.: In: *Origins of Human Cancer,* Cold Spring Harbor Laboratory, Cold Spring Harbor, New York, 1977, p. 1009.
67. Takemoto, K. and Mullarkey, M.F.: *J. Virol.* 12:625, 1973.
68. Simmons, D.T., Takemoto, K.K., and Martin, M.A.: *J. Virol.* 24:319, 1977.
69. Lai, C.-J., Goldman, N.D., and Khoury, G.: *J. Virol.* 30:141, 1979.
70. Karjalainen, H.E., Laaksonen, A.M., and Mäntyjärvi, R.A., : *J. Gen. Virol.* 41:171, 1978.
71. Seehafer, J., Downer, D. N., Gibney, D. J., and Colter, J. S.: *Virology* 95:241, 1979.

Evidence Suggesting that Hepatitis B Virus is a Tumor-Inducing Virus in Man: An Estimate of the Risk of Development of Hepatocellular Cancer in Chronic HBsAg Carriers and Controls

Alfred M. Prince

Lindsley F. Kimball Research Institute of the New York Blood Center, New York, New York

Although relatively rare in the United States, hepatocellular carcinoma (HCC) is the commonest malignancy in many parts of the world, particularly in tropical regions of Africa and Asia.

French and American workers in Africa were the first to postulate that the extraordinarily high incidence of this disease in Africa might be related to the high prevalence of viral hepatitis and post-hepatic cirrhosis in these regions.[1,2] This speculation received serologic support when it became possible to test for specific markers of hepatitis B virus (HBV) infection: the HB surface antigen (HBsAg), its antibody (anti-HBs), and antibody to the HB core antigen (anti-HBc), in the serum of HCC cases, their families and controls.[6,11–14]

Some early studies, using insensitive techniques for detection of HBsAg, failed to find a significant association. For example, Simons found HBsAg in only 2% of 156 Chinese patients with HCC in Singapore, as compared to 4% of controls, when sera were tested by counterelectrophoresis. However, when the same sera were retested by the much more sensitive immune adherence (IAHA) assay, HBsAg was detected in 35% of the sera from HCC patients as compared to 7% in controls.[3]

When sensitive methods for HBsAg detection were employed, a striking association between the presence of HBsAg and HCC was observed in almost all reports. The closest association was found in Africa where, in three studies, HBsAg was found by radioimmunoassay (RIA) in 63% of 441 sera of patients with primary liver carcinoma (PLC) as compared to 11.7% in controls. In five studies carried out in Asia,

HBsAg was found by RIA or IAHA in 47% of 801 sera from HCC patients as compared to 8% in controls.[14]

In the United States and Western Europe, HBsAg was initially found less frequently in HCC patients: 12% in the two series which used RIA. Recently, however, Tabor et al.[4] have reported detection of HBsAg in 40% of American HCC patients, and Peters et al. (personal communication) found HBsAg in 50% of HCC livers at autopsy by immunofluorescence. This is markedly higher than the frequency (0.15–0.5%) found in controls in these regions.

The markedly lower frequency of HBsAg in HCC cases from the United States and Western Europe may, in part, reflect the older age of HCC patients in these regions, since the frequency of HBsAg declines with age both in normal populations[5] and in patients with liver cancer.[6] However, this difference may also reflect a greater role of other etiologic factors, e.g., alcoholism, in the United States and Western Europe.

As many studies did not employ properly matched controls, we investigated the prevalence of serologic markers of HB infection in 165 HCC patients in Senegal, in 154 controls with other cancers closely matched with respect to age, sex, ethnic group, and time of hospitalization, and in 328 similarly matched controls without cancer.[6] The prevalence of HBsAg in these three groups, as tested by RIA, was 61.2%, 11.7% and 11.3%, respectively. This study also revealed that essentially all of the HCC patients with HBsAg were chronic carriers.

When tests for anti-HBc were employed as a marker for active recent infection with HBV, even higher frequencies were observed by Maupas and his colleagues: 87%, 70% and 24% of the HCC patients in Senegal, Hong Kong and the United States, respectively, had detectable anti-HBc as compared to 34%, 36%, and 4% of the corresponding control groups.[7]

Does this striking association have etiologic significance? The possibility has been raised that this association reflects an increased risk of carrier state infection secondary to a presumed immunologic defect in HCC patients. Several observations argue against this hypothesis: (a) Immunologic defects have been searched for in HCC patients but were not found;[8] (b) Infections with HBV in the tropics are mostly acquired during the first few years of life, years before the appearance of most causes of HCC;[6] (c) A strikingly high prevalence of HBsAg has been found in mothers of HCC patients in Senegal (71.6% vs 16.6% in mothers of matched controls), suggesting that most HCC patients had acquired their infections early in life by maternal-fetal or maternal-infant transmission.[9]

These considerations strengthened the hypothesis that infection with HBV may play a role in the etiology of HCC. Such a role could involve a direct oncogenic effect, or a mechanism dependent on an intervening stage of hyperplasia due to cirrhosis. However, the latter does not appear to be a prerequisite, since 59 of 94 cases of PLC which we observed in Senegal, and in which the presence of coexisting cirrhosis could be evaluated by peritoneoscopy, surgery, or autopsy, did not reveal cirrhosis.[6]

It is possible that HBV serves as a cocarcinogen with a chemical carcinogen such as aflatoxin. Due to its extraordinarily potent hepatocarcinogenicity in some experimental animals, and its detection in many mold-contaminated cereals eaten in tropical regions, this compound has received extensive attention as a possible human hepatocarcinogen. Indeed, Peers and Linsell observed a correlation between levels of aflatoxin in food and in the incidence of HCC in three regions in Kenya.[10]

To attempt to gain some insight into the possible role of aflatoxins, we have estimated the risk of development of HCC in chronic HBsAg carriers in Mozambique, where aflatoxin ingestion is common and where the incidence of HCC has been carefully studied, and in the United States, where aflatoxin is probably extremely rare.[22] The estimate was made as follows: (a) In Mozambique the age-standardized incidence of HCC is reported to be 106.9 cases/100,000 males/year. Incidence in this and other populations is estimated from death rates since survival of patients with HCC is seldom more than a few months after clinical presentation. (b) At least 60% of HCC cases in Mozambique show presence of HBsAg, thus we can estimate at least 60 HCC deaths in HBsAg carriers/100,000 males/year. (c) At least 9% of males in Mozambique are HBsAg carriers, thus the 60 HCC deaths occur in a subpopulation of 9,000 male carriers, which corresponds to a risk of at least one case of HCC occurring among 150 male HBs carriers (all ages) per year.

In the United States, assuming an age-standardized incidence of HCC of 2.2/100,000 males/year,[17] we estimate 50% of HCC cases to be HBs carriers,[4] and 0.25% of males to be HBsAg carriers. The same calculation yields a risk of one case of HCC/186 male HBsAg carriers (all ages) per year. The similar estimated risk in American carriers does not support a cocarcinogenic or contributory role of aflatoxins in Africa, and further suggests that the earlier age of infection with HBV in Africa is not a prerequisite for carcinogenesis by HBV. Thus, perinatal infection does not appear to be an important factor in carcinogenesis with HBV, as it is with some other oncogenic viruses. Age at infection may, however, influence age of appearance of HCC: the peak incidence of this neoplasm is in the age group 30–40 in Senegal[6] as compared to 50–60 in the United States.

The above estimates are recognized to be crude and may be underestimated, due to underreporting of HCC cases and underassessment of HBsAg-carrier states, due to limitations inherent in current serologic methods. Prospective studies in chronic HBsAg carriers are needed to provide more exact data. Preliminary results from such studies are already available: Obada in Japan has followed with cirrhosis prospectively for three and a half years to observe the incidence of HCC.[18] Six of 25 (24%) such patients with HBsAg developed HCC, in contrast to none of 17 with anti-HBs, and one of 43 with neither marker. Sakuma et al.[19] observed three cases of HCC among 341 HBsAg carriers (all adult ages), as compared to no cases among 17,843 controls, followed prospectively for a half to three and a half years. Similar results have been obtained by Beasley in Taiwan (personal communication).

Additional data underlining the probable importance of HBV in HCC carcinogenesis has come from molecular hybridization studies: Summers et al. found HBV DNA by this technique in ten of 14 HCC tumors examined, including one case in which the serum contained anti-HBs.[20] The viral DNA's found in the above tumors did not appear to be integrated into host cellular DNA.[20]

Recently a virus morphologically and biochemically similar to HBV has been found to be very prevalent in woodchucks.[21] It is provocative that HCC has been observed in 29% of woodchucks over the age of four.[21] The tumor-bearing animals generally had chronic active hepatitis, and/or cirrhosis.

All of the above lines of evidence point to an important role for HBV in HCC carcinogenesis. It must be recognized, however, that other actual or potential etiologic factors exist: e.g., other hepatitis viruses (non-A, non-B), alcoholism, aflatoxins, vinyl chloride, certain steroids, etc.[22] The relative importance of different etiologic factors may vary in different geographic regions and occupational groups. None, however, is as closely associated or as high an apparent risk factor as HBV.

Estimation of Risk of Development of HCC in HBsAg Carriers and Controls

Source Data

Quantitative predictions have been derived from the following data base: (a) Standardized death rates for primary liver cancer; these data (Table 1) were obtained from the Bureau of Health Statistics and Analysis, New York City Department of Health, and collated by Dr. W. Szmuness.[17] The death rates are for a six-year period and thus must be divided by six to provide an estimate of annual rates. These data are for Code 155 (Primary Liver Cancer) and thus include Code 155.0 (Hepatocellular Carcinoma), as well as the etiologically distinct cancer, Bile Ductular Carcinoma (Code 155.1). Since 1979, computer tabulations in the New York City Department of Health have separated these two categories.

Table 1. Deaths from Hepatocellular Carcinoma (HCC) in Residents of New York City by Sex, Age, and Race and Age-Standardized Death Rates (SDR) for 1971-1976 (Code 155)

Age (yr)	Whites Deaths from HCC M[a]	F	Population (x 10^3)	Blacks Deaths from HCC M	F	Population (x 10^3)
20	4	4	1,743	3	1	693
20-34	4	3	1,284	5	1	384
35-49	23	8	1,061	13	10	307
50	367	227	2,004	133	46	281
Total	398	242	6,092	154	58	1,665
SDR	12.5	6.8	–	33.5	10.0	–

Age (yr)	Chinese Deaths from HCC M[a]	F	Population (x 10^3)	All Deaths from HCC M	F	Population (x 10^3)
20	2	0	25	9	5	2,461
20-34	1	0	17	10	4	1,685
35-49	3	0	15	39	18	1,383
50	40	3	15	540	276	2,300
Total	46	3	72	598	303	7,828
SDR	130.9	16.0	–	16.3	7.3	–

[a] M = males; F = females.

The data reveal that only 12 of 152 (7.8%) male liver cancers in 1978 were of the bile ductular variety. Thus the data are not significantly distorted by pooling of the two categories. (b) Incidence rates by race; the data from Table 1 provided the estimate of incidence rates shown in Figure 1.[17] As survival in HCC cases is almost always less than one year, death rates and incidence rates are essentially identical. (c) The proportion of HCC cases which occur in HBsAg carriers is estimated to be 50%, based on data of Peters et al. (personal communication) and Tabor et al.[4] (d) The distribution of New York City volunteer blood donors, HBsAg-positive and negative, by age and sex which is shown in Tables 2 and 3. (e) A comparison of the age distribution of HBsAg

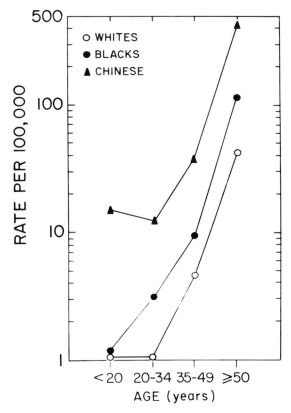

Figure 1. Age-specific death rates from HCC in residents of New York City by race (males only, 1971-1976); (Code 155.0).

carriers with that of the overall donor population shown in Figure 2. (f) The racial distribution of the New York Blood Center (NYBC) HBsAg carrier population (male only)[16] which is 88.6% White, 10.4% Black and Hispanic, and <1% Chinese.[16] (g) The prevalence of HBsAg carriers in the New York City blood donor population by race which is shown in Table 4.[16,17]

Much of the source data was derived from previous epidemiological studies,[15-17] which were not designed for the purpose of the present analysis. Hence, there are obvious inadequacies, e.g., different age groupings in different analyses, pooling of male and female data in some but not all tabulations, pooling of different races in some but not all tabulations. As the data base resides in the NYBC computer system, these differences are being remedied by re-analysis of the source data. It must also be recognized that blood donor populations do not represent

Table 2. Distribution of New York City HBsAg(+) Blood Donors by Age and Sex

Age	Males		Females	
	No.	(%)	No.	(%)
< 20	94	(1.0)	35	(1.9)
20-24	602	(7.0)	188	(10.2)
25-29	1569	(17.9)	356	(19.3)
30-34	1927	(22.0)	337	(18.2)
35-39	1287	(14.7)	211	(11.4)
40-44	900	(10.3)	149	(8.1)
45-49	716	(8.2)	117	(6.3)
50-54	641	(7.3)	137	(7.4)
55-59	502	(5.7)	135	(7.3)
60-64	277	(3.2)	79	(4.2)
65-69	141	(1.6)	61	(3.3)
> 70	80	(0.9)	41	(2.2)
Totals[a]	8736		1846	

[a] 1972-1979.

Table 3. Distribution of New York City HBsAg(−) Blood Donors by Age and Sex

Age	Males		Females	
	No.	(%)	No.	(%)
< 20	401	(5.7)	362	(9.9)
20-24	860	(12.2)	713	(19.5)
25-29	850	(12.1)	571	(15.6)
30-34	1112	(15.8)	417	(11.4)
35-39	982	(13.9)	366	(10.0)
40-44	772	(10.9)	301	(8.2)
45-49	682	(9.7)	273	(7.4)
50-54	596	(8.4)	289	(7.9)
55-59	475	(6.7)	250	(6.8)
60-64	254	(3.6)	98	(2.6)
65-69	37	(0.5)	8	(0.2)
70- +		(0.0)		(0.0)
Total[a]	7021		3648	

[a] A random consecutive sample (1979).

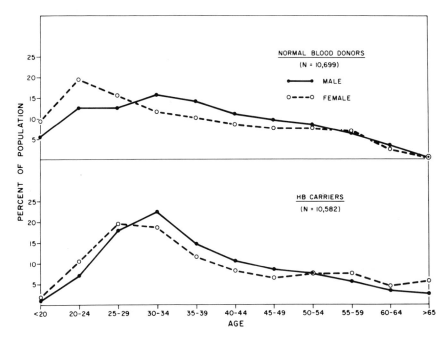

Figure 2. Age distribution of HBsAg-positive and HBsAg-negative blood donors in New York City.

Table 4. Age-Specific Prevalence of HBsAg Carriers in New York City by Race (Rate per 1,000)

Age	White[a]	Black[a]	Chinese
< 20	0.2	3.0	55.0
20-29	1.5	5.0	200.0
30-39	1.4	7.0	170.0
40-49	1.5	10.0	175.0
> 50	0.5	3.5	130 (50-59 yr)
			80 (60-69 yr)
			15 (> 70 yr)
All ages	1.26	5.48	23.17[a]
			100.3[b]

[a] Blood donors, both sexes.

[b] New York City residents, males only.

an unbiased sample of the overall New York City population. The present data are, however, sufficiently precise for the purpose of this analysis.

Predictions Based on the Above Source Data

On the basis of the data summarized above, we can estimate age-specific incidence rates for HCC in male HBsAg-positive blood donors (Table 5 and Figure 3), as well as the incidence in HBsAg-negative donors (Table 6), and the risk ratio between the two rates (Table 6 and Figure 4). It will

Table 5. Expected Incidence (Rate/100,000/Six Years) of HCC in HBsAg-Carrier Male Blood Donors (NYBC)

Race	Age	HCC Incidence in Males[a] (a)	Proportion of Males Who are Carriers[b] (β)	HCC Incidence in Male Carriers[c] (Cases/100,000 per Six Years) (γ)
White				
	< 20	0.45	0.0002	1100.7
	20-34	0.6	0.0014	214.3
	35-49	4.7	0.0015	153.3
	> 50	37.0	0.0005	37000.0
	ASI[d]	12.5	0.0012	5166.7
Black				
	< 20	0.87	0.003	143.3
	20-34	2.6	0.006	216.7
	35-49	8.7	0.008	543.7
	> 50	95.0	0.003	15833.0
	ASI[d]	33.5	0.005	3340.0
Chinese				
	< 20	8.0	0.055	130.8
	20-34	5.9	0.20	26.4
	35-49	20.0	0.17	105.8
	> 50	266.7	0.175	1371.6
	ASI[d]	130.9	0.10	1177.0

[a] Cases/100,000/six years. Taken from Table 1. We have assumed that the overall population is 50% male.

[b] Taken from Table 4.

[c] 50% of HCC cases are assumed to occur in HBsAg carriers among New City Whites and Blacks; therefore, incidence = 0.5 x $(a)/(\beta)$. Among Chinese, we assumed 90% of HCC to occur in HB carriers; therefore, incidence = 0.9 x $(a)/(\beta)$.

[d] ASI equals Age Standardized Incidence Rate.[17]

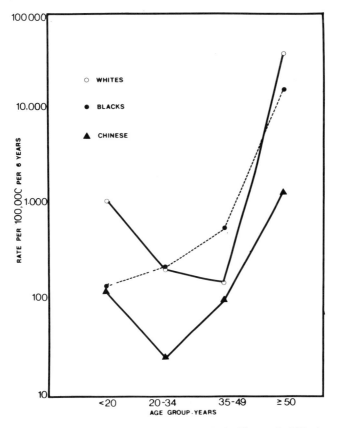

Figure 3. Incidence of HCC in New York City male HBsAg carriers by race.

be noted that the risk ratio tends to fall in early middle age and then rises to maximal rates in the >50-year age group (Figure 4). The racial difference between the incidence of HCC in HBsAg carriers and non-carriers, as well as the resulting racial differences in risk ratios, may not be as significant as they appear. These rates depend very strongly on the estimate of the proportion of HCC arising in HB carriers: assumed to be 50% of Whites and Blacks and 90% for Chinese. Further refinement of these estimates, best carried out by immunologic tests for HB serologic markers on autopsy liver tissue, will further refine these calculations. It should be noted that the risk ratio for development of HCC between HBsAg carriers and noncarriers estimated in Table 6 is the highest risk ratio postulated for any suspected human carcinogen. On the basis of the above data, and the assumptions indicated in footnotes to the tables, estimates of the number of HCC cases which should occur among NYBC

Table 6. Estimated Risk Ratio for Incidence of HCC, by Age and Race Between HBsAg(+) and HBsAg(−) Male Blood Donors in New York City

Race	Age	Incidence of HCC[a]		Risk Ratio[c]
		HBsAg(+)	HBsAg(−)	
White				
	< 20	1100.7	0.23	5000
	20-34	214.3	0.3	670
	35-49	153.3	2.2	710
	> 50	37000.0	18.2	2030
	ASI[b]	5166.7	6.2	833.3
Black				
	< 20	143.3	0.4	358.2
	20-34	216.7	1.3	166.7
	35-49	543.7	4.2	129.5
	> 50	15833.0	47.0	336.8
	ASI[b]	3340.0	16.7	233.2
Chinese				
	< 20	130.8	0.84	155.7
	20-34	26.4	0.74	35.6
	35-49	105.8	2.4	44.0
	> 50	1371.6	32.3	42.5
	ASI[b]	1177.0	14.5	81.1

[a] Cases/100,000/six years; assumes that 50.0% of HCC cases occur in HBsAg carriers among Whites and Blacks, and that 90% of HCC cases occur in HBsAg carriers among Chinese. Thus, among Whites and Blacks, incidence in noncarriers equals 0.5 x incidence in male population as a whole/proportion of male population who are not carriers; incidence in carriers equals 0.5 x incidence in male population/proportion of male population who are HBsAg carriers; among Chinese the incidence in noncarriers = 0.1 x incidence in male population as a whole/proportion of male population who are not carriers; in carriers = 0.9 x incidence in male population as a whole/proportion of male population who are carriers.

[b] ASI = Age Standardized Incidence Rate.[17]

[c] Risk Ratio = HCC incidence in HBsAg(+) subjects/HCC incidence in HBsAG(−) subjects.

HBsAg carriers is shown in Table 7. This analysis provides the basis for the quantitative prediction that at least 69.6 cases of PLC will be observed annually if all NYBC male HBsAg carriers who do not die of other causes are followed prospectively for one year. The annual rate may be even higher if source data are seriously biased by underreporting.

This extraordinary and shocking estimate would imply that 6.2% per

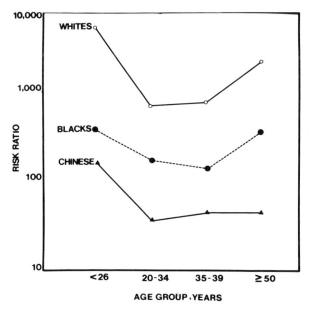

Figure 4. Estimated risk ratio for incidence of HCC between HBsAg-positive and HBsAg-negative subjects.

Table 7. Expected Number of HCC Cases in New York Blood Center Male HBsAg Carrier Population per Year

Age	Number HBsAg Carriers[a]				Number HCC Cases Expected[c]			
	Total	White[b]	Black[b]	Chinese[b]	White	Black	Chinese	Total
<20	90	80	10	< 1	0.1	<0.01	<0.01	0.1
21-35	3670	3252	418	<36	1.1	0.01	<0.01	1.1
36-50	2273	2013	260	<23	0.5	0.23	<0.01	0.73
≥51	1175	1041	134	<12	64.2[d]	3.5	<0.01	67.7
Total	7208	6386	822	<72	65.9	3.74	<0.01	69.6

[a] From Table 2. Carriers with unknown ages are not included in this table.

[b] Racial distribution calculated from Reference 16.

[c] Incidence rate in HBsAg carriers (Table 5) x numbers of carriers in each group, ÷ 6 to convert to annual incidence rates from six-year incidence rates.

[d] Example of calculation:
Number of HCC cases expected in white male HBsAg carriers aged ≥ 51 years:
1. Incidence = 37 cases/100,000 males/6 years = 6.1/100,000/year.
2. Incidence of HB (+) HCC cases (assume 50%) = 3.0/100,000 males/year.
3. Incidence of HB (+) HCC in HB (+) male carriers ≥ 51 years old = 3.0 cases/50 male HBsAg carriers/year [since only 50 of 100,000 males (0.05%) are HBsAg carriers in this age group].
4. Annual incidence in 1041 white male HBsAg carriers = 3.0 x 1041/50 = 64.2 cases HB (+) HCC/year = 6.2% per year.

year of male white HBV carriers will die of HCC if they survive into the high risk age group (>50 years).

It is therefore worthwhile to review the basis for this estimate. This is done in Footnote 4, Table 7. Because of the relative crudity of the source data, this estimate may be somewhat in error (±2-fold); however, the essential conclusion appears likely to be correct. This surprising prediction does not accord well with general clinical experience. Two explanations can be considered: (a) a high proportion of male carriers die of cirrhosis before developing clinical evidence of liver cancer; or (b) many cases of liver cancer may not come to surgery or autopsy and may thus escape definitive diagnosis and inclusion in death statistics. It is likely that both phenomena play a role. The quantitative role of these phenomena can only be evaluated in a well carried out prospective study.

The prediction that most male HB carriers will die in their 50's is compatible with the observed age distribution of male and female HB carriers (Figure 2). Note the more rapid (ca 75%) decline in the number of male carriers between 50 and 65 as compared to the relatively small (ca 25%) decline in the number of female carriers. This is seen more clearly when age distribution is plotted in absolute numbers (Figure 5) rather than as percent of population, as in Figure 2. Females are well known to have a much lower risk of development of HCC than do males.

Figure 5. Age distribution of HBsAg-positive NYBC blood donors.

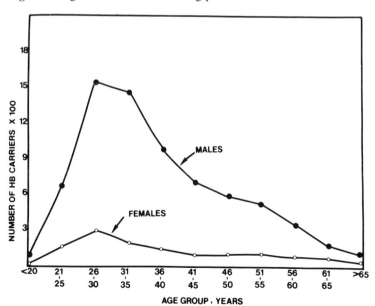

Conclusions

Intensive prospective studies are clearly needed to provide accurate estimates of the incidence of chronic active hepatitis, cirrhosis and hepatocellular carcinoma, and other possible medical complications in high-risk subsets of the HBsAg carrier population. A comparison of results from studies carried out in regions of high aflatoxin prevalence with those obtained in regions of low aflatoxin contamination will permit evaluation of the importance of aflatoxin in these risks. The prospective nature of the data obtained will further evaluate the etiologic significance development of primary liver cancer. Such studies will also permit estimation of the possible utility of prospective α-fetoprotein follow-up in providing clinically useful early diagnosis of primary liver cancer, and may provide patients in a relatively early stage of HCC for controlled treatment trials.

It should also be emphasized that documentation of an etiologic association between HBV infection and hepatocellular carcinoma would intensify efforts to make HB vaccines available throughout the world, and especially in high prevalence regions, to attempt prevention of the establishment of the HBsAg-carrier state. This may contribute to the prevention, by immunization with HB vaccine, of a major human cancer.

Summary

The literature concerning the association between hepatitis B virus (HBV) and hepatocellular carcinoma (HCC) has been reviewed. In addition, a theoretical estimate, which can be tested by prospective studies, has been presented which suggests that the risk of development of HCC in white male HBV carriers in New York is on the average 833 times as high as in noncarriers. This is the highest ratio postulated for any suspected human carcinogen. The incidence of HCC in male white carriers >50 years of age in New York is estimated to be 6% per year.

References

1. Payet, M., Camain, R., and Pene, P.: *Rev. Int. D'Hepatol.:* 6:1, 1956.
2. Steiner, P.E. and Davis, J.N.P.: *Br. J. Cancer* 11:523, 1957.
3. Simmons, M.J., Yap, E.H., Yu, M., and Shanmugaratnam, K.: *Int. J. Cancer* 10:320, 1972.
4. Tabor, E., Gerety, R.J., Vogel, C.L., Bayley, A.C., Anthony, P.P., Chan, C.H., and Barker, L.F.: *J. Natl. Cancer Inst.* 58:1197, 1977.
5. Szmuness, W., Prince, A.M., Diebolt, G., Leblanc, L., Baylet, R., Masseyeff, R., and Linhard, J.: *Am. J. Epidemiol.* 98:104, 1973.

6. Prince, A.M., Szmuness, W., Michon, J., Demaille, J., Diebolt, G., Linhard, J., Quenum, C., and Sankale, M.: *Int. J. Cancer* 16:376, 1975.

7. Maupas, P., Larouzé, B., London, W.T., Werner, B., Millman, I., O'Connell, A., Blumberg, B.S., Saimot, G., and Payet, M.: *Lancet* 2:9, 1975.

8. Primack, A., Vogel, C.L., and Barker, L.F.: *Br. Med. J.* 1:16, 1973.

9. Blumberg, B.S., Larouzé, B., and London, W.T.: *Am. J. Pathol.* 81:669, 1975.

10. Peers, F.G. and Linsell, C.A.: *Br. J. Cancer* 27:473, 1973.

11. Prince, A.M.: In: *Liver Cancer,* IARC Scientific Publications, No. 1 International Agency for Research on Cancer, WHO, Lyon, 1971, p. 51.

12. Prince, A.M., Leblanc, L., Krohn, K., Masseyeff, R., and Alpert, M.E.: *Lancet* 2:717, 1970.

13. Prince, A.M.: *Gastroenterology* 60:913, 1971.

14. Prince, A.M.: In: *The Liver, Part B,* F.F. Becker (ed.), Marcel Dekker, New York, 1975, p. 575.

15. Szmuness, W., Prince, A.M., Brotman, B., and Hirsch, R.L.: *J. Infect. Dis.* 127:17, 1973.

16. Szmuness, W., Hirsch, R.L., Prince, A.M., Levine, R.W., Harley, E.J., and Ikram, H.: *J. Infect. Dis.* 131:111, 1975.

17. Szmuness, W., Stevens, C.E., Ikram, H., Much, M.I., Harley, E.J., and Hollinger, B.: *J. Infect. Dis.* 137:822, 1978.

18. Obada, H.: *Clinician* 24:63, 1977.

19. Sakuma, K., Ohtake, H., Okuda, K., and Mayumi, M.: Hepatitis Scientific Memoranda, October, 1977.

20. London, W.T.: In: *Viral Hepatitis,* G.N. Vyas, S.N. Cohen and R. Schmid (eds.), The Franklin Institute Press, Philadelphia, 1978, p. 455.

21. Snyder, R.L.: *Am. J. Pathol.* 52:32, 1968.

22. Popper, H.: In: *Viral Hepatitis,* G.N. Vyas, S.N. Cohen and R. Schmid (eds.), Franklin Institute Press, Philadelphia, 1978, p. 451.

23. Prince, A.M.: In: *Viral Hepatitis,* G.N. Vyas, S.N. Cohen and R. Schmid (eds.), Franklin Institute Press, Philadelphia, 1978, p. 732.

Inhibition of Chemical Transformation *in Vitro* and Tumor Induction *in Vivo* by Inhibition of Viral Expression

Paul J. Price

*U.S. Department of Health, Education and Welfare, Public Health Service,
Center for Disease Control, Atlanta, Georgia*

Three previous studies led us to examine *in vitro* cell systems as a means of studying the cocarcinogenic role of leukemia viruses in chemically induced cell transformation. They were the studies by Lieberman on the activation of type "C" RNA viruses in mice that had been irradiated,[12] by Toth[3] and Igel[4] on activation of the viruses after mice had been treated with chemicals (Toth), and simultaneous studies by Whitmire that showed a relationship between viral expression (antigenic) and tumors arising spontaneously or after mice had been treated with chemicals.[5-7] Our results were extended by Huebner and Fish, who used *in vivo* systems.[8-12]

We initially turned to rat cells as a possible model system. The inbred rat is like the human in that, normally, it does not show leukemia viral expression during its normal life span and has virus-free leukemias and other cancers late in life. It soon became evident that non-transforming type "C" RNA viruses play a significant and specific role in promoting the expression of transformation. Because this system is based on an interaction between the omnipresent RNA tumor viruses and the carcinogenic chemicals, it may accurately reflect what is happening in the intact animal.

In our initial experiments,[13] we treated secondary cultures of Fisher, Osborne-Mendel, and Wistar rat embryo cells with 0.1 mM diethylnitrosamine (DENA) and simultaneously infected the cells with either the ectropic Rauscher murine leukemia virus (RLV) or the ecotropic CF-1 leukemia virus. The chemically treated cells were fed repeatedly for 21 days with media containing DENA; the chemical was then permanently removed. Sister cultures were left untreated or were treated with either DENA or virus. By the 12th subculture after chemical treatment, cultures treated with both DENA and virus were transformed, but the untreated controls and cultures treated with either DENA or virus were normal and were still normal at the end of the experiment 50 subcultures later. Fortunately, we used secondary cultures of rat embryo since with increased subculturing, the cultured rat cells progressively lose their metabolic competence with respect to DENA (J. Wolff, personal communication). We, or other investigators working independently, confirmed our initial observations, using 3-methylcholanthrene,[14-16] benzo(a)pyrene,[17-18] residues of city smog,[17] dimethylbenzanthracine,[19] and dimethylnitrosamine.[15] In general, low-passage rat embryo cell cultures appear to be resistant to spontaneous transformation or transformation by type "C" RNA leukemia virus (MuLV). Cultures chronically infected with MuLV, however, have an increased sensitivity to transformation by chemicals shown to be carcinogenic by *in vivo* studies (Table 1). Depending upon the cell strain, the need for adding an exogenous source of virus for increased transformation efficiency disappears between subcultures 35 and 60. At this time, rat leukemia virus (RaLV) antigens are more easily demonstrated.[20] Between subcultures 100 and 120, the background rate of spontaneous transformation renders the cell system unusable as a carcinogen screen. The life history of the rat embryo cell, therefore, passes through three stages characterized in terms of susceptibility to chemically induced transformation, endogenous "C" type virus expression, and rate of spontaneous transformation. Freeman[21] has described this subculture-dependent phenomenon in rat cells on the basis of the promoting effects of the virus. To be transformed by a carcinogenic chemical, low-passage, Stage I Fischer rat embryo cells have an absolute requirement for virus. This requirement appears to be due to the absence or low expression of the endogenous RaLV. Stage II cells, which express the endogenous RaLA, do not require exogenous virus infection for chemical transformation.

Role of the Exogenous Virus in the Sensitivity of Stage I Cells to Transformation by Chemical Carcinogens

We do not know exactly how the virus functions as a cocarcinogen. Perhaps the chemical carcinogen causes a DNA lesion in which the viral DNA is incorporated, resulting in a frameshift mutation. Perhaps the role of the virus is to directly transport cellular genetic information from cell to cell and, in doing so, the virus functions as a means of multiplying cellular oncogene sequences. Perhaps the virus-producing cells are more susceptible to transformation. Perhaps the chemical carcinogen induces transient expression of the xenotropic virus, resulting in the formation of

Table 1. Cell Cultures Transformed by the Combined Action of Carcinogenic Chemicals and C-Type RNA Viruses

		Virus Status	Transformation	Transplantability	Reference
Diethylnitrosamine	Fischer rat	RLV+[a]	+	−	(13,17,20,21)
	O-M rat	RLV−	−	−	(13,17,20,21)
	Fischer rat	CF-1+[b]	+	−	(13,17,20,21)
	Wistar rat	CF-1−	−	−	(13,17,20,21)
Dimethylnitrosamine	Fischer rat	RLV+	+[c]	NT[d]	(15,23)
Methylcholanthrene	Fischer rat (2 different embryo pools)	RLV+	+	+	(14,22,24,25,28-32)
		RLV−	−	−	(14,22,24,25,28-32)
	Fischer rat	RLV+	+[c]	NT	(15,23)
		RLV−	−	NT	(15,23)
	Fischer rat	RaLV+[e]	+	+	(16)
		RaLV−	−	−	(16)
Dimethylbenzanthracene	Fischer rat	RLV+	+	+	(19,33)
		RLV−	−	−	(19,33)
Benzo(a)pyrene	Fischer rat	RLV−	−	−	(18)
		RLV+	+	+	(18)
	Fischer rat	RLV+	+	+	(13,17,20,21)
		RLV−	−	−	(13,17,20,21)
City Smog Residues	Fischer rat	RLV+	+	+	(13,17,20,21)
		RLV−	−	−	(13,17,20,21)

[a] Rauscher leukemia virus.

[b] A mouse leukemia virus isolated from CF-1 mice.

[c] Growth in soft agar.

[d] NT = Not tested.

[e] Rat leukemia virus.

recombinant viruses which, in turn, rescue or express transforming genes or oncogenes. We do know that the virus must be integrated into the cellular genome before chemical treatment. If the low-passage rat cells are infected with the virus only after chemical treatment,[22] then no cocarcinogenic effect occurs. Mishra has shown that if ethidium bromide, an inhibitor of putative virus-specific cDNA integration, was added to the FRE cells immediately before virus infection, transformation was not demonstrable after challenge with a chemical carcinogen. However, if ethidium bromide was added after one cycle of viral infection, no such inhibition was observed. If viral protein synthesis was inhibited by puromycin or cycloheximide, chemically induced transformation was also inhibited. On the other hand, purified rat interferon, which is thought to interfere with intact virion assembly, but not with virus-specific macromolecular synthesis, does not inhibit chemical-viral cocarcinogenesis. Mishra has interpreted his results to mean that a virus-specific protein may be required for virus-induced promotion of chemical transformation.[23] If low-passage, Fischer rat embryo cells chronically infected with RLV were treated before and during treatment with a chemical carcinogen with neutralizing antibody having high titers against both the ecotropic RLV and the xenotropic AT124 virus, then transformation was inhibited. Low-titered antibody, antibody specific for only the xenotropic virus[24] or for an antigenically different ecotropic virus,[25] or antibody having low titer against either the xenotropic or ecotropic virus, does not protect the cells from transformation (Table 2). Data from our experiment with the Stage I Fischer rat system have therefore demonstrated that active viral synthesis is a prerequisite for chemically induced transformation and that if this synthesis is inhibited by specific antiviral antisera, chemically induced cell transformation is also inhibited. The role of the virus is still not completely known. Zimmerman et al. have demonstrated that there is not a significant difference between control cells and chronically infected cells with regard to carcinogen uptake, binding to nucleic acids or protein, or metabolism.[26] However, a recent study by Waters et al. demonstrated that infection with a type "C" RNA virus inhibits cellular postreplication repair synthesis.[27] The defect in the cellular repair mechanism in the virus-infected FRE cell can be seen after insult with a chemical carcinogen, 4 nitroquinoline oxide (4NQO), or after exposure to ultraviolet irradiation.

Role of the Endogenous Virus of Stage II Cells

Even though the Stage II Fischer rat embryo cells appear to be virus-free by both complement fixation and by testing for RNA-dependent DNA polymerase, the rat xenotropic virus RaLV is inducible with halogenated pyrimidines, and RaLV antigens are occasionally detected

Table 2. Immunoprevention of Transformation of F115[a]

Antisera Dilution	RDDP Activity at the Time of Carcinogen Treatment[e]	Growth in Agar	Transformed Foci	Tumors[j]
	0.05γ 4-NPO[b]			
Goat anti-RLV[f]				
1:480	1.2	−	− (P17)	ND[g]
1:960	1.7	−	− (P17)	0/13 (118)
Control	3.7	+	− (P11)	ND
Goat anti-AT124[h]				
1:480	3.3	+	+ (P11)	ND
1:960	4.3	+	+ (P11)	12/12 (47)
1:1920	5.3	+	+ (P12)	ND
	0.05γ 4NQO[c]			
Goat anti-RLV				
1:480	1.2	−	− (P17)	ND
1:960	1.7	ND	− (P17)	ND
1:1920	3.8	+	+ (P11)	ND
Control	3.7	+	+ (P9)	ND
Goat anti-AT124				
1:480	3.3	+	+ (P11)	ND
1:960	4.3	+	+ (P9)	ND
	0.5γ MCA[d]			
Goat anti-RLV				
1:480	0	−	− (P15)	ND
1:960	.07	−	− (P15)	ND
1:1920	9.5	+	+ (P7)	ND
Control				
Goat anti-RadLV[i]				
1:480	1.1	+	+ (P13)	ND
1:960	2.7	+	+ (P7)	ND
1:1920	10.8	+	+ (P7)	ND

[a] Fischer rat embryo cells chronically infected with RLV.

[b] Nitropyridine-1-oxide.

[c] Nitroquinoline-1-oxide.

[d] 3-methylcholanthrene.

[e] pmoles ^{3}H-TMP incorporated/ml supernatant.

[f] Goat antisera produced against the Rauscher murine leukemia virus and having high titers against RLV and AT124.

[g] Not done.

[h] Goat antisera produced against the Swiss mouse AT124 xenotropic virus.

[i] Goat antisera produced against the Kaplan radiation leukemia virus and having high titer against AKR but low titer against AT124.

[j] Number of animals with tumors/number of animals inoculated (number of days).

after transformation. We have shown that streptonigrin,[28] cordycepine,[29] geldanamycin,[30] 9-B-D-Arabinofuronosyladenine,[31] and rimantadine,[32] antiviral antibiotics which inhibit either the activation of endogenous virus by the halogenated pyrimidines, virus spread, absorption, penetration, uncoating, or integration, can protect the high-passage cells (but not the chronically infected low-passage cells) from chemically induced transformation (Table 3). One explanation of this protective action would be that the carcinogenic chemical acts by turning on a transient xenotropic virus infection, which either by itself or after recombination acts as a carrier and a means of multiplying cellular oncogene sequences. If this is true, then IgG specific to the endogenous virus should also protect the cells from chemical or spontaneous transformation. In two separate experiments, four neutralizing units of RaLV-specific goat IgG protected the high-passage cells from transformation normally induced by the carcinogen 4NQO if the goat IgG was added to the cells two or three days before chemical treatment (Table 4). In contrast, if the cells were treated with low-titered RaLV IgG or if the high-titered IgG was added after chemical treatment, transformation was not inhibited, and the cells appeared to be even more sensitive to chemically induced transformation. These observations have not been repeatable with other high-titered lots

Table 3. Prevention of Transformation of Stage II Fischer Rat Cells by Antiviral Antibiotics

Treatment	Transformed Foci	Tumors[a]
0.1 μg MCA/ml	+ (P1)	13/13 (56)
0.1 μg MCA + 0.16 mg SN/ml	− (P27)	0/6 (76)
0.1 μg MCA + 0.33 mg SN/ml	− (P27)	0/6 (76)
0.1 μg MCA/ml	+ (P4)	11/11 (29)
0.1 μg MCA/ml	+ (P3)	9/9 (27)
0.1 μg MCA + 10 μg Cd/ml	− (P9)	1/9 (90)
0.1 μg MCA + 5 μg CD/ml	− (P7)	1/9 (60)
0.1 μg MCA/ml	+ (P1)	6/7 (90)
0.1 μg MCA + 0.3 μg Gl d/ml	− (P14)	0/4 (90)
0.2 μg MCA/ml	+ (P3)	11/12 (82)
0.2 μg MCA + 1.0 μg Ara-A/ml	− (P8)	0/10 (94)
0.2 μg MCA + μg Ara-A/ml	− (P8)	0/13 (94)
0.1 μg MCA/ml	+ (P3)	ND[b]
0.5 μg B(a)P/ml	+ (P3)	ND
0.1 μg MCA + 0.5 μg Rd/ml	− (P9)	ND
0.5 μg B(a)P + 0.5 μg Rd/ml	− (P9)	ND

[a] Number of animals with tumors/number of animals inoculated (number of days).

[b] ND = Not done.

Table 4. Inhibition of Chemical Transformation of Fischer Rat-Embryo Cells By Pretreatment with Rat Leukemia Virus (RaLV) Specific IgG

RaLV IgG Treatment	0.05γ 4NQO Treatment	Exp. No.	Transformation		Tumorigenicity[b]
			Phenotypic	Growth in Agar	
Day 1	Day 4	A	−D15[a]	−D4, −D7	0/12
		B	−D15	−D4, −D7	ND[c]
Day 2	Day 4	A	−D15	−D4, −D7	0/8
		B	−D15	−D4, −D7	ND
Day 3	Day 4	A	+ D11	−D4, −D7	12/12 (77)
		B	−D15	−D4, −D7	ND
Day 4	Day 4	A	+ D4	+ D4, + D7	13/13 (21)
		B	+ D8	−D4, −D7	ND
Day 5	Day 4	A	+ D4	+ D4, + D7	11/11 (189)
		B	+ D7	−D4, + D7	ND
Day 6	Day 4	A	+ D4	+ D4, + D7	13/13 (175)
		B	+ D4	+ D4, + D7	ND
No IgG	Day 4	A	+ D8	−D4, −D7	11/11 (126)
		B	+ D10	−D4, −D7	ND
No IgG	No 4NQO	A	−D15	−D4, −D7	2/19[d]
		B	−D15	−D4, −D7	ND

[a] D = Number of population doublings

[b] Number of animals with tumors/number of animals inoculated (number of days). Numbers in parentheses represent number of days to 100% tumor incidence. Animals inoculated SQ with 10^6 cells from D15 and held 200 days.

[c] ND = Not done.

[d] First tumor observed on day 105. Second tumor observed on day 140. Remaining animals still tumor-free on day 200.

of RaLV-specific goat IgG; so the role of the endogenous virus in this system is still unclear.

Summary of *in Vitro* Model Systems

The increased sensitivity to chemical transformation in the presence of virus is not limited to rat cells. The efficiency of chemically induced transformation of hamster cells is also greatly increased if the cells are preinfected with the hamster leukemia virus.[17] Rhim et al. demonstrated that in the presence of the AKR leukemia virus, Swiss-mouse-embryo cells are also more sensitive to chemically induced transformation.[33] Increased efficiency with respect to chemically induced transformation has also been noted by Rapp[34] in type "C" RNA virus-inoculated C3H10T 1/2 mouse cells.[34,35]

It also appears that untreated cells propagated *in vitro* eventually die or transform spontaneously. The subculture at which this occurs depends upon the genus, species, or even the strain and culture conditions. Transformation is therefore a predictable event. This event in the rodent cells (rat, mouse and hamster) which we have studied is minimally accelerated after infection with a nontransforming type "C" RNA virus, moderately accelerated after exposure to a chemical carcinogen, and greatly accelerated if exposure to a chemical carcinogen follows stimulation of endogenous virus expression or infection with an exogenous oncornavirus.

In Vivo Model Systems

In 1972, Whitmire, Huebner and Salerno reported that vaccination with radiation leukemia virus (RadLV)[1,2] significantly reduced the incidence of sarcomas induced in C57B1/6 mice by inoculation with the polycyclic hydrocarbon 3-methylcholanthrene (MCA). Vaccination with a heterotypic virus, Graffi leukemia, induced no protection.[5-7] Their work, summarized in Table 5, demonstrated that immunity to specific viral antigens could provide protection against chemically induced cancer.

More recently, Hartley demonstrated that spontaneous leukemia in AKR mice appears at about the same time as a new recombinant virus, which she called MCF. This virus appears to be a stable recombinant of an endogenous ecotropic and xenotropic virus, and it can induce leukemia in mice and transformation in mink fibroblasts.[36] In four separate experiments (summarized in Table 6), Huebner and Fish demonstrated that

Table 5. Prevention of 3MCA Tumors in Newborn C57B1/6 CUM Mice By Active Immunization with RadLV

Experiment	Immunogen	3MCA Dosage (Mg)	Sarcomas	
			Frequency	(%)
1	RadLV	150	4/18	(22)
	PBS controls	150	16/20	(80)
2	RadLV	25	9/31	(29)
	PBS controls	25	19/30	(63)
3	RadLV	100	12/27	(44)
	PBS controls	100	20/21	(95)
4	Graffi LV	100	15/25	(60)
	HBSS controls	100	15/28	(54)

Table 6. Prevention of 3MCA Tumors in Weanling C3H MTV-Mice By Passive Immunization with Anti-Viral IgG

Goat IgG Used	Neutralization Titer Versus:		150 μg 3MCA Administration on Day:	Tumor Incidence (day)	Percent Tumors
	AKR	AT-124			
RadLV	3200	3200	3	14/27 (122)	52
Control	–	–	3	25/29 (122)	86
RadLV	3200	3200	12	11/30 (122)	37
Control	–	–	12	29/39 (122)	74
RadLV	1600	400	4	16/29 (122)	55
Control	–	–	4	20/30 (122)	67
Normal Goat	< 100	< 100	2	8/10 (122)	80
Control	–	–	2	6/9 (122)	67
RadLV	1600	800	4	7/20 (250)	35
Control	< 100	< 100	4	17/22 (250)	77
GLV	800	200	4	13/22 (250)	59
C57/L	100	800	4	16/22 (250)	73
RadLV	1600	1600	4	8/30 (190)	27
RadLV	100	200	4	20/30 (190)	67
RLV	400	1600	4	24/27 (190)	89
Control	–	–	4	27/29 (190)	93

passive immunity induced by inoculation with RadLV or Gross leukemia virus (GLV) antisera could protect weanling C3H/f mice from tumor induction by MCA. To be effective, the IgG had to have titers against both the xenotropic and ecotropic components of the recombinant viruses (in this case RadLV or GLV). Mixing IgG's prepared against either a xenotropic or ecotropic virus was ineffectual. IgG of low titer or IgG having a low titer against either component provided poor protection.[10] These studies demonstrated that recombinant viruses contain species-specific transforming proteins, which can induce antibodies capable of preventing chemically induced sarcomas in mice having no or low virogene expression.

Huebner et al. also demonstrated that the same anti-RadLV antibodies that protected C3H mice from tumors could also prevent spontaneous leukemia in AKR mice. This work is summarized in Table 7. They also found that they could prevent or modify the spontaneous leukemia incidence that normally occurs in the Fl offspring of C57L/AKR or NIH/AKR mice by active immunization. AKR males were mated with NIH or C57L females previously immunized with purified cobalt-killed GLV. At

166

Table 7. Prevention of Leukemia in AKR Mice by Specific Anti-Viral Antibody

Goat IgG Used	Leukemia Incidence at 300 Days		Leukemia Incidence at 365 Days	
	Frequency	(%)	Frequency	(%)
RadLV	2/30	(6.6)	6/30	(20)
Control	11/24	(45.8)	20/24	(83.3)
RadLV	NR[a]		10/52	(19)
RadLV	NR		0/30	(0)
Control	NR		62/86	(72)
RadLV	2/22	(9)	NR	
AT124	15/33	(45)	NR	
RLV	14/41	(34)	NR	
Control	32/75	(43)	NR	

[a] NR = Not reported.

about mid-pregnancy the pregnant females were vaccinated with live murine sarcoma virus [MSV (GLV)]. At ten days of age the Fl mice were vaccinated with live MSV (GLV). Table 8 summarizes their results and demonstrates significant protection against spontaneous leukemia.[12]

Using immunoprevention of cancer in rats as a model system akin to cancer in man, Huebner and his associates attempted to prevent tumor induction in Fischer (F344)- and Wistar Furth (WF)-inbred rats by vaccination with oncornavirus-associated tumor cells [allogenic Kirsten (Ki) MSV nonproducer (NP) or syngeneic Ki MSV (Rasheed)]. Both tumor cell lines are readily rejected by 25 days postinoculation. The various syngeneic tumor cells used for challenge produce lethal tumors in control rats. Table 9 summarizes several experiments and demonstrates that transformed allogeneic and syngeneic sarcogene-transformed cells contain tumor antigens that are crossreactive with a variety of tumors and transformed cells. These Ki MSV antigens induced highly significant protection.[10]

Conclusion

Low-passage or Stage I rat cells appear to be resistant to spontaneous transformation, transformation by a type "C" RNA leukemia virus, or transformation by a chemical carcinogen. Cultures chronically infected with the virus, however, have an increased sensitivity to transformation by carcinogenic chemicals. If the same chronically infected cells are treated before and during treatment with a chemical carcinogen that has

Table 8. Prevention of Leukemia by Immunization[a]

	Incidence of Spontaneous Leukemia on Day:							
	300		400		500		600	
	Vaccinated	Control	Vaccinated	Control	Vaccinated	Control	Vaccinated	Control
C57L/AKR	0/65	0/45	5/69 (8%)	6/44 (14%)	7/59 (12%)	14/44 (32%)	11/59 (19%)	24/44 (55%)
NIH/AKR	1/107 (1%)	5/105 (5%)	10/107 (9%)	20/105 (19%)	20/107 (19%)	30/105 (29%)	29/106 (27%)	45/105 (43%)
SWR/AKR	1/43 (2%)	5/38 (13%)	4/42 (10%)	7/35 (20%)	6/42 (14%)	11/35 (31%)	12/40 (30%)	18/32 (56%)

[a]Weanling females of C57L, SWR and NIH Swiss Strains were immunized SQ with purified GLV and then bred to AKR males. At mid-pregnancy, the mice were injected SQ with live MSV (GLV). At 10 days of age all F1 offspring of immunized mothers were challenged with live MSV (GLV).

Table 9. Prevention of Transplantable Tumors in F344 Weanling Rats Using a Tumor Cell Vaccine

Immunogen	Challenge	No. of Tumors at Day 21-23
KiMSV (NP)	4NQO sarcoma cells[a]	0/5
Control	4NQO sarcoma cells[a]	4/5
KiMSV (NP)	DMH colon carcinoma cells[a]	0/5
Control	DMH colon carcinoma cells[a]	5/5
KiMSV (NP) – double immunization	4NQO sarcoma cells[a]	4/10
Control	4NQO sarcoma cells[a]	24/25
Rat sarcoma tumor cells	Polyoma tumor[a]	0/15
Control	Polyoma tumor[a]	6/10
KiMSV (Rasheed)	4NQO tissue culture cells[b]	0/5
Control	4NQO tissue culture cells[b]	4/5
KiMSV (Rasheed)	8613 M-MSV tumor line[b]	0/5
Control	8613 M-MSV tumor line[b]	5/5
KiMSV (Rasheed)	CL3KiMSV transformed rat liver line	0/5
Control	CL3KiMSV transformed rat liver line	3/5

[a] 10^5 cells.
[b] 10^6 cells.

the proper viral-specific neutralizing antibody or if active viral synthesis is inhibited by chemical means, then transformation is also inhibited.

Rat cells serially passaged for a period of time, and which now show endogenous rat leukemia virus expression, do not require exogenous virus infection for increased sensitivity to transformation by chemical carcinogens. Specific antibody or antiviral antibiotics inhibiting either the activation of endogeneous virus, virus spread, absorption, penetration, uncoating, or integration can protect these cells from transformation.

As in the *in vitro* system, the *in vivo* models have shown that antibody to a recombinant between the ecotropic and xenotropic virus is effective in reducing or eliminating oncogenesis. In addition, the *in vivo* data has shown that antibody to a common tumor antigen can also effectively protect the host.

By inhibiting the putative cellular oncogene induction or expression, all cancers, regardless of causative agent, may be preventable.

Summary

Low-passage rat embryo cultures which have been chronically infected with a non-transforming leukemia virus have an increased sensitivity to transformation by chemicals shown to be carcinogenic by *in vivo* studies. Antiviral antibody having high titers against the xenotropic and ecotropic components of a recombinant murine leukemia virus inhibits the chemical transformation if present during the period of chemical treatment. Depending upon the cell strain, the need for adding an exogenous source of virus for increased transformation efficiency disappears between subcultures 35 and 60. At this time, rat leukemia viral antigens are more easily demonstrated. Some lots of high titered RaLV antibody, as well as several antiviral antibiotics, can now suppress chemical or irradiation-induced malignant transformation of these "virus-free" cells. This same recombinant antibody can also prevent spontaneous leukemia in AKR mice and generally reduce the incidence of chemically induced tumors in C57B1/6 or C_3H mice.

References

1. Lieberman, M. and Kaplan, H.S.: *Science* 130:387, 1959.
2. Lieberman, M., Haran-Chera, N., and Kaplan, H.S.: *Nature* 203:420, 1964.
3. Toth, B.: *Proc. Soc. Exp. Biol. Med.* 112:873, 1963.
4. Igel, H.J., Huebner, R.J., Turner, H.C., Kotin, P., and Falk, H.L.: *Science* 166:1624, 1969.
5. Whitmire, C.E., Salerno, R.A., Rabstein, L.S., Huebner, R.J., and Turner, H.J.: *J. Natl. Cancer Inst.* 47:1255, 1971.
6. Whitmire, C.E. and Salerno, R.A.: *Proc. Soc. Exp. Biol. Med.* 144:674, 1973.
7. Whitmire, C.E.: *J. Natl. Cancer Inst.* 51:473, 1973.
8. Huebner, J.J., Gilden, R.V., Toni, R., Hill, R.W., Trimmer, R.W., Fish, D.C., and Sass, B.: *Proc. Natl. Acad. Sci.* 73:4633, 1976.
9. Huebner, R.J.: In: *Tumors of Early Life in Man and Animal (Sixth Perugia Quadrennial International Conference on Cancer, 1977)*, L. Severi (ed.), Division of Cancer Research, Perugia, Italy, 1980 (in press).
10. Huebner, R.J. and Fish, D.C.: In: *Carcinogens: Identification and Mechanisms of Action*, A.C. Griffin and C.R. Shaw (eds.), Raven Press, New York, 1979.
11. Fish, D.C., Gilden, R.V., Bare, R.M., Trimmer, R.M., and Huebner, R.J.: *J. Natl. Cancer Inst.* 62:943, 1979.
12. Fish, D.C., Bare, R.M., Hill, P.R., and Huebner, R.J.: *Int. J. Cancer* 23:269, 1979.
13. Freeman, A.E., Price, P.J., Igel, H.J., Young, J.C., and Maryak, J.M.: *J. Natl. Cancer Inst.* 44:65, 1970.
14. Price, P.J., Freeman, A.E., Lane, W.T., and Huebner, R.J.: *Nature New Biol.* 230:144, 1971.
15. Mishra, N.K. and Ryan, W.L.: *Int. J. Cancer* 11:123, 1973.
16. Rasheed, S.A., Freeman, A.E., Garner, M.B., and Huebner, R.J.: *J. Virol* 18:776, 1976.
17. Freeman, A.E., Price, P.J., Bryan, R.J., Gordon, R.J., Gilden, R.V., Kelloff, G.J., and Huebner, R.J.: *Proc. Natl. Acad. Sci.* 68:445, 1971.
18. Traul, K.A., Kachevsky, V., and Wolff, J.: *Int. J. Cancer* 23:193, 1979.
19. Rhim, J.S., Vass, W., Cho, H.Y., and Huebner, R.J.: *Int. J. Cancer* 7:65, 1971.

20. Freeman, A.E., Gilden, R.V., Vernon, M.L., Wolford, R.G., Hugunin, P.E., and Huebner, R.J.: *Proc. Natl. Acad. Sci.* 70:2415, 1973.

21. Freeman, A.E., Igel, H.J., and Price, P.J.: *In Vitro* 11:107, 1975.

22. Price, P.J., Suk, W.A., and Freeman, A.E.: *Science* 177:1003, 1972.

23. Mishra, N.K., Pant, K.J., Thomas, F.O., and Price, P.J.: *Int. J. Cancer* 18:852, 1976.

24. Price, P.J., Auletta, A.E., King, M.P., Hugunin, P.M., and Huebner, R.J.: *In Vitro* 12:595, 1976.

25. Price, P.J., Bellew, T.M., King, M.P., Freeman, A.E., Gilden, R.C., and Huebner, R.J.: *Proc. Natl. Acad. Sci.* 73:152, 1976.

26. Zimmerman, E.M., Kouri, R.E., Higuchi, K., Laird, F., and Freeman, A.E.: *Cancer Res* 35:139, 1975.

27. Waters, R., Mishra, N., Bouck, N., DiMayorca, G., and Regan, J.D., *Proc. Natl. Acad. Sci.* 74:238, 1977.

28. Price, P.J., Suk, W.A., Spahn, G.J., Chirigos, M.A., Lane, J.A., and Huebner, R.J.: *Proc. Soc. Exp. Biol. Med.* 145:1197, 1974.

29. Price, P.J., Suk, W.A., Peters, R.L., Martin, C.E., Bellew, T.M., and Huebner, R.J.: *Proc. Soc. Exp. Biol. Med.* 150:650, 1975.

30. Price, P.J., Suk, W.A., Skeen, P.C., Spahn, G.J., and Chirigos, M.A.: *Proc. Soc. Exp. Biol. Med.* 155:461, 1977.

31. Price, P.J., Skeen, P.C., and Hassett, C.M.: *Proc. Soc. Exp. Biol. Med.* 159:253, 1978.

32. Price, P.J., Mansfield, J.I., and Hassett, C.M.: *In Vitro* 15:82, 1979.

33. Rhim, J.S., Creasy, B., and Huebner, R.J.: *Proc. Natl. Acad. Dci.* 68:2212, 1971.

34. Nowinski, R.C. and Miller, E.C.: *J. Natl. Cancer Inst.* 57:1347, 1976.

35. Reznikoff, C.A., Brankow, D.W., and Heidelberger, C.: *Cancer Res.* 33:3231, 1973.

36. Hartley, J.W., Wolford, N,K., Old, L.J., and Rowe, W.P.: *Proc. Natl. Acad. Sci.* 74:189, 1977.

The Feline Leukemia Virus: An Animal Oncovirus Model for Human Leukemia

William D. Hardy, Jr., and
Alexander J. McClelland

Memorial Sloan-Kettering Cancer Center, New York, New York

Endogenous and exogenous oncoviruses (oncogenic RNA containing viruses) exist in many species of animals. Endogenous oncovirus genes are an integral part of the host species genome and are transmitted from one cell generation to the next and from the adult animal to its offspring as an inherited Mendelian trait—a process known as vertical transmission. Exogenous oncovirus genes are not incorporated into the genome of their host species and the viruses are transmitted infectiously (horizontally) between members of their host species (Table 1). During evolution some endogenous oncoviruses apparently escaped from host control and became infectious either to their host species or to other unrelated species (Table 2).[1] After transpecies infection, some oncovirus genes were incorporated into the genetic material of the recipient species and transmitted vertically in the new species. For example, the vertically transmitted endogenous RD114 oncovirus of cats originated in Old World monkeys and infected ancestors of the domestic cat 3-10 $\times$ 10^6 years ago.[2] However, other oncovirus genes did not become incorporated into the genome of the recipient species. For example, the exogenous gibbon ape leukemia virus is thought to have originated in ancestral Asian mice but is now spread infectiously between gibbons.[3] Like the gibbon ape leukemia virus, feline leukemia virus (FeLV) originated in another species. In this paper we will describe FeLV and, in particular, its usefulness as a model for studying the putative viral etiology of human leukemia.

Table 1. Species with Contagious Oncoviruses[a]

Species	Oncoviruses
Mouse	Many laboratory strains of MuLV and MSV (murine leukemia and sarcoma viruses)
Cat	FeLV (feline leukemia virus)
	FeSV (feline sarcoma virus)
Cattle	BLV (bovine leukemia virus)
Primates	
Woolly monkey	SSV-1 (simian sarcoma virus)
Gibbon ape	GALV (gibbon ape leukemia virus)

[a] Genomes not found in normal tissues of the species. (Adapted from Todaro.[1])

Feline Leukemia Virus Diseases

The feline leukemia virus (FeLV) was transmitted from an ancestor of the rat to an ancestor of the cat approximately 10^6 years ago and although FeLV related genes are incorporated into the genome of the domestic cat, the virus is transmitted horizontally between cats.[4] FeLV replicates in several different types of cells and can cause proliferative or degenerative diseases of each of the cell types it infects (Table 3).[5] The diseases caused by FeLV are invariably fatal and are probably the most common cause of death among pet cats in the United States. The disease that is most commonly associated with FeLV is feline lymphosarcoma (LSA),

Table 2. Examples of Cross-Species Transmission of Oncoviruses[a]

Recipient Species	Donor Species	Mode of Transmission in Recipient Species
Cat (domestic)	Old World monkey	RD114 virus-genetic transmission
	Rat ancestor	FeLV – contagious transmission
Pig (ancestor)	Mouse ancestor	Genetic transmission
Mink-weasel-ferret ancestor	Rodent-unknown ancestor	Genetic transmission
Cattle	Unknown species	Contagious transmission
Primates		
Gibbon apes	Rodent-Asian	Contagious transmission
Woolly monkeys	(Mus caroli)	
Possibly humans	(Mus cervicolor)	

[a] Adapted from Todaro.[1]

Table 3. FeLV Caused or Associated Diseases

Cell type	Proliferative Diseases (Neoplastic)	Degenerative Diseases (Blastopenic)
Lymphoid	Lymphosarcoma	Thymic atrophy (kittens)
	Reticulum cell sarcoma	Immunosuppressive diseases (adults)
Erythroid	Erythroleukemia	Non-regenerative anemia (erythroblastopenia)
	Erythremic myelosis	
Myeloid	Myeloproliferative diseases	Panleukopenia-like syndrome (myeloblastopenia)
	Myelogenous leukemia	
Placenta-uterus		Abortion and resorption

a proliferative disease of lymphoid cells. The cat has the highest incidence of LSA of any mammal. LSA occurs in 44/100,000 cats per year in the general cat population.[6] FeLV is known to cause feline LSA but approximately 25% of cats with the disease do not replicate the virus (i.e., are negative for FeLV antigens and do not have infectious virus).[7-9] There are four forms of LSA which differ in the location of the primary tumor and occurrence of FeLV. The disease is characterized by solid lymphoid tumor masses and occasionally by a leukemic blood profile. The other major FeLV induced diseases are: (a) FeLV non-regenerative anemia, a progressive degenerative disease of the erythroid cells, (b) FeLV panleukopenia-like disease, a fatal degenerative disease of the granulocytes, (c) myelogenous leukemia, a malignant proliferation of the granulocytes and (d) thymic atrophy, a degenerative disease of the thymus.[10] In addition to these diseases, FeLV is associated with, but has not yet been proved to cause, several other proliferative and degenerative bone marrow disorders as well as fetal abortions and resorptions.[11] FeLV is immunosuppressive in experimental cats and is now known to be indirectly responsible for numerous secondary infectious diseases of pet cats.[12,13] More cats die from these FeLV associated immunosuppressive diseases than die from LSA.

Immune Response to FeLV Exposure

Although the diseases caused by FeLV are progressive and fatal, the fate of an exposed cat depends on its ability to respond immunologically to the viral and viral-induced antigens.[14] Much is now known about these antigens and about how cats may respond to them. There are two major classes of FeLV related antigens—the viral structural antigens and the nonviral, but virally-induced tumor-specific feline oncornavirus-associated cell membrant antigen (FOCMA).[15,16] The FeLV structural antigens consist of proteins located inside the virus or glycoproteins which are found primarily on the viral envelope. The internal viral proteins are used as markers for detecting FeLV in the cytoplasm of infected cells by the indirect immunofluorescent antibody (IFA) test.[15] The envelope antigens divide FeLV into three subgroups (A, B and C) and antibody to these envelope antigens (serum neutralizing [SN] antibody) protects cats from FeLV infection.[17] FOCMA is not an FeLV structural antigen and is found only on the surface of cells transformed by feline oncoviruses, thus FOCMA is transformation specific.[14,18-20] Cats with high titered antibody to FOCMA are protected from the development of LSA but can still be infected with the virus and remain susceptible to the other nonneoplastic diseases caused by FeLV.[14,21] The antibody response of a cat to the virus and to FOCMA determines its fate. As a result of our studies it has become clear that a healthy cat can be classified into one of six classes depending on its FeLV status and FeLV SN and FOCMA antibody response (Table 4).[14] These classes are: (a) Class 1, FeLV uninfected cats susceptible to both FeLV infection and LSA, (b) Class 2, uninfected cats susceptible to FeLV infection but resistant to LSA, (c) Class 3, uninfected cats resistant to FeLV infection but susceptible to LSA, (d) Class 4, uninfected cats resistant to both FeLV and LSA, (e) Class 5, infected cats susceptible to LSA and (f) Class 6, infected cats resistant to LSA development. Cats belonging to each of these six classes have been found in household environments.

Contagious Transmission of FeLV

Early observations of the clustering of cases of feline LSA were the first indication that FeLV is transmitted infectiously between cats.[22-24] Initially these observations were doubted because the leukemia viruses of laboratory mice were transmitted vertically and because the reports of clusters were often anecdotal and difficult to evaluate. In addition, an epidemiologic survey of LSA development in cats did not detect infectious spread of the disease.[25] The continuing high occurrence of LSA in households that had a history of previous cases of LSA convinced us that further investigations into the question of whether or not FeLV is horizontally transmitted were necessary. Using the sensitive IFA test for FeLV that we developed in 1970, we studied the distribution of FeLV in the pet cat population.[15,26] We found that FeLV is transmitted horizontally between pet cats living in household environments and that 30% of the cats exposed to FeLV become infected with the virus, 42% become immune to FeLV infection and 28% remain uninfected and susceptible to infection (Table 5).[8,27] Our discovery that FeLV is infectious for cats was subsequently confirmed by other investigators using different methods of

Table 4. Immune Classes of Healthy Cats — Classes of Healthy Cats as Based on Their FeLV Status and Their Antibody Responses to FeLV and FOCMA

Class of Healthy Cat	Exposure History	FeLV Status	Protective FeLV Neutralizing Antibody (≥ 1:10)	Protective FOCMA Antibody (≥ 1:32)	Susceptibility or Resistant	
					to FeLV Infection	to LSA Development
1	Not exposed	−	−	−	Susceptible	Susceptible
2	Exposed	−	−	+	Susceptible	Resistant
3	Exposed	−	+	+	Resistant	Susceptible
4	Exposed	−	+	−	Resistant	Resistant
5	Exposed	+	−	−	Infected	Very susceptible
6	Exposed	+	−	+	Infcted	Resistant chronic carrier

176

Table 5. Consequences of Healthy Cat Exposure to FeLV

Percent of Cats Exposed	Result of Exposure		Possible Outcome of FeLV Exposure
	FeLV Status	Immune Status	
30%	+	75% have no immunity; 25% immune to LSA (class 5 and 6 cats in Table 4)	20% of these cats develop FeLV positive LSA (class 5 cats only, Table 4)
40%	−	These cats are immune to FeLV or LSA or both (class 2, 3, or 4 cats in Table 4)	3% of these cats develop nonproducer LSA's (class 3 or 4 cats, not class 2 cats, see Table 4)
30%	−	These cats are not immune to FeLV or LSA (class 1 cats in Table 4)	

monitoring the spread of the virus in the environment.[28] FeLV is thus similar to the exogenous oncoviruses of chickens, wild mice, cattle, woolly monkeys and gibbon apes in that it is transmitted horizontally and causes disease in the species it infects. However, unlike the lymphoid tumors of these species, approximately 25% of feline LSA's do not contain any evidence of FeLV infection.[7,8,29]

FeLV-Induced Nonproducer Lymphosarcomas

The etiology of FeLV nonproducer (NP) LSA's was, until recently, uncertain, since NP LSA cells do not contain FeLV provirus sequences additional to the FeLV-related sequences that are found in FeLV uninfected normal cat cells.[30,31] However, we have found that FOCMA is expressed on NP LSA cells as well as on producer LSA cells.[19,20] Although there is no direct evidence that FeLV codes for FOCMA, indirect evidence does exist. For example, FOCMA is known to be induced only by FeLV or the feline sarcoma virus (FeSV) and FOCMA antibody is induced in dogs after FeLV infection.[32] This observation is significant since it shows that, like FeSV which is known to code for FOCMA, FeLV can induce FOCMA in a non-feline species. The expression of FOCMA on feline NP LSA cells thus suggests that these cells are transformed by FeLV. If feline NP LSA cells are indeed transformed by FeLV, these feline NP cells might be an appropriate model for the study of the "virus negative" human leukemia.

In an attempt to determine if NP LSA is caused by FeLV, we recently conducted a prospective study of a large group of FeLV unexposed and exposed cats for the development of LSA, in order to determine if exposure to FeLV was associated with the development of NP LSA to the same extent that it is with FeLV producer LSA.[8,29] In addition to comparing the occurrence of LSA in unexposed and exposed cats, we compared the data we obtained to the previously published "baseline" incidence of LSA in the general cat population. We found a highly significant difference ($p < 0.001$) between the occurrence of LSA in the 1074 unexposed and 538 exposed cats that we studied (Table 6). Although none of the unexposed cats developed LSA, 41 of the exposed cats developed the disease. Thirty of the 149 FeLV exposed and infected cats developed producer LSA and 11 of the 389 exposed but uninfected cats developed NP LSA (Table 7). The relative risk of developing LSA, that is, the number of observed cases of LSA over the number of expected LSA cases (from the published baseline data) for the infected and uninfected exposed cats was similar ($39\times$ and $42\times$ respectively) suggesting that, like producer LSA, NP feline LSA is caused by FeLV.

Possible Mechanisms of Virus Nonproducer Tumor Induction

The mechanism by which FeLV causes NP LSA is unknown but several possibilities exist.[33] FeLV provirus sequences additional to those found in uninfected cat cells have not been detected in NP LSA cells even though they are present in producer LSA cells.[30,31] The apparent lack of FeLV proviral sequences in NP LSA cells may be due to the fact that only a small fragment of the FeLV provirus is integrated into the genome of the host cell. This fragment may be just sufficient to cause transformation of the cell, but not virus production, and may be too small to be detected by current technology. Another possible hypothesis is the "hit and run" theory of FeLV NP LSA induction. This theory postulates that the FeLV provirus is integrated into the host cell DNA and causes transformation, but is then lost by deletion, or some other event, and thus does not produce virus. Yet another theory of FeLV induction of NP LSA postulates that FeLV infects nonlymphoid cells. As a result of infection these cells produce abnormal regulator substances that cause neoplastic growth of the lymphoid cells resulting in NP LSA. In a variation of this theory, it is suggested that the FeLV infected nonlymphoid cells release DNA fragments containing enough information for transformation, but not enough to induce viral production, and that these fragments transfect lymphoid cells.

These models are not the only possible models by which an oncovirus may induce a NP leukemia, but are the most consistent with available knowledge. The feline NP LSA system provides us with a unique opportunity to test these models. We have established two FeLV NP LSA cell cultures in our laboratory which do not produce infectious

Table 6. Occurrence of Lymphosarcoma in Pet Cats

Cat Exposure History	Observation Years Based on:	No. of Cats[a]	Observation Years		Expected Cases of Lymphosarcoma	Observed Cases of Lymphosarcoma	Relative Risk
			Total	Average per Cat			
Cats never exposed	Ages of cats	1074	3235	3.1	1.4	0	0
Exposed cats	From time of FeLV exposure	558	2334	4.3	1.03	41	40

[a] Total number of cats = 1632; this includes 1074 unexposed cats and 558 exposed cats.

Table 7. Search for Evidence of FeLV Infection in Humans

Species	FeLV IFA Test		Neutr. Antibody	
	No. Tested	No. Positive	No. Tested	No. Positive
Human				
Exposed				
Healthy	167	0	78	0
Cancer	12	0	8	0
	179		86	
No known exposure				
Healthy	67	0	18	0
Cancer	359	0	10	0
	426		28	

FeLV or FeLV antigens, but which do express FOCMA, the marker of FeLV or FeSV induced transformation.[34,35] Using these cell cultures we may be able to determine how FeLV induces NP LSA. That information might enable us to understand how an oncovirus can transform human lymphoid cells without viral production resulting in the apparently virus-negative human leukemia. Using such knowledge, it may be possible to design experiments to determine if human tumors are, in fact, caused by an oncovirus(es). It is already clear from the research that has been done into the infectious spread of FeLV that epidemiological studies cannot answer the question of whether or not human leukemia is caused by an infectious oncovirus. The epidemiological studies of the distribution of LSA in the cat population that were done in 1969/70, before the IFA test for FeLV was available, failed to detect the infectious spread of the disease.[25] Only when the etiological agent could be readily identified could the infectious nature of this agent (FeLV) be established. In retrospect, it is obvious that the reasons for the failure of the epidemiological studies of disease development to detect the infectious nature of FeLV, as opposed to the seroepidemiological studies of viral transmission, are: (a) that there is often a long and highly variable latent period between infection and LSA development and, (b) the overall incidence of LSA in the general cat population is low. Epidemiological surveys of the occurrence of human leukemia are subject to these same two limitations and thus it is not surprising that no evidence for the infectious nature of human leukemia (assuming it is infectious) has been obtained. The lesson from FeLV research is that the nature of the etiological agent must be known before an epidemiological survey can be designed to answer the question of whether or not human leukemia is infectious. The importance of the FeLV system is that it provides a model for elucidating the mechanism of oncovirus transformation. Using this information we may be able to discover if a human leukemia virus exists and, if so, whether or not it is infectious.

Public Health Considerations of FeLV

Since FeLV appears to be a suitable model for a putative human leukemia virus, the question of whether or not FeLV can infect humans and thus pose a public health risk arises.[36-38] There is no conclusive evidence showing that FeLV causes disease in humans.[39] We tested several hundred people for both FeLV antigens and FeLV SN antibody but none were found to be positive (Table 7).[14] However, it should not be concluded from these results that FeLV poses no potential risk to humans. FeLV can grow in human and canine tissue culture cells and causes LSA when injected into puppies.[40,41] Some human patients in the acute blast crisis phase of myelogenous leukemia have been found to have immunoglobulins on their tumor cells which react with the FeLV replicative enzyme, reverse transcriptase.[42] This finding suggests, but does not prove, that FeLV infects humans. A recent epidemiological survey of veterinarians aged 45 or older showed that the mortality due to lymphoma in this group was 80% greater than in the general U.S. population.[43] Veterinarians are more likely to be exposed to large quantities of FeLV from leukemic cats than members of the general population and the relatively high occurrence of lymphoma among veterinarians might be related to this exposure, although, of course, the high occurrence might be due to other factors. Although no evidence has been found to suggest that FeLV causes disease in humans, in view of these findings it is clear that all possible precautions to limit the exposure of humans to FeLV should be taken. In this regard it should be mentioned that FeLV has been classified as a "moderate risk biohazard agent" by the National Cancer Institute of the United States and must be handled with "sufficient biohazard controls" in laboratories.[44] The reasons for this classification are that FeLV has the ability to grow in human cells, and, like other oncoviruses, can "rescue" defective sarcoma virus genomes from species other than the cat (hamsters).[45] It is thus possible that FeLV could "rescue" a defective human sarcoma virus which could then cause disease in humans. In view of what is known about FeLV, we feel that it is extremely important that immunosuppressed individuals, such as patients on immunosuppressive drugs, and the fetuses of pregnant women and young children who are more susceptible to viral infections than healthy adults, not be exposed to FeLV until the public health implications of FeLV infection are clarified. At present, cat owners can have their cats tested for FeLV by a simple blood test to determine if their cat is infected.[15] By removing infected cats from households it is now possible to prevent the infectious spread of the virus and to prevent human exposure to cats shedding large quantities of FeLV in their saliva.[46,47]

Concluding Remarks

Feline lymphosarcoma (LSA) is caused by an oncovirus, FeLV, which is transmitted infectiously between cats. Although most cats with LSA are overtly infected with FeLV (i.e., are FeLV producers) approximately 25% of cats with the disease are negative for the virus (i.e., are FeLV nonproducers). FeLV nonproducer (NP) LSA's express the FeLV induced tumor-specific antigen FOCMA on the tumor cell surface and, like FeLV producer LSA's are epidemiologically associated with exposure to FeLV. For these reasons it is now thought that FeLV NP LSA's are, in fact, caused by FeLV. FeLV is therefore an appropriate and potentially valuable model for studying how oncoviruses transform cells and how an oncovirus might induce "virus-negative" leukemias such as human leukemia. Since FeLV is infectious and can cause NP LSA in cats, it is possible that the virus could infect humans and cause disease. Although no conclusive evidence showing that FeLV poses a public health risk has been obtained, in view of what is known about FeLV and its ability to rescue "defective" viruses it seems prudent to prevent exposure of humans to the virus until all the public health questions associated with FeLV are resolved.

ACKNOWLEDGMENTS
This work was supported by grants CA-16599, CA-08748 and CA-19072 from the National Cancer Institute and a grant from the Cancer Research Institute, Inc. During this study Dr. Hardy was a Scholar of the Leukemia Society of America, Inc.

References

1. Todaro, G.J.: In: *Origins of Human Cancer,* H.H. Hiatt, J.D. Watson and J.A. Winsten (eds.), Cold Spring Harbor Laboratory, Cold Spring Harbor, New York, 1977, p. 1169.

2. Livingston, D.M. and Todaro, G.J.: *Virology* 53:142, 1973.

3. Benveniste, R.E. and Todaro, G.J.: *Proc. Natl. Acad. Sci., USA* 70:3316, 1973.

4. Benveniste, R.E., Sherr, C.J., and Todaro, G.J.: *Science* 190:886, 1975.

5. Hardy, W.D., Jr.: In: *The Immunopathology of Lymphoreticular Neoplasms,* J.J. Twomey and R.A. Good (eds.), Plenum Press, New York, 1978, p. 129.

6. Dorn, C.R., Taylor, D.O.N., Schneider, R., Hibbard, H.H., and Klauber, M.R.: *J. Natl. Cancer Inst.* 40:307, 1968.

182   W. D. Hardy, Jr. and A. J. McClelland

7. Hardy, W.D., Jr., Geering, G., Old, L.J., deHarven, E., Brodey, R.S., and McDonough, S.: *Science* 166:1019, 1969.

8. Hardy, W.D., Jr., McClelland, A.J., Zuckerman, E.E., Snyder, H.W., Jr., MacEwen, E.G., Francis, D.P., and Essex, M.: In: *Viruses in Naturally Occurring Cancer,* M. Essex, G.J. Todaro, and H. zur Hausen (eds.), Cold Spring Harbor Laboratory, Cold Spring Harbor, New York, 1980 (in press).

9. Francis, D.P., Essex, M., Cotter, S.M., Jakowski, R., and Hardy, W.D., Jr.: Submitted for publication.

10. Hardy, W.D., Jr. and McClelland, A.J.: *Vet Clinics of N. America* 7:93, 1977.

11. Cotter, S.M., Hardy, W.D., Jr., and Essex, M.: *J. Am. Vet. Med. Assoc.* 166:449, 1975.

12. Perryman, L.E., Hoover, E.A., and Yohn, D.S.: *J. Natl. Cancer Inst.* 49:1357, 1972.

13. Cockerell, G.L., Krakowka, S., Hoover, E.A., Olsen, R.G., and Yohn, D.S.: In: *Comparative Leukemia Research 1975,* Y. Ito and R.M. Dutcher (eds.), Karger, Basel, Switzerland, 1975, p. 81.

14. Hardy, W.D., Jr., Hess, P.W., MacEwen, E.G., McClelland, A.J., Zuckerman, E.E., Essex, M., Cotter, S.M., and Jarrett, O.: *Cancer Res.* 36:582, 1976.

15. Hardy, W.D., Jr., Hirshaut, Y., and Hess, P.: In: *Unifying Concepts of Leukemia,* R.M. Dutcher and L. Chieco-Bianchi (eds.), Karger, Basel, Switzerland, 1973, p. 778.

16. Essex, M., Klein, G., Snyder, S.P., and Harrold, J.B.: *Nature* 233:195, 1971.

17. Sarma, P.S. and Log, T.: *Virology,* 54:160, 1973.

18. Stephenson, J.R., Essex, M., Hino, S., Hardy, W.D., Jr., and Aaronson, S.A.: *Proc. Natl. Acad. Sci. USA* 74:1219, 1977.

19. Hardy, W.D., Jr., Zuckerman, E.E., MacEwen, E.G., Hayes, A.A., and Essex, M.: *Nature* 270:249, 1977.

20. Hardy, W.D., Jr., Zuckerman, E.E., Essex, M., MacEwen, E.G., and Hayes, A.A.: in: *Differentiation of Normal and Neoplastic Hematopoietic Cells,* B. Clarkson, P.A. Marks and J.E. Till (eds.), Cold Spring Harbor Laboratory, Cold Spring Harbor, New York, 1979, p. 601.

21. Essex, M., Sliski, A., Cotter, S.M., Jakowski, R.M., and Hardy, W.D., Jr.: *Science* 190:790, 1975.

22. Schneider, R., Frye, F.L., Taylor, D.O.N., and Dorn, C.R.: *Cancer Res.* 27:1316, 1967.

23. Brodey, R.S., McDonough, S., Frye, F.L., and Hardy, W.D., Jr.: In: *Comparative Leukemia Research,* R.M. Dutcher (ed.), Basel, Switzerland, 1970, p. 333.

24. Hardy, W.D., Jr.: *J. Am. Vet. Med. Assoc.* 158:1060, 1971.

25. Schneider, R.: *Int. J. Cancer* 10:345, 1972.

26. Hardy, W.D., Jr., Old, L.J., Hess, P.W., Essex, M., and Cotter, S.M.: *Nature* 244:266, 1973.

27. Essex, M., Sliski, A., Hardy, W.D., Jr., and Cotter, S.M.: *Cancer Res.* 36:640, 1976.

28. Jarrett, W., Jarrett, O., Mackey, L., Laird, H., Hardy, W.D., Jr., and Essex, M.: *J. Natl. Cancer Inst.* 51:833, 1973.

29. Hardy, W.D., Jr., Zuckerman, E.E., McClelland, A.J., Snyder, H.W., Jr., MacEwen, E.G., Essex, M., and Francis, D.: In: *Advances in Comparative Leukemia Research, D.S. Yohn and B. Lapin (eds.), Elsevier/North Holland (in press).*

30. Levin, R., Ruscetti, S.K., Parks, W.P., and Scolnick, E.M.: *Int. J. Cancer* 18:661, 1976.

31. Koshy, R., Wong-Staal, F., Gallo, R.C., Hardy, W.D., Jr., and Essex, M.: *Virology,* 1980 (in press).

32. Essex, M.: *Adv. Cancer Res.* 21:175, 1975.

33. Gallo, R.C., Saxinger, W.C., Gallagher, R.E., Gillespie, D.H., Ruscetti, F., Reitz, M.S., Aulakh, G.S., and Wong-Staal, F.: In: *Origins of Human Cancer,* H.H. Hiatt, J.D. Watson and J.A. Winsten (eds.), Cold Spring Harbor Laboratory, Cold Spring Harbor, New York, 1977, p. 1253.

34. Snyder, H.W., Jr., Hardy, W.D., Jr., Zuckerman, E.E., and Fleissner, E.: *Nature* 275:656, 1978.

35. Hardy, W.D., Jr., Zuckerman, E.E., MacEwen, E.G., and Markovich, R.: In preparation.

36. Hardy, W.D., Jr., McClelland, A.J., Hess, P.W., and MacEwen, E.G.: *J. Am. Vet. Med. Assoc.* 165:1020, 1974.

37. Levy, S.B.: *N. Engl. J. Med.* 290:513, 1974.

38. Essex, M., and Francis, D.P.: *J. Am. Animal Hosp. Assoc.* 12:386, 1976.

39. Krakower, J.M. and Aaronson, S.A.: *Nature* 273:463, 1978.

40. Jarrett, O., Laird, H.M., and Hay, D.: *Nature* 224:1208, 1969.

41. Rickard, C.G., Post, J.E., Noronha, F., and Barr, L.M.: *J. Natl. Cancer Inst.* 42:987, 1969.

42. Jacquemin, P.C., Saxinger, C., and Gallo, R.C.: *Nature* 276:230, 1978.

43. Gutensohn, N., Francis, D.P., Hardy, W.D., Jr., and Essex, M.: In: *Viruses in Naturally Occurring Cancer,* M. Essex, G.J. Todaro and H. zur Hausen (eds.), Cold Spring Harbor Laboratory, Cold Spring Harbor, New York (in press).

44. National Cancer Institute: Minimum standards of biologic safety and environmental control for contractors of the special virus cancer program, National Cancer Institute, Bethesda, Maryland, 1972.

45. Sarma, P.S., Log, T., and Huebner, R.J.: *Proc. Natl. Acad. Sci. ESA* 65:81, 1970.

46. Hardy, W.D., Jr., McClelland, A.J., Zuckerman, E.E., Hess, P.W., Essex, M., Cotter, S.M., MacEwen, E.G., and Hayes, A.A.: *Nature* 263:326, 1976.

47. Francis, D.P., Essex, M., and Hardy, W.D., Jr.: *Nature* 269:252, 1977.

Human Leukemia *in Vitro* and the Expression of a New Virus

Abraham Karpas

University of Cambridge Clinical School, Cambridge, England

The continuous search for a causative agent for human leukemia stems from the overwhelming evidence that retroviruses play a major role in the induction of animal leukemias, including our closest relatives, the subhuman primates.[1]

The demonstration that viruses are involved in the development of animal leukemia often followed *in vivo* studies in which the disease developed following an injection of subcellular viral material into new-born animals. However, such studies are not feasible in man for obvious reasons. The use of experimental animals for the isolation of human viruses has turned out to be a fruitless effort, mainly because most animal species carry their own retroviruses or because of the inability of human virus, if such a virus exists, to cause leukemia in the experimental animal.

Repeated efforts in numerous laboratories to isolate a retrovirus *in vitro* directly from fresh human leukemic cells failed, or the few reported isolates turned out to be a laboratory contamination by various animal leukemia viruses.

The extensive study of the biology of the animal leukemia viruses have provided us with most valuable information which could be used as a guideline in the search for a human virus. We now know that although the genetic material of retroviruses is RNA, the RNA-directed DNA polymerase (reverse transcriptase)[2] which they contain enables them to code for a DNA copy which, in turn, is integrated in the chromosomes. This proviral DNA can, but does not always, code for virus production and release by the affected cells, whether normal or malignant. The presence of the integrated proviral DNA can cause malignant transformation with or without virus release. The factors involved in turning a phenotypically normal cell, which contains the proviral DNA, into a malignant cell are not yet known.

The naturally occurring animal models of leukemia in which vertical (genetic) transmission of proviral information without the expression and release of virus particles takes place could explain what might happen in human leukemia. From the studies of the naturally occurring animal leukemias, it has been established that if the leukemic cells are grown for prolonged periods *in vitro,* they might spontaneously start to produce and release retroviruses. In all cultures of leukemic cells which do not spontaneously release detectable levels of viruses it was possible to induce virus release following the addition of certain chemicals, such as the halogenated pyrimidine nucleosides (IUDR or BUDR), to the growth medium.[3]

In face of past failures to isolate an etiological agent from fresh human leukemic cells, and the limited scope of experimental studies with human material, but with the information gained from the animal leukemias, it occurred to us that a promising way to investigate whether a virus is involved in the development of the human disease could be the continuous *in vitro* proliferation of the leukemic cells.

Unlike adherent human cells, such as normal and malignant fibroblasts and epithelial cells, which have been successfully grown with relative ease in numerous laboratories for many years, human hemic cell lines from leukemic patients have been established only by a few investigators. Human hemic cell lines have also been established from the peripheral blood and bone marrow of normal individuals. However, until recently it was not possible to determine with certainty the nature of the hemic cell lines and whether those which have been derived from leukemia do indeed represent an *in vitro* proliferation of the patient's malignant cells. Cytological and cytochemical characteristics are usually sufficient to establish the nature of the fresh cells, but are often insufficient in determining the nature of hemic cells after long-term *in vitro* growth. In tissue culture conditions, hemic cells often dedifferentiate after long-term *in vitro* proliferation, and may lose certain cytochemical characteristics. A very important development in the study of cultured human hemic cells was the discovery of the anti-complement immunofluorescence (ACIF) test by Reedman and Klein.[4] This test can also detect a cell which is latently infected with Epstein-Barr virus (EBV). The recent development of a panel of immunological surface marker tests helps in determining the nature of the hemic cell lines and their relation to the fresh cells of the patients.

Since the majority of the human hemic cell lines, whether established from normal individuals or from leukemic patients, are infected with

EBV, this chapter is devoted to the biology of this virus in spite of the fact that it is not involved in the development of human leukemia.

Epstein-Barr Virus and Human Hemic Cells

EBV is a human herpesvirus which was discovered in a hemic cell culture established by Epstein and Barr from a biopsy of Burkitt's lymphoma.[5,6] Henle et al.[7] were the first to show that the newly discovered herpes-type virus was infectious and that it could transform normal human white blood cells, following the cocultivation of irradiated Burkitt's lymphoma cells with white blood cells from fetal cord. This finding was extended by Pope et al.[8] who were the first to show that a cell-free filtrate which contained EBV was sufficient to infect and transform normal human hemic cells. However, the most important discovery about the biology of this virus was the finding of Henle et al.[9] that EBV is the causative agent of a very common human illness, infectious mononucleosis (glandular fever). These findings opened the door to understanding the role of EBV infection in man and to the observation that during the course of life most individuals become infected by the virus, develop antibodies and could remain latent carriers of the virus for the rest of their lives. In serum-positive, normal individuals, the virus is probably carried latently in a very small number of lymphoblasts. The occasional EBV-positive cells will escape detection when a fresh sample of cells is tested for the EBV-determined nuclear antigen (EBNA), but during *in vitro* growth, the various normal leukocytes which cannot grow in culture medium will die out, while the EBV-positive cells will proliferate rapidly and dominate the culture. A similar situation also occurs with leukocytes cultured from leukemic patients. Leukemic cells, whether lymphoid or myeloid, are EBNA-negative, but since many leukemic patients have been exposed to the virus, the few circulating EBV-carrying cells are often sufficient to outgrow the leukemic cells *in vitro;* or occasionally, in the absence of circulating anti-EBV antibodies, they also infect and transform cells of myeloid origin *in vitro*. This explains our observation that the study of newly established EBNA-positive cell lines from leukemic patients provided evidence that such cultures are heterogenic[10] and that in some cases myeloid precursors can become infected with EBV.[11]

Electron microscopic examination of many of our EBNA-positive cell lines did not reveal any morphologically detectable herpes-type viruses. This can be due either to a very low rate of virus production or to lack of virus synthesis. Zur Hausen and Schulte-Holthausen[12] were the first to report the presence of EBV nucleic acid in "virus free" cells from Burkitt's lymphoma, the finding that explains the latent state of the virus. However, the establishment of a cell line from Burkitt's lymphoma tissue which is EBV-free,[13] when measured by the ACIF test and by molecular hybridization, raises at least the theoretical possibility that this virus might not be essential for malignant transformation *in vivo,* or that the few EBV-negative African Burkitt's lymphomas are separate entities, as are the American Burkitt's lymphomas which are EBV-negative.[14]

In conclusion, it could be stated that although EBV is the causative agent of infectious mononucleosis and is closely associated with Burkitt's lymphoma and nasopharyngeal carcinoma, it is not involved in the development of human leukemia, and when an EBNA-positive culture arises from a sample of human leukemic cells, in most cases the culture represents an *in vitro* proliferation of the EBV-infected B-lymphoblasts or an *in vitro* infection by the virus of other cell types.

Human Leukemia *in Vitro*

Fresh leukemic cells are invariably EBV-free, therefore the examination of cells for EBNA is one of the first tests used to determine whether a newly established line from a leukemic blood or bone marrow represent a proliferation of the patient's malignant cells.

Another important parameter in the study of leukemic cell lines is the characterization of immunological surface markers. The immunological profile of leukemic cells after long-term culture often remains similar, if not identical, to the surface marker characteristics of fresh leukemic cells which gave rise to the culture. Morphologically, after long-term culture, the leukemic cells appear to undergo dedifferentiation; namely, the ratio of nucleus to cytoplasm decreases, cytoplasmic granules may disappear in the case of cells of the myeloid series, and characteristic nuclear configuration, such as Rieder cell formation, is no longer obvious. This will explain why certain cytochemical staining properties, present in the fresh cells or after short-term culture, will disappear after many months of *in vitro* growth. On the other hand, our findings with alkaline phosphatase cytochemistry are very interesting.[10] This enzyme is not normally detectable cytochemically in substantial quantities in any hemic cells of blood, bone marrow or lymph nodes, other than granulocytes from about the metamyelocyte stage and onwards, or in macrophages. Therefore, the occurrence of this enzyme in EBNA-positive blasts of 13 of our 28 leukemia-derived cell lines studied was quite unexpected.[10]

Another most interesting observation has been reported recently about line K562, which has been established from the pleural effusion of a patient with chronic myeloid leukemia (CML).[15] Earlier studies of this cell line indicated that it represented an *in vitro* proliferation of myeloid cells.[15,16] However, recent reports from a different laboratory claimed that it has properties compatible with an erythroid cell.[17,18] On the other hand, when Lozzio et al.[19] tried recently to establish whether their cell line, which was grown only in their own laboratory, had erythroid properties, they claimed that it retained its earlier reported myeloid and not erythroid characteristics. Therefore it appears that a subculture of their cell line, which was grown in a different laboratory for several years, for some unknown reason expresses erythroid properties. This might be explained by gene(s) derepression. It is not entirely surprising since undifferentiated stem cells could give rise to either cell lineage.

Cytogenetic studies might be useful in relating cultured cells to the patient's malignant cells. However there are two factors which limit the value of such studies: (a) only half the number of patients with acute leukemia have gross chromosomal abnormalities; (b) after long periods of *in vitro* growth, there could be an increase in the number of chromosomes of all groups as well as the appearance of unusual marker chromosomes which often result from translocation and rearrangements.

In recent years there have been a number of reports on the successful continuous culture of presumably malignant hemic cells from leukemic patients. Most of these cells have been established from patients with acute lymphoblastic leukemia (ALL) and include T cells,[10,20-23] B cells,[24] and null cells.[25,26] EBNA-negative B cell lines have also been established from lymphocytic lymphoma,[27] Burkitt's lymphoma,[13] and histiocytic lymphoma.[28] Fewer cell lines have been established from patients with acute myeloid leukemia. These include two lines from patients with chronic granulocytic leukemia,[15,29] three from patients with acute myeloid leukemia,[30-32] and from a patient with acute myelomonocytic leukemia.[33] A phenotypically unusual cell line has been established from a patient with acute monocytic leukemia supervening on a longstanding non-Hodgkin's lymphoma.[34] The properties of each of the above mentioned cell lines have been described in detail (see corresponding references). The phenotypic properties of our five cell lines are summarized in Table 1. Of these five cell lines, three were found to produce cytoplasmic inclusion bodies which contained virus-like particles. To date, similar inclusions have been reported only in fresh human leukemic cells, but not in cell cultures.

Ultrastructural Study

Electron microscopic examination of 25 EBNA-positive cultures and two EBNA-negative leukemic cell cultures (T cell line 45 and null cell line 190) did not reveal any morphologically detectable virus particles. However in three EBNA-negative leukemic myeloblastoid and lymphoblastoid cultures (lines 230, 241 and 330) I have been able to demonstrate the spontaneous appearance of virus-like particles (VLP) within cytoplasmic inclusion bodies. Systematic ultrastructural examination revealed that intracytoplasmic inclusion bodies were found in approximately 5% of the sectioned cells of the three EBNA-negative cell lines (Tables 1,2). They

Table 1. Properties of Leukemic Cell Lines

Cell Line	Origin Sex/Age(Yr)	EBNA	Alkaline Phosphatase	Rosette Formation				Intracellular Ig	Ia-like Antigen	HAT1 Antigen	Karyotype	Inclusion Bodies	References
				E	FC	C3	SmIg						
Karpas 45	T-ALL M 5	–	Lymphoid	+	–	–	–	–	–	+	Normal	–	(10)
Karpas 190	Null ALL M 5	–	NT	–	–	–	–	–	+	NT	Abnormal	–	(25)
Karpas 230	AMML M 35	–	Myeloid	–	–	–	–	–	+	–	Abnormal	+	(33)
Karpas 241	Lymphoma/AMoL M 35	–	Lymphoid	+	–	–	–	–	–	–	Abnormal	+	(34)
Karpas 330 Kien 330	AML M 5	–	Myeloid	+	–	–	–	–	–	–	Abnormal	+	(32)

Table 2. Frequency of Cytoplasmic Inclusion Bodies in Leukemic Cell Lines

Cell Line	Growth Medium[a]		Growth Medium + BUDR (30 μg/ml)		Growth Medium + Me$_2$SO (1.5%)	
	Proportion of Cells with Cytoplasmic Inclusions	Average Number of Inclusions per Cell[b]	Proportion of Cells with Cytoplasmic Inclusions	Average Number of Inclusions per Cell	Proportion of Cells with Cytoplasmic Inclusions	Average Number of Inclusions per Cell
230	5/100	0.15	76/100	7.6	74/100	5.2
241	6/100	0.18	81/100	7.3	83/100	6.6
330	4/100	0.12	70/100	5	81/100	7.3

[a] Control cultures.
[b] Relates to cell section.

were often membrane bound and contained numerous electron-dense particles, often with an electron-lucent core. In the inclusion-positive cells the number of inclusions per cell varied greatly but averaged three per cell section. Also the appearance of the inclusions varied, and this we interpreted as due to differences in the stage of their development (Figures 1, 2). Some were composed of electron-dense material, some

Figure 1a, b. Electron micrograph of Karpas 241 cell line (**a**) showing a viable cell which contains numerous inclusion bodies in the cytoplasm. (↑). (× 5,600) (**b**) Section through the cytoplasm of a dying cell with numerous inclusion bodies which are packed with virus-like particles (v). The only cell organelles which are recognizable are the mitochondria (M).(× 25,000)

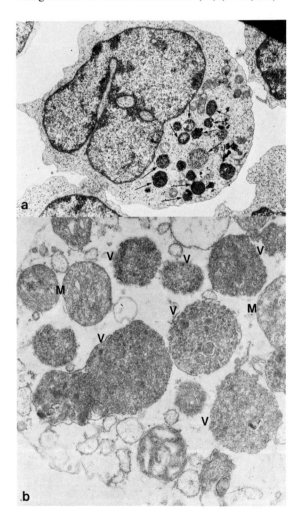

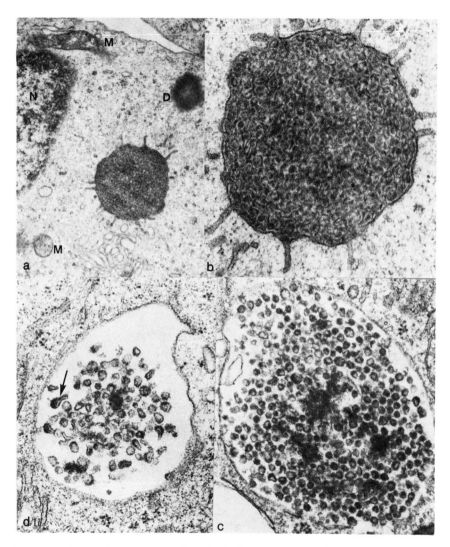

Figure 2a-d. Electron micrograph of inclusion bodies from Karpas 230 cell line. (a) Part of a cell showing a membrane-bound cytoplasmic inclusion body with tubular structures together with a cytoplasmic dense body (D), mitochondria (M) and the edge of the nucleus (N).($\times$ 17,000) (b) Higher magnification of the same inclusion as in (a) showing the fragmentation of the electron-dense material into subunits.($\times$ 45,000) (c) An inclusion tightly packed with discrete particles, most with an electron-lucent and some with an electron-dense core.($\times$ 45,000) (d) A membrane bound lumen contains some particles with tail formation ($\uparrow$).($\times$ 45,000)

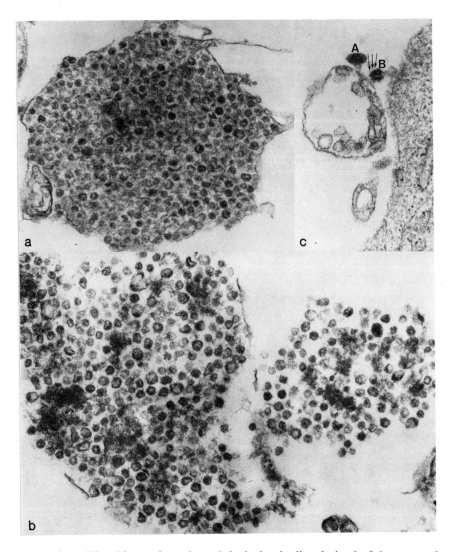

Figure 3a-c. Ultrathin sections through inclusion bodies derived of degenerated BUDR-treated Karpas 230 cells. (**a**) A membrane-bound inclusion showing the formation of numerous electron-dense particles.(× 37,000) (**b**) A pack of numerous virus-like particles. Some with electron-dense cores.(× 48,000) (**c**) A vesicular structure from a disrupted cell with two virus-like particles: A. longitudinal section showing the tail formation, and B. horizontal section showing knob-like projections (↑). In addition membrane formations with an electron-lucent center can be seen within the vesicle.(× 42,000)

contained electron-lucent areas, each surrounded by a denser ring so that an aggregation of such particles resembled a honeycomb. Inclusion bodies containing tightly-packed, ring-shaped virus-like particles with an electron-lucent core might represent an intermediate stage of development. In the postulated end stage loosely packed VLP, most with electron-lucent core, lay within the lumen of a membrane bound vesicular structure (Figure 2). Some of the inclusion bodies could be seen adjacent to the centriole. Inclusion bodies could not be found in the cytoplasm of five EBNA-positive cell lines studied.

Effect of BUDR and Me₂SO

After culture in the presence of 5-bromodeoxyuridine (BUDR) (30 μg/ml for three days) and dimethylsulfoxide (Me$_2$SO) (1.5% for three days), cytoplasmic inclusions could be found in nearly 80% of the cells in all three lines.[48] In addition the average number of inclusions per cell increased approximately three-fold, while the average size and particle density of the inclusions appeared to be unchanged. However, since the number of inclusion-positive cells had increased approximately 16-fold, the increase in the total number of inclusion bodies was between 40-50-fold (see Table 2). While before treatment most inclusions contained similar particles with an electron-lucent core, in the BUDR and Me$_2$SO-treated cells, the contents of the inclusions ranged between (a) small 30-40 nm electron dense particles, (b) ring-shaped particles of approximately 50 nm, and (c) membranous profiles (myelin?) forming into units. The cytoplasm of dead and dying cells in both the treated (BUDR and Me$_2$SO) and non-treated cultures was packed with inclusions (Figure 3). What appears to be a complete virus-like particle could be seen associated with a vesicular structure arising from a disrupted BUDR-treated cell (Figure 2c).

Serological Studies

To determine whether the virus expressed by the leukemic cell lines was related to any of the major groups of animal retroviruses, specific antisera were used. Antisera against avian myeloblastosis virus, murine leukemia virus, feline leukemia virus, bovine leukemia virus, woolly monkey virus, and baboon endogenous virus were used in immunofluorescent (IF) tests against the virus-producing human cell lines and in immuno-diffusion against cell-free, high-speed pellets of the virus-producing lines. These six antisera, which were kindly provided by the National Cancer Institute (Bethesda, Maryland, USA), represent the major groups of animal retroviruses. They failed to cause an immunofluorescence staining of any of the cells, and also failed to form precipitating lines with the virus suspension. However, eight out of the 34 human leukemia sera tested caused IF staining of the virus-producing cells.

Thus these preliminary serological tests indicate that the virus differs from the animal oncornaviruses. The fact that antibodies could be found in some human sera support the ultrastructural studies which indicate that it might be a genuine human virus.

Transformation of Normal Bone Marrow Cells

Fialkow et al.[35] and later Thomas et al.[36] reported that in a female leukemic patient irradiated and transfused with normal male marrow cells, recurrent acute leukemic cells were of male karyotype. This observation suggests an *in vivo* transmission of human leukemia by a virus. The availability of a virus-producing human leukemic cell line enables us to try and repeat the transformation *in vitro*. For this purpose, leukemic cells (line 241) were lethally irradiated (10,000 rads) and were added to a fresh culture of bone marrow cells obtained from a hemato-logically normal female. In addition, irradiated 241 cells alone and bone marrow cells alone were set up in separate cultures and incubated at 37°C. The bone marrow cells which were incubated with irradiated 241 cells proliferated actively, while the bone marrow cells cultured alone, or the irradiated 241 cells, died out. Karyotype analysis revealed that bone marrow cells which were cocultivated with the irradiated 241 cells were EBV-negative and had a female karyotype (XX). Line 241 was derived from a male (XY). Ultrathin sections of these cells reveal the presence of inclusion bodies containing virus-like particles similar to those seen in line 241. Thus our studies provide the experimental counterpart to Fialkow's observation.[35]

Attempts to induce the continuous proliferation of hemic cells from other normal bone marrow cell samples have so far failed. Furthermore, Dr. P. Fischer, of the Cancer Institute in Vienna (personal communica-tion), succeeded in transforming normal human cord leukocytes with an irradiated, virus-producing, leukemic cell line. The infrequent rate of success in the induction of *in vitro* malignant transformation and contin-uous proliferation of human hemic cells can be explained by the very low rate of success in establishing human leukemic cells in a continuous *in vitro* proliferation; namely the inability of most malignant hemic cells to proliferate indefinitely *in vitro*. In our experience, out of 500 samples of cells from leukemia patients, we were only able to obtain five continuous cell lines. In spite of this very low rate of success, to the best of our knowledge these are the only EBV-negative human leukemic cell lines established in Great Britain. An inability to obtain continuous proliferation of human hemic cells following cocultivation with the virus-producing irradiated cells does not necessarily mean lack of infectivity or malignant transformation. Therefore, in order to be able to reproduce the transformation experiment, many more bone marrow and cord

leukocytes will have to be cocultivated with the irradiated virus-producing leukemic cell lines.

Discussion

One of the most important areas in experimental oncology is the
development of continuous tissue culture lines derived from human
tumors. A wide variety of human solid tumor (carcinoma and sarcoma)
lines have been established and used for studies of cell biology, cytoki-
netics, cytogenetics, cellular differentiation and intracellular growth
regulation in response to biochemical stimuli, as well as for comparative
studies of the cytotoxic effects of new cytotoxic drugs and radiosensitive
agents. While human solid tumors have been generally easier to establish
as continuous lines *in vitro*, there has been difficulty in establishing lines
derived from human hematological malignancies. However, in recent
years there were several reports on the successful culture of a relatively
small number of genuine human leukemic cell lines (see Human Leukemia
In Vitro).

My primary reason for attempting to establish human leukemia in
culture has been the belief that *in vitro* such cells may express a genuine
human leukemogenic virus. Virologists who have studied the ultrastruc-
ture of fresh human leukemic cells concentrated their attention on the
cell membrane where budding C-type viruses are readily found in the
animal leukemias. The failure to demonstrate and isolate a genuine
human retrovirus directly from fresh human leukemic cells does not rule
out a possible viral involvement in the induction of this malignancy. For
reasons which were stated in the introduction of this chapter, the strategy
of trying to look for a potential human leukemogenic virus in leukemic
cells after long-term culture seems to have paid off. The successful
continuous culture of human leukemic cells *in vitro* and the study of
their properties revealed three cell lines which express virus-like particles
(VLP) within cytoplasmic inclusion bodies. Similar VLP aggregated into
inclusion bodies have been noted in fresh human leukemic cells, in
lymphoid and myeloid leukemic cells,[37,38] and in one case of myeloma.[39]
The most recent and only systematic search for such inclusions was
undertaken by Smith[37] who reported their presence in the leukemic cells
of 12 of 28 children with acute lymphoblastic leukemia.[37] It is impossible
at this stage to establish how the human VLP relate to the animal
retroviruses, but comparison with the reports on the ultrastructural
expression of incomplete virus particles in murine cells reveals a certain
similarity.[40,41] The ability of a halogenated pyrimidine deoxyribonucleo-
sides to induce the expression of cell integrated RNA viral information
is well documented,[33] and a similar effect of Me_2SO on viral expression
in murine cells has been reported.[41] In the cell lines 230, 241 and 330,

treatment caused a 40- to 50-fold increase in the number of cytoplasmic inclusions (Table 2) and the cytoplasm of degenerating cells was often packed with inclusion bodies containing VLP. The increase in the number of inclusion bodies following incubation of the cells with BUDR and Me$_2$SO supports the notion that these bodies are the sites of synthesis of viral structural proteins.[48]

The reason for the dominance of what can be interpreted to be incomplete particles in the human leukemic cells is not yet known. Particle formation may be incomplete or there may be a block in particle assembly. Luftig et al.[41] demonstrated that treatment of Friend erythro-leukemic cells with interferon decreased mature virus formation and increased the number of immature particles.

Any discussion of the nature of these particles and their possible relation to leukemia in man must first take into account two major sources of potential confusion and error. One is the possibility of a laboratory-borne contamination of the human cells with one or more animal viruses. The second concerns the differentiation of VLP from recognizable cellular organelles which have a certain morphological resemblance to viruses.[42]

We think that the possibility of cross-contamination of our leukemic cell lines with an animal virus is unlikely for the following reasons:

1. No animal viruses were handled in the same laboratory during the culture of the hemic cell lines.
2. The characteristic features of animal B, C and D-type particles, namely the budding and shedding of free virus particles, were never observed.
3. There was a complete absence of cytopathic effect when the leukemic cells were cocultured with a wide range of human and animal cell lines.
4. Serological studies failed to reveal any crossreaction between the various antisera against the major groups of C-type viruses and our leukemic cell lines.[49]

The difficulty in differentiating VLP from the microvesicles and vesicles of multivesicular bodies sometimes found in lymphoblastoid cell lines has been well discussed by Dalton,[42] who points out that type-C members of the RNA tumor virus group do not possess ultrastructural characteristics allowing their certain identification, and that evidence of replication is needed to establish their viral nature. Among the membrane bound particles probably of nonviral nature described and illustrated by Dalton are multivesicular bodies (MVB) and phagocytic vacuoles containing microvesicles. The former are believed to represent a form of digestive vacuole for both exogenous and endogenous materials, corre-

sponding to prelysosomes or the "autosomes" of De Duve and Wat-
tieux's classification. Their nature and genesis has been explored and
described by Smith and Farquhar,[43] whose illustrations depict the stages
in their formation. It also indicates how sharply they differ from the
VLP, which form the subject of the present paper (Figures 1-3), as does
Figure 4, an electron micrograph of a typical MVB for one of our
cultured hemic cell lines.

The vesicles of MVB are usually few in number, variable in diameter
and in shape, and commonly set against a moderately electron-dense
matrix, whereas the VLP described here are frequently very numerous—
up to several hundreds within a single inclusion—are generally round or
oval with less variability in diameter, and are mostly within an electron-
lucent matrix. Again, because of their small size, MVB can rarely be
recognized by light microscopy, whereas the VLP are readily seen in
cultured cells treated with halogenated pyrimidines and have been
observed in fresh leukemic cells.[37,44] Furthermore, the 50-fold increase

Figure 4. Ultrathin section through a multivesicular body (MVB) of a lymphoblastoid cell line.(× 84,000)

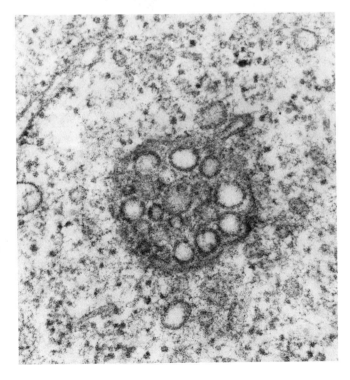

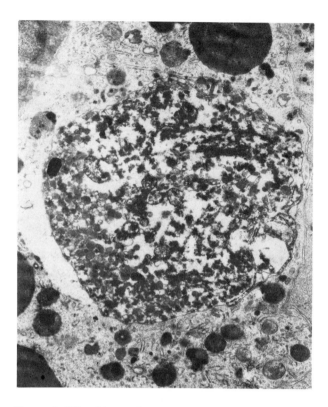

Figure 5. Ultrathin section through a phagocytic vacuole illustrating its variable contents.($\times$ 11,000)

in VLP seen on treatment of the inclusion-forming cells with Me$_2$SO or BUDR has no parallel in increase of MVB when other lymphoblastoid cell lines are similarly treated.

Phagocytic vacuoles may occur in lymphoblastoid cells and may contain microvesicles, possibly derived from degenerating mitochondrial cristae or sometimes from particulate components of fetal bovine serum.[42] The fact that only three of some 30 established cell lines manifest the VLP inclusions reported here, whereas occasional phagocytic vacuoles occur in all the lines, and that treatment with IUDR or BUDR greatly increases the frequency and size of the former while not affecting the latter, might also be sufficient evidence of discrimination. In addition, however, the contents of phagocytic vacuoles usually show considerable variability in size, shape and structure, as illustrated in Figure 5, while the VLP are relatively uniform in size whether within inclusion bodies or liberated from disrupted cells.

A major problem at present is that these human leukemic cell lines produce only small numbers of extracellular particles. This situation can be compared with the murine retroviruses of restricted tropism which are not released from murine cells, but replicated readily in heterologous host cells.[1] A similar situation has been reported in baboon cells infected with the endogenous virus (BaEV), which expresses viral structural proteins but produces only small amounts of complete extracellular virus.[50] In the baboon system, restriction of endogenous virus seems to be the rule rather than the exception.[45,46] A similar restriction of endogenous retroviruses may explain the difficulty of isolating endogenous virus from human cells. We are therefore searching for a cell line that will allow continuous productive replication and release of large quantities of extracellular particles which may help in the study of its possible role in human leukemia.

The successful transformation of human bone marrow cells[47] and cord leukocytes (Dr. P. Fischer, personal communication) following cocultivation with virus-producing, irradiated cells may have resulted from the fusion of the irradiated cells with the normal hemic cells. So far, infection of similar cultures with cell-free virus has not led to transformation nor has it led to the productive infection of the heterologous cell types tested. However, the availability of large quantities of VLP from cells following BUDR and Me_2SO treatment should enable us to proceed with the study of the biochemical and biological properties of the VLP. If these particles prove to be a human leukemia virus or the structural proteins of such a virus, they might eventually be used as a source for viral antigen for vaccination.

References

1. Kaplan, H.S.: *Leukemia Res.* 2:253, 1978.

2. Temin, H.M. and Baltimore, D.: *Adv. Virus Res.* 17:128, 1972.

3. Lowy, D.R., Row, W.P., Teich, N., and Hartley, J.W.: *Science* 174:155, 1971.

4. Reedman, B.M. and Klein, G.: *Int. J. Cancer* 11:499, 1973.

5. Epstein, M.A. and Barr, Y.M.: *Lancet* 1:252, 1964.

6. Epstein, M.A., Henle, G., Achong, B.G., and Barr, Y.M.: *J. Exp. Med.* 121:761, 1965.

7. Henle, W., Diehl, V., Kohn, G., zur Hausen, H., and Henle, G.: *Science* 157:1064, 1967.

8. Pope, J.H., Horne, M.K., and Scott, W.: *Int. J. Cancer* 3:857, 1968.

9. Henle, G., Henle, W., and Diehl, V.: *Proc. Natl. Acad. Sci. USA* 59:94, 1968.

10. Karpas, A., Hayhoe, F.G.J., Greenberger, J.S., Barker, C.R., Cawley, J.C., Lowenthal, R.M., and Maloney, W.C.: *Leukemia Res.* 1:35, 1977.

11. Karpas, A., Hayhoe, F.G.J., Greenberger, J., and Neumann, H.: *Science* 202:318, 1978.

12. Zur Hausen, H. and Schulte-Holthausen, H.: *Nature* 227:245, 1970.
13. Klein, G., Lindahl, T., Jondal, M., Leibold, W., Menezes, J., Nilsson, K., and Sundstrom, C.: *Proc. Natl. Acad. Sci. USA* 71:3283, 1974.
14. Pagano, J.S., Huang, C.H., and Levine, P.: *N. Eng. J. Med.* 289:1395, 1973.
15. Lozzio, C.B. and Lozzio, B.B.: *Blood* 45:321, 1975.
16. Klein, E., Ben-Bassat, H., Neumann, H., Ralph, P., Zeuthen, J., Polliack, A., and Vanky, F.: *Int. J. Cancer* 18:421, 1976.
17. Andersson, L.C., Nilsson, K., and Gahmberg, C.G.: *Int. J. Cancer* 23:143, 1979.
18. Rutherford, T.R., Clegg, J.B., and Weatherall, D.J.: *Nature* 280:164, 1979.
19. Lozzio, C.B., Lozzio, B.B., Machado, E.A., Fuhr, J.E., Lait, S.V., and Bamberg, E.G.: *Nature* 281:709, 1979.
20. Golde, D.W., Quan, S.G., and Cline, M.J.: *Blood* 52:1068, 1978.
21. Kaplan, J., Shope, T.C., and Peterson, W.L.: *J. Exp. Med.* 139:1070, 1974.
22. Minowada, J., Ohnuma, T., and Moore, G.E.: *J. Natl. Cancer Inst.* 49:891, 1972.
23. Morikawa, S., Tatsumi, E., Baba, M., Harada, T., and Yasuhira, K.: *Int. J. Cancer* 21:166, 1978.
24. Hiraki, S., Miyoshi, I., Masuji, H., Kubonishi, I., Matsuda, Y., Nakayama, T., Kishimoto, H., Chen, P., and Kinura, I.: *J. Natl. Cancer Inst.* 59:93, 1977.
25. Karpas, A., Sandler, R.M., and Thorburn, R.J.: *Br. J. Cancer* 36:177, 1977.
26. Rosenfeld, C., Goutner, A., Choquet, C., Venaut, A.M., Kayabanda, B., Pico, J., and Greaves, M.F.: *Nature* 267:841, 1977.
27. Nilsson, K. and Sundstrom, C.: *Int. J. Cancer* 13:808, 1974.
28. Kaplan, H.S., Goodenow, R.S., Garther, S., and Bieber, M.M.: *Cancer* 43:1, 1979.
29. Minowada, J., Tsuboia, T., Greaves, M.F., and Walters, T.R.: *J. Natl. Cancer Inst.* 59:83, 1977.
30. Collins, S.J., Gallo, R.C., and Gallagher, R.E.: *Nature* 270:347, 1977.
31. Kauffler, H.P. and Golde, D.W.: *Science* 200:1153, 1978.
32. Fischer, P., Karpas, A., Nacheva, E., Haas, O., Winterleither, H., and Krepler, P.: *Br. J. Hematol.* 45, 1980 (in press).
33. Karpas, A., Khalid, G., Burns, G., And Hayhoe, F.G.J.: *Br. J. Cancer* 37:308, 1978.
34. Karpas, A., Worman, C.P., Khalid, G., Neumann, H., Hayhoe, F.G.J., Newell, D., and Stewart, J.W.: *Br. J. Haematol.,* 44:415, 1980.
35. Fialkow, P.J., Thomas, E.D., Bryant, J.I., and Neimann, P.E.: *Lancet* 1:251, 1971.
36. Thomas, E.D., Bryant, J.I., Buckner, C.D., Clift, R.A., Fefer, A., Johnson, F., Neimann, P.E., Ramberg, R., and Strab, R.: *Trans. Assoc. Am. Physicians* 84:248, 1971.
37. Smith, H.: *Leukemia Res.* 2:133, 1978.
38. Tanaka, Y., Bell, W., and Brindley, D.: *J. Natl. Cancer Inst.* 38:629, 1967.
39. Sorenson, G.D.: *Exp. Cell Res.* 25:219, 1961.
40. Hall, W.T., Gazdar, A.F., Hobbs, B.A., and Chopra, H.C.: *J. Natl. Cancer Inst.* 52:1337, 1974.
41. Luftig, R.B., Conscience, J.F., Skoultchi, A., McMillan, P., Revel, M., and Ruddle, F.H.: *J. Virol.* 23:799, 1977.
42. Dalton, A.J.: *J. Natl. Cancer Inst.* 54:1137, 1975.
43. Smith, R.E. and Farquhar, M.G.: *J. Cell Biol.* 31:319, 1966.

44. Berrebi, A., Oberling, A., Mayer, S., and Waitz, R.: *La Nouvelle Presse Medicale* 14:894, 1974.
45. Todaro, G.J., Sharr, C.J., Benveniste, R.E., Lieber, M.M., and Melnick, J.L.: *Cell* 2:55, 1974.
46. Todaro, G.J., Sharr, C.J., and Benveniste, R.E.: *Virology* 72:278, 1976.
47. Karpas, A., Wreghitt, J.G., and Nagington, J.: *Lancet* 2:1016, 1978.
48. Karpas, A., Fischer, P.: *Leukemia Research* 4:315, 1980.
49. Karpas, A.: *Lancet* 2:110, 1978.
50. Lavelle, G., Foote, L., Heberling, R.L., and Kalter, S.S.: J. *Virol.* 30:390, 1975.

A Comment on Retroviruses in Human Leukemia

Yechiel Becker

Hebrew University-Hadassah Medical School, Jerusalem, Israel

Particles morphologically resembling viruses that cause leukemia in animals have been isolated from leukemic cells from patients with acute and chronic leukemia after cultivation of the cells under laboratory conditions.[1] However, the role of these viruses in the disease process in humans is not yet known.

Two approaches have been used to demonstrate the association of viruses with human leukemia. The first approach used by Spiegelman[2,3] was to search for virus-like particles that contain reverse transcriptase and nucleic acid homologous to that of a mouse leukemia virus, Rauscher leukemia virus (RVL), in leukemic cells. The studies of Spiegelman's group suggested the presence of viral genetic information in leukemic cells. It was therefore necessary to isolate viruses from the leukemic cells to be able to study the properties of the virus particles and the nature of their association with the leukemic cells.

The second approach was to induce virus particles in leukemic cells, since fresh cells do not produce any virus. One way was to induce virus particles in cells that were kept in the laboratory for a short period (several days). Under such induction conditions, virus particles resembling retroviruses were induced only in leukemic cells.[4] Gallo's group[5] had isolated a C-type virus from a human leukemic cell line grown under laboratory conditions for a prolonged period. Subsequent studies[6] to characterize the isolated virus revealed that the viral reverse transcriptase was antigenically similar to the reverse transcriptase of monkey leukemia viruses. However, unpublished studies by Henry Kaplan's group showed that the reverse transcriptase from virus particles released from human leukemic cell lines can be freed from a contaminating protein that crossreacted with the reverse transcriptase of the monkey leukemia viruses.[7] Thus, it is possible that the virus released from the human leukemia cells might be a human-derived virus. Further studies on this problem are necessary.

These studies showed that leukemic cells contain a virus hidden in the cell nucleus. Under experimental conditions the virus can be activated, synthesized by the leukemic cells and released from them. Such a virus was not seen in normal lymphocytes but was seen in normal placenta.[8] Therefore, further research is necessary to study the nature of the association of these viruses with human leukemia.

References

1. Kaplan, H.S., Goodenow, R.S., Epstein, A.L., Gartner, S., Decleve, A., and Rosenthal, P.N.: *Proc. Natl. Acad. Sci. USA* 74:2564, 1977.

2. Hehlmann, R., Kufe, D., and Spiegelman, S.: *Proc. Natl. Acad. Sci. USA* 69:435, 1972.

3. Baxt, W., Hehlmann, R., and Spiegelman, S.: *Nature New Biol.* 240:72, 1972.

4. Kotler, M., Weinberg, E., Haspel, O., Olshevsky, U., and Becker, V.: *Nature New Biol.* 244:197, 1973.

5. Gallagher, R.E. and Gallo, R.C.: *Science* 187:350, 1975.

6. Okabe, H., Gilden, R.V., Hatanaka, M., Stephenson, J.R., Gallagher, R.E., Gallo, R.C., Tronick, S.R., and Aaronson, S.A.: *Nature* 260:264, 1976.

7. Goodenow, R.S. and Kaplan, H.S.: *Proc. Natl. Acad. Sci. U.S.A.* 76:4971, 1979.

8. Kalter, S.S., Helmke, R.J., Heberling, R.L., Panigel, M., Fowler, A.K., Strickland, J.E., and Hellman, A.: *J. Natl. Cancer Inst.* 50:1081, 1973.

Type B Virus and Human Breast Cancer

Nurul H. Sarkar

Memorial Sloan-Kettering Cancer Center, New York, New York

The etiology of breast cancer in women, like that of many other forms of human cancer, is still unknown. The interplay of several factors, such as the genetic, hormonal, immunological and physiological status of the host, dietary habits, exposure to various chemical carcinogens and oncogenic viruses, is thought to be involved in the process of mammary tumorigenesis. Some of these factors may act as initiators of the tumorigenic process while others may act as promotors, resulting in the transformation of normal mammary gland cells into cancer cells. Extensive investigations to determine the relationship between human mammary tumorigenesis and the various factors mentioned above have been done, but have often provided inconclusive results which are difficult to interpret. For example, epidemiologic studies have revealed that women whose relatives have had breast cancer have double the risk of developing the disease as compared to women with no familial history of breast cancer.[1] This finding, however, does not prove that there is a genetic basis for breast cancer, since shared living habits and a shared environment could account for the observed familial association. Thus, an understanding of the etiology of human breast cancer can only be obtained when the precise roles of the various factors suspected of being involved in tumorigenesis are identified. In this paper I would like to discuss one possible etiologic factor of human breast cancer, namely oncogenic virus(es), that has received a great deal of attention recently.

As late as the early 1950's, viruses were not even considered to be a possible cause of cancer in animals, let alone human cancer. However, by the early 1960's, viruses had been proven to cause cancer in several species of animals, including mammary tumors in mice, and it was then considered probable that at least some human tumors, especially breast tumors, might be caused by similar viruses. By biological experimentation, Bittner[2] discovered that the murine mammary tumor virus (MuMTV) was the etiologic agent of murine mammary tumors, but such experiments are not possible in humans. The putative viral etiology of human tumors can thus only be investigated using an appropriate animal model, such as murine mammary cancer. Attempts have been made to identify virus particles in human mammary tumor tissue by electron microscopy, and immunological techniques have been used in an effort to detect virus antigens in tumor cells and viral antibodies in human sera. Biochemical methods have also been used to determine if viral genes are expressed and integrated into the DNA of mammary tumor cells. Since type B virus (MuMTV)-derived reagents have been used in most of these studies, it is appropriate to first briefly describe some of the characteristic properties of MuMTV and then discuss the work that has provided both positive and negative evidence for the association of MuMTV with human breast cancer.

Structural Properties of MuMTV

MuMTV, a type B virus, after being assembled at the cell membrane, is released from the cell by a process called budding (Figure 1).[3] Mature extracellular MuMTV is spherical and between 100-200 nm in diameter, but under certain conditions it exhibits a "head and tail" configuration. Regularly spaced spikes consisting of knobs and stalks are the major structural components of the virus envelope. The knobs are composed of gp52, a glycoprotein of 52,000 dalton molecular weight while another glycoprotein (gp34) is located inside the membrane bilayer. The viral core contains four polypeptides (p28, p23, p14, and p10), 35S single-stranded RNA, and an 80,000-100,000 dalton molecular weight reverse transcriptase, which prefers Mg^{++} over Mn^{++} in poly(rC)·oligo(dG)-directed DNA synthesis. The buoyant density of the virus is 1.19 g/ml in sucrose and 1.22 g/ml in CsCl gradients.

Studies to Identify a Putative Human Breast Cancer Virus

Morphological Studies

An extensive search for a putative human breast cancer virus in human milk and breast tumors has been done using both thin sectioning and negative staining electron microscopy. The etiologic significance of the particles (100-200 mμ in diameter) which resemble type B or type C (leukemia-sarcoma) viruses or M-PMV (a virus found in simian mammary tumors) and which have been found in thin sections of human breast

Structure of MuMTV

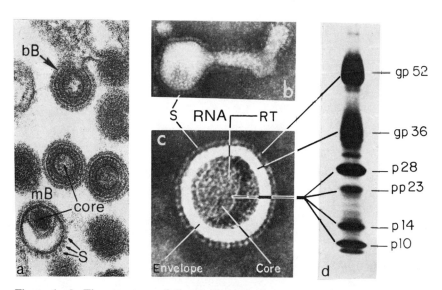

Figure 1a-d. The structure of the murine mammary tumor virus (MuMTV or B-particle). The core of the budding virus (bB) is spherical, and consists of two concentric protein layers, whereas the core of the mature virus particle (mB) is condensed. The virus envelope has "spikes" (s) on its surface. **Panel a** is a thin section electron micrograph of a virus producing cell. MuMTV particles stained with phosphotungstic acid often exhibit a head and tail configuration (**Panel b**), but when fixed with gluteraldehyde, pH 7.0, for 30 min or more, they appear spherical and the nucleoprotein strands become visible (**Panel c**). The molecular weight of the proteins (P) and glycoproteins (gp) are expressed in units of 1,000 (**Panel d**). RT denotes reverse transcriptase. (Panels a and b, × 130,000; Panel c, × 169,000)

tumors and milk, is not known.[4,5] The particles observed in sections of human breast tumor cells are most probably of cellular origin since no budding particles resembling oncornaviruses (as shown in Figure 1) have been seen.[5] A thorough search of an established human breast cancer cell line, MCF-7, revealed no budding oncornavirus-like particles, even though particles resembling oncornaviruses have been seen in the culture supernatants of the MCF-7 cells.[6] Using negatively stained preparations of particulate material isolated from human milk, Moore and his associates,[7] for the first time, detected a few particles that were morphologically indistinguishable from MuMTV. Further extensive studies revealed the presence of three different types of particles resembling oncornaviruses in human milk. One type of particle (Figure 2) designated MS-1, which

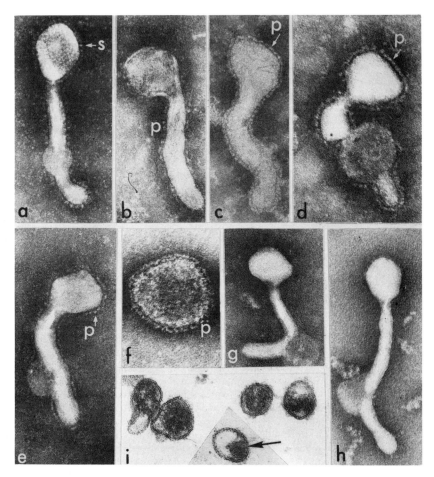

Figure 2a-i. Virus-like particles in human milk. The particles shown in **Panels a-h** were observed in negatively-stained preparations of milk isolates. The spikes (s) of the particle in **Panel a** are identical to those of MuMTV (compare this figure with Figure 1, **Panel b**). This type of particle is designated MS-1. The morphology of the surface projections (p) of the particles (designated MS-2) shown in **Panels b-f** is variable and appears to be different from those of the particles shown in **Panel a**. The particles shown in **Panels g** and **h** have smooth membranes and resemble type-C or M-PMV particles. The appearance of the human milk particles in thin sections are shown in **Panel i;** note the eccentricity of the core (shown by arrow) in one of these particles. (Panels a-f, × 114,000; Panel i, × 83,000)

has the characteristic features of murine type B virus morphology (i.e., head and tail forms, 10 nm "spikes" covering the surface of the particle, spaced about 7 nm apart and with knobs at the distal ends), has been seen only occasionally. Only 16 such particles were found in milk specimens from more than 1,000 women.[5] The second type of particle (Figure 2) designated MS-2, contains surface projections which are not identical to the surface spikes of type B particles. About 10-15% of human milk samples contain MS-2 particles.[4] The other types of particles seen frequently in human milk are MS-3 particles, which have heads and tails but not surface projections (Figure 2). These particles resemble type C viruses or M-PMV.[8,9] Many, if not all, of the MS-3 particles are probably cellular debris. As has been emphasized previously,[4] cell membrane fragments or other cellular structures can assume head and tail shapes and resemble MS-2 or MS-3 particles. It is also possible that MS-1 particles are first converted to MS-2 particles, and then to MS-3 particles as a result of degradation. Whatever the origin of MS-1 particles, their presence in human milk and their morphological similarity to type B particles is unique. It should be emphasized, however, that the occurrence of neither these particles nor the MS-2 and MS-3 particles in milk correlates with the familial breast cancer history of the donors (Table 1).

Table 1. Distribution of the Oncornavirus-Like Particles in Milk from Women With or Without a Family History of Breast Cancer

Group	No. of Milk Donors	Percent of Milk Samples Positive for Particles of Types		
		MS-1	MS-2	MS-3 or M-PMV-like
Women with family history of breast cancer				
a. Maternal[a]	90	4.4	16.7	36.7
b. Maternal and paternal[b]	90	NR[c]	NR	12.3
Women with family history of other types of cancer[b]	190	NR	NR	10.0
Women without family history of cancer				
a. Reference 4	173	9.5	11.6	39.9
b. Reference 9	180	NR	NR	11.0

[a] Sarkar and Moor.[4]

[b] Chopra et al.[9]

[c] NR, the authors did not report or discuss MS-1 or MS-2 type particles.

Biochemical Studies

The discovery of an RNA-dependent DNA polymerase, commonly referred to as "reverse transcriptase" (RT), as a unique enzyme of retroviruses[10,11] and the finding of a few type B virus-like particles in human milk,[4,7,12] led several investigators, using a variety of approaches, to search for the presence of such an enzyme in human milk and breast tumor tissues. Endogenous RNA, that is, RNA derived from the putative virus particles of human milk or tumor tissues and exogenous oncornavirus RNA, served as templates in the search for the enzyme in these studies; synthetic template primers were also used. It was found that a high percentage of human milk samples contained an RNA-directed DNA polymerase (Table 2). The DNA polymerase activity reported by Schlom et al. was found for the first time in milk fractions containing virus-like particles with an apparent density of 1.17 to 1.19 g/ml in sucrose gradients.[13] The criteria used to identify the polymerase activity in these experiments were the sensitivity of the endogenous reactions to RNAse and the requirement for all four deoxyribonucleoside triphosphates (dXTP). However, it is not certain that the DNA polymerase detected in these experiments and in those experiments that used the synthetic template primer poly(rA)·oligo(dT)[14] is RT, since (a) a DNA-directed DNA polymerase primed by short oligomers is, like RT, sensitive to ribonuclease,[15] and (b) normal cellular DNA polymerase as well as RT can synthesize DNA using the template primers poly(rA)·oligo(dT).[16]

Attempts were made by Gerwin and her associates[14] to partially purify the DNA polymerase from human milk by phosphocellulose chromatography and compare its properties to that of RNA tumor-virus RT. Two enzymatic activities were detected in human milk. One, eluting at 0.6 M KCl was detected by a poly(rA)·oligo(dT) template, while the other eluting at 0.2 M KCl was detected by an activated calf thymus DNA template. However, no enzymatic activity eluting at 0.3 M KCl, the characteristic elution position of oncornaviral RT, was detected. The enzyme eluting at 0.2 M KCl is probably alpha polymerase while the enzyme eluting at 0.6 M KCl is probably the DNA polymerase III (gamma) characterized by Lewis et al.[16] which, like viral RT, prefers poly(rA)·oligo(dT) to DNA as a template and elutes from phosphocellulose columns at high salt concentrations.

In spite of the uncertainty of the nature of the DNA polymerase(s) detected in these studies, other studies have been done which indicate, with a degree of certainty, that a DNA polymerase associated with a particulate fraction of human milk is RNA directed and thus possibly similar to the RT of oncornaviruses. These studies include: (a) simultaneous detection of a 60-70S RNA (a sedimentation value characteristic of oncornaviral RNA and of an enzyme synthesizing DNA that cosedi-

Table 2. DNA Polymerase(s) Detected in Particles Isolated from Human Milk and Breast Tumor

Specimen	Template	Criteria for Identification of the Enzyme	No. Positive/ Total Samples (%)	Reference
Milk	Endogenous	RNAse sensitivity; requirement for 4 dXTP	4/13 (30)	(13)
	Endogenous	RNAse sensitivity; requirement for 4 dXTP	8/20 (40)	(4)
	Endogenous	Product sediments with 60-70 RNA	10/20 (50)	(17)
	Endogenous	Simultaneous detection	9/24 (37)	(18)
	Endogenous	Simultaneous detection	8/53 (16)	(19)
	Endogenous	RNAse sensitivity	14/94 (15)	(14)
	Endogenous	Simultaneous detection	31/40 (75)	
	Poly(rA) · oligo(dT)	Poly(A) utilization	12/33 (36)	
	Poly(rC) · oligo(dG)	Mg^{++} activity $>$ Mn^{++}	10/25 (40)	(20)
		Simultaneous detection	7/25 (28)[a]	
	Poly(rCm) · oligo(dG)	Poly(rCm) utilization by purified RT	–	(25)
Breast tumor	Endogenous	Simultaneous detection	30/38 (79)	(27)
Normal breast tissue	Endogenous	Simultaneous detection	0/4 (0)	
Fibroadenoma	Endogenous	Simultaneous detection	0/6 (0)	
Breast tumor	Poly(rCm) · oligo(dG)	Specific poly(rCm) utilization	10/19 (53)	(28)
Normal breast tissue	Poly(rCm) · oligo(dG)	Specific poly(rCm) utilization	0/9 (0)	
Breast tumor	Poly(rCm) · oligo(dG)	Heteropolymeric RNA-directed DNA synthesis		(29)
	AMV 70S RNA	Back-hybridization of DNA product to template		
	Poly(rCm) · oligo(dG)	Inhibition by anti M-PMV RT		(30)

[a]7 of the 10 positive samples were also positive by the simultaneous detection test.

ments with the RNA).[14,17-20] The DNA and the 60-70S RNA complex, presumably as a result of hydrogen bonding, sediment in a $(Cs)_2SO_4$ equilibrium gradient at a density of 1.650-1.680 g/ml.[17] In addition, the 60-70S RNA of human milk particles was shown to contain polyadenylic acid with sequences 200 nucleotides in length identical in size to that of the poly(A) stretches of the RNA of oncornaviruses.[21] (b) The DNA polymerase of human milk particles, like the RT of MuMTV and M-

PMV, prefers Mg^{++} over Mn^{++} as a divalent cation in poly(rC)·oligo(dG)-directed DNA synthesis.[20] Although normal cellular DNA polymerase has been found to utilize poly(rC) as a template at low salt concentrations,[22,23] the DNA polymerase detected in human milk using poly(rC) as a template does not appear to be cellular polymerase since it is associated with particles having the density characteristics of MuMTV (1.22 g/ml in CsC1 gradients). The buoyant density of type C viruses, including M-PMV in CsC1 gradients, is 1.15-1.17 g/ml.[20,24] Partially purified DNA polymerase from human milk particulate fractions has been shown[25] to utilize a methylated polycytidylate template, poly(rCm), which is resistant to RNAse and which does not appear to be used by any cellular DNA polymerase under any reaction conditions.[26c] It has been further demonstrated by Kantor et al.[25] that the DNA polymerase that they purified from human milk displays the divalent cation preference characteristic of MuMTV reverse transcriptase and that an antiserum prepared against the enzyme did not inhibit cellular DNA polymerases α,β, or γ although it did, as expected inhibit the DNA polymerase activity of human milk particles. These results suggest that the DNA polymerase from human milk may be similar to oncornaviral reverse transcriptase. Unfortunately, however, it is not known if the antiserum to human milk DNA polymerase can inhibit MuMTV-RT, and inconclusive results were obtained in enzyme neutralization and binding studies with antibody to the M-PMV reverse transcriptase. It is also not known if the purified human enzyme can copy retroviral RNA.[d] Das and his associates[18] not only detected DNA polymerase in human milk particles, but also demonstrated that the synthesized cDNA was directed by 60-70S RNA and could be hybridized to polysomal RNA from an undifferentiated human breast carcinoma; the cDNA probe did not hybridize to similar RNA's derived from normal breast, human placenta or mouse embryos. Although this study does not necessarily indicate that an oncornavirus-like RT in human milk is responsible for the synthesis of such a DNA, it demonstrates the coexistence of a unique enzyme and RNA in human milk particles which may have biological functions associated with human breast tumorigenesis.

The search for a DNA polymerase in human breast tumors was initiated by several investigators as early as 1972. Axel et al.[27] demonstrated, for the first time, that a 60-70S RNA and DNA polymerase was present in particles with a density of 1.17 g/ml in sucrose gradients which they isolated from human breast carcinomas (Table 2). Using poly(rCm)·oligo(dG) as a template-primer, Gerard et al.[28] detected DNA polymerase activity in ten of 19 breast tumors. The activity was associated with particles that had a density of 1.16-1.19 g/ml in sucrose gradients; no polymerase activity was found in any of the nine normal or fibrocystic breast tissues. Adequate characterization of the enzyme was not done in their study, however, and thus the enzyme cannot be considered to be a proven reverse transcriptase. Human breast tumor DNA polymerase has only once been characterized with criteria sufficiently stringent to define it as a reverse transcriptase.[29] Using a three-step procedure involving density gradient fractionation, polyacrylamide-agarose gel and phosphocellulose chromatography, a DNA polymerase was partially purified from breast tumor tissue by Ohno et al.,[29] but was not found in normal or benign breast tissue. The DNA polymerase eluted at 0.18 M phosphate from a phosphocellulose column, sedimented as a 5-6S component and demonstrated a strong preference for oligo(dT)·poly(rA) over oligo(dT)·poly(dA) as a template for the synthesis of poly(dG). Most important, the partially purified breast tumor DNA polymerase was able to synthesize a heteropolymeric cDNA which was further shown to back-hybridize specifically to the template RNA. Further studies on this particular enzyme preparation[30] revealed that it was immunologically related to the reverse transcriptase of M-PMV since (a) isolated IgG against M-PMV polymerase partially inhibited the activity of the human breast tumor DNA polymerase, and (b) the purified human DNA polymerase formed a complex with anti M-PMV polymerase IgG.

It is indeed unfortunate that in the eight years of investigations since the first detection of DNA polymerase in human milk, the question of whether or not the human milk DNA polymerase is related to the human breast tumor DNA polymerase and of how these enzymes are related to the RT of MuMTV, is unanswered. Since a DNA polymerase, apparently resembling the reverse transcriptase of oncornaviruses, is present in breast tumors but not in normal breast tissues, it can, at least, be considered as a potential marker for breast tumors. The establishment of a correlation between the presence of the DNA polymerase and the presence of any of the three types of particles that are found in human milk would indicate that the particles were viruses that might be etiologically related to breast cancer. As I have mentioned earlier (see Table 1), the virus-like particles in human milk are not restricted to women from families with high breast cancer incidence. Naturally, the question then arises of whether or not the occurrence of human milk DNA polymerase can be correlated with the familial breast cancer history of the women whose milk was tested. As is shown in Table 3, we could not assign the DNA polymerase activity to a particular type of virus-like particle or to women with a family history of breast cancer,[4] even though an apparent correlation between the presence of MS-1 particles and DNA polymerase was found in an early study of a limited number of milk samples.[13] Similarly, the results obtained by Gerwin et al.,[14] who examined a large number of milk samples, show that the occurrence of DNA polymerase is not significantly higher in milk donors with a family history

Table 3. Occurrence of the Virus-Like Particles in Human Milk and the RNA-Dependent DNA Polymerase Activity[a]

Group	Sample Number	Type of Particles			RNA-dependent DNA Polymerase
		MS-1	MS-2	MS-3	
Women with a family history of breast cancer	1	−	+	+	+
	2	−	−	+	+
	3	−	−	+	+
	4	−	−	−	−
	5	−	+	+	−
	6	−	−	+	−
	7	−	−	−	−
	8	−	−	−	−
	9	+	+	+	+
	10	−	−	−	−
Milk samples from women with no cancer history	1	−	+	+	+
	2	−	−	+	−
	3	−	−	+	+
	4	−	−	+	+
	5	−	−	−	−
	6	−	−	−	−
	7	+	+	+	+
	8	−	−	−	−
	9	−	−	+	−
	10	−	−	+	−

[a] Data from Reference 4.

of breast cancer, or any other cancer, than in donors with no family history of cancer.

Even in milk samples from women (with or without a family history of breast cancer or other cancer) where no virus-like particles could be found, DNA polymerase activity could be detected by the procedure that monitors simultaneously 60-70S RNA and an RNA-directed DNA synthesis.[19] Obviously, these disparate observations and the lack of correlation between the occurrence of DNA polymerase, virus-like particles and a history of breast cancer could be attributed to many factors; one of them certainly is the concentration of the particles, and/or the particle-associated enzymes and RNA, to be found at the borderline of detectability. Another factor may be the sensitivity and the specificity of the various methods used by different investigators for assaying DNA polymerase, since Gerwin et al.[14] have shown that the percentage of milk samples containing DNA polymerase activity varied as a function of the methods used for detecting the enzyme activity. The observed lack of correlation might also be due to the presence of an enzyme or enzymes, such as phospholipases, proteases or nucleases in some human milk samples. These enzymes would degrade milk particles and/or interfere with the determinations of DNA polymerase and RNA. The following observations provide strong evidence that some human milk contains enzymes detrimental to the morphological integrity, bioinfectivity, and the DNA polymerase activity of MuMTV and it is possible that the effect of such antiviral substances on the putative human milk particles could account for the lack of correlation between DNA polymerase activity and the detection of particles by electron microscopy:

1) When MuMTV is incubated with human milk at 37°C for 12-18 hrs,[31] the morphology of MuMTV is altered (Figure 3), i.e., the core of the virus particles is degraded and viral membranes are damaged and become permeable to phosphotungstic acid (PTA) stain. As a result, the particles appear spherical in contrast to the characteristic head and tail morphology of untreated MuMTV stained with PTA.

2) The infectivity titer of MuMTV exposed to whole human milk has been shown to be reduced by at least 1,000-fold (Table 4). The cream fraction of human milk appears to be more virulytic than whole or skim milk. These studies have been corroborated by Fieldsteel[32] who has recently shown that human milk, especially the cream fraction, contains antiviral substances that essentially destroy the infectivity of Japanese B encephalitis and Friend and Rauscher murine leukemia viruses (MuLV).

3) Three independent studies have established that the reverse transcriptase activity of MuMTV, MuLV and avian myeloblastosis virus (AMV) is severely reduced following exposure to some human milk.[31,33,34] The loss of MuMTV RT has been shown to correlate well with the morphological integrity of the virus.[31] Furthermore, it has been established by McCormick et al.[34] that human milk contains a variable amount of RNAse (2 to 20 ng/ml) and this RNAse can cosediment with retroviruses as a part of the casein micelle. The presence of RNAse in viral preparations would obviously inhibit the RT. However, it should be stressed that since RNAse cannot act on intact whole virions, there must be other factors in human milk that degrade and cause loss in infectivity of MuMTV, Japanese B encephalitis virus and MuLV exposed to human milk. Although the observations described above would account for the difficulties in obtaining reproducible results in various laboratories and correlating the presence of virus-like particles and DNA polymerase activity in milk from women with or without a family history of breast cancer, the clinical significance of the milk particles and the DNA polymerase activity still remains an unsolved question after ten years of investigation.

The detection of RNA, similar in size to the oncornavirus genome, in

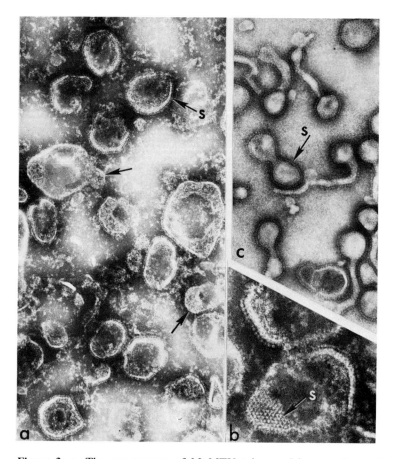

Figure 3a-c. The appearance of MuMTV (observed by negative staining) after exposure to human milk (**Panels a and b**). Note that most of the particles appear to be spherical and are penetrated by stain—the particles appear empty. Some degraded particles (arrows) are also shown in this micrograph and some particles appear to have lost their spikes (s). Compared to the particles seen in Figure 1, untreated MuMTV particles appear to have a head and tail morphology and are not penetrated by stain (**Panel c**). (Panel a, × 58,000; Panel b, × 115,000; Panel c, × 72,000)

experiments to measure DNA polymerase activity in particulate fractions of human milk as described above, prompted the search for nucleic acid sequences, homologous to oncornaviral RNA, in human breast tumors. Molecular hybridization is an efficacious and powerful tool for assaying viral and/or cellular genes in tissues, but it may produce variable results since different hybridization procedures permit varying amounts of mismatching to occur. Using an endogenous RNA template from deter-

Table 4. Infectivity of MuMTV Exposed to Human Milk

Skim Milk from RIII Mice Diluted 1:10 With:	Percent of Mice Infected at Following Dilutions					Approximate 50% Infective Dose/0.1 ml
	10^{-3}	10^{-4}	10^{-5}	10^{-6}	10^{-7}	
A. PBS (control)	67^a	80	54	50	36	$>10^{-6}$
B. Whole human milk	23	7	0	14	7	$<10^{-3}$
C. Skim milk fraction from sample B	64	7	7	0	15	10^{-3}
D. Cream fraction from sample B	7	8	0	0	0	$<10^{-3}$

a For each experiment 12-15 mice were used; data from Reference 31.

gent-disrupted MuMTV and/or MuLV, Axel et al.[35] synthesized complementary DNA (cDNA) and used it as a probe for the detection of putative MuMTV and/or MuLV-related sequences in polysomal RNA preparations from human breast tumors, fibrocystic breast tissue, fibroadenomas, gynecomastias and normal breast tissues. In this study, the RNA-DNA hybrids were detected by isopycnic centrifugation in $(Cs)_2SO_4$ gradients. Although the yield of the specific label recovered in the gradient was very low, 19 of the 29 breast tumors that these investigators tested were positive for MuMTV-related RNA, whereas none of the 15 samples from normal, fibrocystic, fibroadenomatous or gynecomastic breast tissues contained RNA homologous to MuMTV or MuLV-cDNA (Table 5). Other human tissues were also negative, regardless of whether or not they were normal or neoplastic. Das and his associates[18] synthesized DNA complementary to the RNA of MuMTV and of human milk particles, and found in a $(Cs)_2SO_4$ gradient centrifugation assay that the cDNA's hybridized with polysomal RNA from four of the ten human breast tumors tested. It should be mentioned that the $(Cs)_2SO_4$ gradient centrifugation procedure used by Axel et al.[35] and Das et al.[18] although very sensitive, is not quantitative.

In order to further determine the significance of these observations and to quantitate the extent and fidelity of hybridization between cellular RNA's from human breast tumors and the cDNA of MuMTV, two groups of investigators[36,37] used a more stringent, but potentially less sensitive assay in which the degree of hybridization was estimated by measuring the sensitivity of the annealed cDNA to a single strand-specific S_1 nuclease digestion.[38] Vaidya et al.[36] observed that a certain number of human breast tumor-derived RNA preparations (5/17) hybridized up to 77% with MuMTV-cDNA at high $C_r t$ values ($2-8 \times 10^4$ mol/liter·sec). They estimated that the human tumors contained about 1.5 to 8 MuMTV 70S RNA equivalents/cell. By thermal denaturation studies, they estimated the melting temperature (TM) of the human breast tumor

Table 5. Virus-Like Nucleic Acid Sequences in Human Breast Tissue

| | | No. Positive/Total Samples (%) | | | |
Probe	Hybridization Detection Method	Tumor Tissue RNA	Normal Tissue RNA	Tumor Tissue DNA	Reference
MuMTV ^{3}H-cDNA	$(Cs)_2SO_4$-gradient centrifugation	19/22(66)	0/15(0)	NT[c]	(35)
Human milk ^{3}H-cDNA	$(Cs)_2SO_4$-gradient centrifugation	4/10(40)	0/3 (0)	NT	(18)
MuMTV ^{3}H-cDNA	S_1 nuclease digestion	5/17(30)	0/4 (0)	NT	(36)
MuMTV ^{3}H-cDNA	S_1 nuclease digestion	0/19 (0)	0/3 (0)	0/6(0)	(37)
M-PMV ^{3}H-cDNA[a]	S_1 nuclease digestion	0/17 (0)	0/4 (0)	NT	(36)
M-PMV ^{3}H-cDNA[b]	Hydroxylapatite chromatography	7/10(70)	0/11(0)	NT	(39)

[a] Endogenously synthesized with detergent-disrupted M-PMV virions.

[b] Synthesized on isolated M-PMV 70S RNA using purified AMV reverse transcriptase.

[c] NT = Not tested.

RNA-cDNA hybrids to be 62°C, in contrast to 69° for the homologous MuMTV RNA-cDNA hybrids. These results indicate a high degree of base pairing (approximately 5% mismatching) between the RNA of human breast tumors and the genome of MuMTV; the obvious implication of this finding is that human breast tumors contain RNA very closely related to the MuMTV genome. In contrast to these results, Bishop et al.,[37] using a similar S_1 nuclease digestion procedure, found no MuMTV-related RNA in any of the 19 human breast tumor samples they tested. Furthermore they did not find any MuMTV-related sequences in human breast tumor DNA when hybridizations were done at 68°C in the presence of 0.6M Na$^+$, a stringent condition in which duplexes are formed only if extensive complementarity of nucleotide sequences exists between the DNA molecules. However, at 59°C in the presence of 1.5M Na$^+$, a significant degree of hybridization was found to occur between MuMTV-cDNA and DNA from some human breast tumors as well as DNA from normal breast tissues. The latter conditions of hybridization are not stringent since they allow duplexes to form with large numbers of mispaired nucleotides. Furthermore, MuMTV-cDNA was found to hybridize to calf thymus DNA and salmon sperm DNA to the same extent as to DNA from human breast tumors. Thus, the lack of specificity of hybridization in the "nonstringent" conditions casts doubt on the significance of the hybridization observed between MuMTV-cDNA and human breast tumor DNA observed by these investigators. It should be mentioned that although McGrath[39] and his associates, could detect RNA hybridizable to MuMTV-cDNA up to 37% with a $C_r t_{\frac{1}{2}}$ values between 10^3 and 10^4, they could not detect MuMTV-related nucleotide sequences in the DNA of MCF-7 cells even at extremely high $C_r t$ values and very high cellular DNA/cDNA ratios (10^7), a condition in which it is possible to detect less than one genome per cell.

Studies designed to determine if human breast tumors contain RNA related to a primate virus (M-PMV) that was originally isolated from a spontaneous breast tumor of a rhesus monkey yielded conflicting results. Colcher et al.[40] reported that seven of the ten RNA preparations from human malignant breast tumors that they examined annealed to M-PMV cDNA, whereas RNA from all the benign breast tumors and normal tissues that were tested did not anneal to M-PMV cDNA. The cDNA used in these experiments was synthesized using 60-70S M-PMV RNA as a template and purified AMV reverse transcriptase. The hybrids were analyzed by hydroxylapatite chromatography to facilitate both quantitation and assessment of the fidelity of the hybrids that were formed. Although the extent of hybridization between the M-PMV cDNA and human breast adenocarcinoma RNA was only 25% with $C_r t_{\frac{1}{2}}$ values between 1 and 5×10^4 mol/liter·sec, the thermal stability studies showed that the duplexes formed had only a small degree of mismatching. These results would seem to corroborate a recent report showing that the DNA polymerase of human breast cancer particles is antigenically related to the RT of M-PMV,[30] that some human breast tumor antigens crossreact with the major core proteins of M-PMV[41] and that M-PMV-like particles are present in human milk.[8,9] These results thus indicate that some human breast tumors may contain a putative virus related to M-PMV. In contrast to the hybridization results of Colcher et al.[40] however, Vaidya et al.[36] did not find any homology between human breast tumor RNA and the genome of M-PMV. These two disparate observations and, in general, the variation in hybridization results from laboratory to laboratory may be due to differences in the methods used for detecting the RNA-cDNA hybrids, the quality of the cDNA probes, evolutionary differences in the genomes of animal and putative human viruses, or simply because the various tumors tested contained various amounts of MuMTV- or M-PMV-specific RNA. No attempt has yet been made to determine if both MuMTV and M-PMV related RNA can coexist in human breast tumors, although it is known that some human leukemias contain simian sarcoma virus and baboon endogenous virus-related sequences.[42]

Immunological Studies

Since the discovery of a few particles resembling MuMTV in some human milk samples, concurrent with biochemical studies, numerous attempts have been made and continue to be made to search for antibodies reactive to MuMTV in the sera of breast cancer patients. Human sera, milk and breast tumor tissues are also being examined for the presence of MuMTV-related antigen(s). The cell-mediated immune response is being measured to discover whether breast cancer patients, but not normal women, have been specifically exposed to MuMTV. Charney and Moore[43] were the first to report the presence of neutralizing antibody in human sera against a surface component of MuMTV. In their experiments, sera from five breast cancer patients and five normal women were each incubated with various amounts of mouse-milk-derived MuMTV which were then inoculated into low-cancer strain mice so that the infectivity of the serum-treated virions could be determined. It was found that the sera from breast cancer patients had a greater neutralizing effect on MuMTV than did sera from normal individuals (Table 6). Subsequent studies of a large group of human serum samples, however, revealed that about 25% of the serum samples had various degrees of

Table 6. Evidence for the Presence of Anti-MuMTV Antibody in Human Sera

	Serum from			
Method of Detection	Healthy Women	Women with Breast Cancer	Women with Other Diseases	Reference
Virus Neutralization	0/5 (0)[a]	3/5 (60)	NT[b]	(43)
Immunofluorescence				
with MuMTV+ cells	3/20(15)	14/23 (60)	NT	(44)
Immunofluorescence				
1) with MuMTV+ cells	3/20(15)	15/23 (65)	NT	(45)
2) with MuMTV− cells	4/20(20)	2/23 (7)	NT	(45)
Immunofluorescence				
with MuMTV-core	10/96(11)	75/228(33)	95/369(26)	(46)
Immunoperoxidase				
1) with MuMTV	−	3/8 (38)	0/2 (0)	(47)
2) with MuMTV-core	−	0/8 (0)	0/2 (0)	(47)
Antibody dependent				
lysis of MuMTV	5/60 (7)	13/65(20)	2/108 (2)	(48)
Enzyme linked				
immunoassay	3/20(15)	13/33 (39)	−	(50)
Radioimmunoprecipitation				
of ^{125}I-MuMTV	0/20 (0)	0/25 (0)	0/97 (0)	(51)

[a] Number positive/total number (% positive).

[b] NT = Not tested.

neutralizing activity to MuMTV irrespective of whether or not the sera came from breast cancer patients.[5] Although the neutralizing activity of the serum could be absorbed out by MuMTV-containing but not by MuMTV-negative, mouse milk, the significance of the findings remains unknown since no further characterization of the antibody was made. Using indirect immunofluorescence (IF) tests, Priori et al.[44] and Bowen et al.[45] observed that 60-65% of serum samples from breast cancer patients reacted with MuMTV-producing cells compared to only 15% of serum samples from normal women. Since critical absorption analysis of the positive sera with purified MuMTV were not done in these studies, it is not known whether the observed reactions were due to the presence of MuMTV-related antibody in the sera of breast cancer patients. However, Müller and his associates[46] observed that a percentage of serum samples from women with breast cancer, 75/228 (33%); proliferating mastopathy, 29/61 (47%); adenoma and fibroadenoma of the mammary gland, 17/54 (31%); simple fibrocystic disease without proliferation, 55/254 (21%); and healthy pregnant women 16/62 (25.8%), were reactive to sections of mammary tumor cells containing intracytoplasmic A particles, the pronucleocapsids of MuMTV. In contrast, only 11% of the sera from healthy nonpregnant women were positive. The antigen reactive to the human sera appeared to be associated with A particles and the core component of MuMTV since (a) MuMTV-containing tumor homogenates, solubilized MuMTV or purified A particles absorbed the antibody activity of the human sera, (b) the reaction with positive human sera could be blocked by prior incubation of the A particle-containing tissue slices with rabbit anti-A particle antisera, (c) the distribution of the immunofluorescence reaction observed with positive human sera corresponded to the distribution of the fluorescence obtained with anti-A particle antisera and to the tissue distribution of the A particle inclusion bodies and (d) electron microscopic observations of the immunoferritin or immunoperoxidase stained sections of MuMTV-producing mouse cells revealed that only A particles and not the envelope of MuMTV reacted with human sera. In contrast to these observations, Hoshino and Dmochowski[47] using the immunoperoxidase staining technique found that three of the eight sera (positive sera) obtained from breast cancer patients reacted frequently with the surface of budding and mature MuMTV; but reached only rarely with A particles. Absorptions of positive human sera with intact MuMTV completely removed the reactivity with mature MuMTV particles, indicating that the reactions were MuMTV-specific and that human sera contained antibody which probably reacted with the major glycoprotein (gp52) of MuMTV. That sera of breast cancer patients contain antibody reactive to the surface antigens of MuMTV has also been reported recently by Witkin et al.[48,50] using two independent immunoassays. One of the assays is based on the fact that when MuMTV is incubated with anti-MuMTV serum, the virus is lysed releasing RT, the amount of which is dependent of the titer of the serum. Using this assay Witkin et al.[48] showed that sera from breast cancer patients had consistently greater virolytic activity [13/65 (20%)] than sera from patients with benign breast disease [2/63 (3%)]; colon cancer [0/45 (0%)]; or normal women [5/60 (7%)]. By using an enzyme linked immunoassay originally developed by Voller et al.,[49] these investigators found that 13 of the 33 (39%) sera from breast cancer patients they tested, but only three of the 20 (15%) sera from women without any cancer history, reacted to the surface of MuMTV.[50] Using a sensitive radioimmunoprecipitation test with intact MuMTV, Newgard and his associates[51] could not detect any antibody against a surfact antigen of MuMTV in any of the 25 sera from breast cancer patients. Obviously, the positive results mentioned above suggest either that human sera contains antibodies reactive to the surface as well as internal proteins(s) of MuMTV or that the reactions observed by various investigators are fortuitous. Certainly some of the reactions could be due to heterophile and Forssman-type antigens or some unknown antigens that are specifically present in MuMTV-infected cells. The antigenic structure of the major polypeptides of MuMTV is at present well known.[52] It is now necessary to identify immunochemically the antigen or antigens in MuMTV preparations or MuMTV-producing cells that are recognized by human sera, especially sera from breast cancer patients.

The search for MuMTV-related antigens in human tissues and milk has also provided results that give additional weight to the concept that similarities exist between human and murine mammary neoplasms. Using immunodiffusion techniques, Müller et al.[53] found a soluble antigen in the sera of breast cancer patients which was precipitated by anti-MuMTV serum and formed a line of identity with ether-disrupted MuMTV (Table 7). Dion and Moore have recently isolated, by DEAE-cellulose chromatography, a component from a large pool of human milk samples from hundreds of women which produces a line of identity with ether-disrupted MuMTV when analyzed in the Ouchterlony test against anti-MuMTV serum.[54] Using a radioimmunoassay with a crude extract of MuMTV surface antigen (MuMTV-gp52), we have detected small quantities of an antigen that partially crossreacts with MuMTV-gp52 in the milk of women both with and without a family history of breast cancer (Table 8).

The most compelling evidence for the presence of MuMTV-gp52 related antigen in human breast tumors has been provided by Spiegelman and his associates. Using an indirect immunoperoxidase labeling technique these investigators[58] have observed specific staining of certain areas of breast tumor tissue sections when anti MuMTV-gp52 serum is used (Table 7). The immunohistochemical reactions could only be abro-

Table 7. MuMTV Antigen in Human Specimen

Specimen	Immunodiffusion with Anti-MuMTV [53]	Radioimmunoassay		Immunoperoxidase Labeling for MuMTV-gp52 [58]
		with MuMTV-gp52 [60]	with MuMTV-p28 [61]	
Sera from women:				
Normal	0/30 (0)[a]	0/107(0)	0/50 (0)	
Breast cancer	10/36(28)	0/89 (0)	0/157 (0)	
Benign breast disease	0/5 (0)	0/65 (0)	0/131 (0)	
Breast tumor extracts			8/24 (33)[b]	
Mammary cyst fluid		1/20 (5)		
Breast tissue sections:				
Normal				0/18 (0)
Cancerous				51/131(39)
Benign breast disease				0/119 (0)
Malignant tissue sections				1/107 (1)

[a] Number positive/total samples (%).
[b] Weakly positive.

Table 8. MuMTV Related Antigen(s) in Human Milk[a]

	No. of Milk Samples	Antigens (ng/ml of Milk)
Women with no family history of breast cancer	28	ND[b]
	3	10-25
	3	30-40
	1	45-50
Women with family history of breast cancer	11	ND
	1	20-30
	2	35-55[c]

[a] Unpublished results (Sarkar, N.H. and Whttington, E., 1975).

The amount of MuMTV-related antigen in human milk was estimated as follows: MuMTV purified from RIII mouse milk was surface labeled with ^{125}I:[55] Following exhaustive dialysis for the removal of free iodine, the virus was solubilized by Tween-80 (2%) and ether treatment;[56] the lipid phase was removed and the aqueous phase was centrifuged at 100,000 x g for 1 hr. The supernatant was collected, concentrated by vacuum dialysis or by lyophilization, reconstituted to a desired concentration and used in a competition radioimmunoassay.[55,57] Using polyvalent anti-MuMTV serum and unlabeled MuMTV antigen (prepared as above) as the competing antigen we found that as little as 5 ng of MuMTV protein (MuMTV-gp52) could be detected. Soluble extracts of defatted and decaseinated human milk were prepared and concentrated by the methods that were used for the preparation of MuMTV antigen. The human milk extracts were reconstituted to a desired volume and the amount of MuMTV-related antigen was estimated by comparing the ability of the extracts to compete with known amounts of MuMTV antigen. The human milk antigen appeared to compete partially (60-70%) with MuMTV antigen. This observation and the fact that high protein concentrations of human milk extracts were needed to observe the competition reaction, made it difficult for accurate estimations of the MuMTV-related antigens in human milk. It is important to note that human milk must be thoroughly defatted and decaseinated to obtain specific competition between the human milk antigen and MuMTV antigen (gp52).

[b] ND = Not detectable.

[c] The amount of MuMTV antigen in the milk of RIII mice (up to the 6th lactation), measured under identical conditions, was found to contain $5 \times 10^4 - 3 \times 10^5$ ng/ml.

gated by preabsorbing the serum with purified MuMTV or MuMTV-gp52, indicating that the reactions were specific. Further studies have established that the crossreactivity observed by Ohno et al. between the human and murine antigens was due to the polypeptide rather than to the polysaccharide component of MuMTV-gp52.[59] An important aspect of the results obtained by Spiegelman and his associates was that none of the tissue sections from 119 benign breast disease contained MuMTV-gp52 related antigens. With only one exception, 99 carcinomas from 13 organs other than the breast and eight cytosarcomas were also all negative. In contrast to these observations, other investigators[60,61] using a sensitive radioimmunoassay could not detect any antigen related to MuMTV-gp52 or -p28 in breast cancer tissue extracts (Table 7). It is possible that the quantity of MuMTV-related antigen expressed in human breast tumor is so miniscule that radioimmunoassays cannot successfully detect the antigen in crude tissue extracts. Attempts must therefore be made to partially purify the human antigen that crossreacts with MuMTV, using biochemical and/or immunological techniques, so that quantitation and immunochemical characterization of the antigen can be done.

Support for the possibility of a relationship between MuMTV and human breast carcinoma has been obtained with cell-mediated immune assays. Black et al.[62] reported that approximately 30% (25/80) of breast cancer patients exhibit higher cellular hypersensitivity responses [as measured by an *in vitro* leukocyte migration inhibition (LMI) test] to MuMTV-containing RIII mouse milk than to MuMTV-free C57BL and RIIIf mouse milk, and that leukocytes from only 5% of normal women responded to RIII mouse milk (Table 9). In subsequent studies,[63] they found that the leukocytes from 43% of the breast cancer patients tested responded to MuMTV. An average of 60% (12/20) of the patients with positive responses (MI < 0.80) to RIII MuMTV responded to MuMTV-gp52 (0.05 to 5 μg/ml), but only 25% of the patients responded to M-PMV, and none (0/4) to MuLV.[64] Only 20% of the breast cancer patients that reacted to MuMTV-gp52 responded to MuMTV-p28 and to MuLV-gp70 in the LMI assay, and none of these patients reacted to MuMTV-gp36.[65] It was also observed[65] that leukocytes responsive to MuMTV and MuMTV-gp52 reacted preferentially to lymphoreticular endothelial positive autologous and homologous breast cancer tissues in simultaneous tests and that this responsiveness occurred preferentially in breast cancer patients with a favorable prognosis (stage 0 patients). The LMI reactivity could be completely blocked by prior treatment of the antigens and breast cancer tissue sections with anti-MuMTV-gp52.

Using an LMI assay similar to that of Black et al.,[62] Fukuda et al.[66] observed a significant difference (p < 0.001) in the response of breast cancer patients to MuMTV, compared to that of normal people, benign breast tumor patients and patients with head and neck cancer (Figure 4, Table 9). Leukocytes from 29% of the breast cancer patients responded to M-PMV, but this response did not significantly differ from that observed in normal women (14%) or from that of patients with benign breast disease (20%). An insignificant number (only 11%) of the breast cancer patients responded to MuLV. The percentage of breast cancer patients that responded to MuMTV (49%) in this study agrees with the value (43%) obtained by Black et al.[63] However, McCoy et al.[67] found a very high number of responses to MuMTV in both breast cancer patients (83%) and in patients with benign breast diseases (60%) compared to normal donors; LMI with MuMTV-gp52 was observed in 65% of patients with breast cancer and in 53% with fibrocystic disease. Furthermore, these investigators found that the leukocytes from a significantly higher

Table 9. Cell-Mediated Immune Response of Women to Oncornaviruses

Method of Detection		Reactivity with	Source of Leukocyte			
			Normal	Breast Cancer	Other Breast Disease	Other Cancers
LMI[62]	(MI < 0.75)	RIII milk (MuMTV+ve)	2/41 (5)[a]	25/80 (31)		
		C57BL milk (MuMTV−ve)	0/10 (0)	0/18 (0)		
LMI[63]	(MI < 0.80)	RIII-MuMTV		6/14 (43)		
LMI[66]	(MI < 0.87)	MuMTV	9/67 (13)	46/94 (49)	2/32 (6)	2/20 (10)
	(MI < 0.87)	M-PMV	3/21 (14)	10/35 (29)	2/10 (20)	2/10 (20)
	(MI < 0.85)	MuLV	2/21 (10)	4/35 (11)	0/10 (0)	1/10 (10)
LMI[67]	(MI = 0.89)	MuMTV	1/16 (6)	15/18 (83)	3/5 (60)	0/9 (0)
	(MI = 0.92)	MuMTV-gp52	2/24 (8)	39/60 (65)	10/26 (38)	3/15 (20)
	(MI = 0.92)	MuSV-gp70	1/12 (8)	11/28 (39)	1/10 (10)	1/11 (9)
	(MI = 0.92)	MuLV-gp70	0/16 (0)	14/32 (44)	3/16 (19)	—
LT[68]		MuMTV	13/52 (25)	34/68 (50)	31/42 (50)	5/20 (25)

[a] Number positive/total number (percent positive).

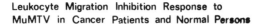

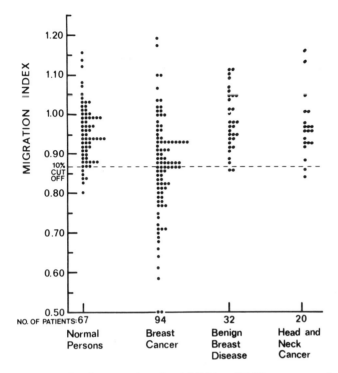

Figure 4. Leukocyte migration inhibition (LMI) response of patients with breast cancer, benign breast disease, head and neck cancer, and healthy persons. Patients showing a migration index corresponding to the 10% cut-off point for LMI (MI±0.87) were considered positive. A significant difference in LMI response was observed between patients with breast cancer and normal persons (p < 0.001), patients with benign breast disease (p < 0.001), and patients with head and neck cancer (p < 0.01).

proportion (40%) of breast cancer patients reacted to the gp70 of MuLV and MuSV (murine sarcoma virus). Since none of the polypeptides of MuLV and MuMTV are thought to share any antigenic determinant, these results indicate that the cellular immune response of breast cancer patients must be directed against at least two antigenic determinants, one associated with MuMTV-gp52 and the other with MuLV-gp70. Using an *in vitro* lymphocyte transformation assay (LT), Cunningham-Rundles et al.[68] found that about 50% of patients with malignant or benign breast disease responded positively to MuMTV-containing, but not to MuMTV-free, mouse milk. In contrast, the cell-mediated immune response to this antigen was found in 25% of normal women or women with other gynecological malignancies. Although these results show that some normal women are responsive to MuMTV-containing mouse milk and can be identified by the LT assay, the significance of this responsiveness in terms of the disposition of this group of women to cancer or other diseases is unknown. It should be mentioned that McCoy et al., using the lymphocyte proliferation assay, found that a much lower percentage of breast cancer patients responded to MuMTV and MuMTV-gp52 than responded to the antigens in the LMI assay.[67] In spite of all these inconsistencies, it appears that the cell-mediated immune response to MuMTV, MuMTV-gp52 and breast cancer tissue antigen(s) in breast cancer patients is higher than in normal women. The molecular characteristics of the antigenic component(s) responsible for the cell-mediated immunity in breast cancer patients is unknown at present and therefore one must be cautious when considering the data described above as evidence of an etiologic association of MuMTV with human breast cancer.

Cultivation of a Putative Human Breast Cancer Virus

As has been discussed earlier, the evidence for a viral involvement in human breast cancer is contradictory and inconclusive. One approach that seems to have the best prospects for resolving the contradictions, and for determining whether or not a virus is the etiologic agent of human breast cancer, is cultivation of human breast cancer cells in tissue culture. A human tumor cell line would be a favorable source for a putative human breast tumor virus and would enable investigators working in different laboratories to obtain comparable results and thus permit the unequivocal characterization of any putative virus. A large number of human tumor cell lines have been established and these cells have been examined, primarily by electron microscopy, for a putative human breast tumor virus. As yet, only one candidate with human breast tumor virus occurring in the MCF-7 cell line has been found. In 1974, McGrath et al.[6] reported the isolation of an RNA tumor virus-like particle from the MCF-7 culture medium. The biochemical and biophysical properties of the particle, designated 734B, resemble those of other oncornaviruses, and several of its polypeptides have similar molecular weights to the polypeptides of M-PMV and MuMTV.[39] However, the migration pattern of the nonglycosylated polypeptides of MuMTV, M-PMV and 734B particles are different, suggesting that 734B is distinct from MuMTV and M-PMV. Immunological tests have also shown that 734B particles are not related to MuLV or M-PMV. However, cross-reactivity between 734B and MuMTV has been found using a polyvalent anti-MuMTV serum. Subsequent experiments using monospecific antisera prepared against MuMTV-gp52 and -p28 have shown that antigenic determinants crossreactive with MuMTV-p28 are present in 734B-producing (MCF$^+$) cells. The extent of crossreactivity between 734B and MuMTV-p28 has been evaluated in immunoprecipitation experiments. Polypeptide(s) from Triton X-disrupted and iodinated 734B particles, but not M-PMV or MuLV polypeptides, was found to be immunoprecipitated with anti-MuMTV-p28 serum. The similar rate of precipitation of Mu-MTV and 734B and the fact that the precipitation of 734B is competitively inhibited with solubilized MuMTV (but not M-PMV or MuLV) polypeptides suggests that the determinants on the MuMTV-p28 are crossreactive with determinants on a 734B polypeptide(s).

In hybridization experiments,[39] RNA from 734B has been found to react only with MuMTV-cDNA but not with cDNA from several other oncornaviruses, indicating that 734B and MuMTV are apparently related. However, a significant degree of mismatching has been detected in the hybrids suggesting that, although 734B and MuMTV may be related, they are not identical. The fact that cDNA from 734B does not hybridize with DNA from mouse cells strongly suggests that 734B particles are not of mouse origin. Furthermore, a cDNA probe made from 734B has been found to hybridize with the DNA from MCF-7 and other human breast tumor cells, but not with nonhuman cellular DNA's. These results strongly support the theory of a human origin for the 734B particle. However, the MuMTV-cDNA probe does not hybridize with the DNA of MCF-7 which are producing 734B despite the fact that the probe does hybridize with both MCF-7 cell RNA and 734B RNA. These results do not conform to the known replicative cycle of oncornaviruses which integrate into their host cells' genome, and suggest that 734B may not, in fact, be an oncornavirus. It should be emphasized that no other investigators have confirmed the existence of 734B-like particles in MCF-7 cells by biochemical and/or immunological studies, and therefore, the findings reported by McGrath et al.[39] have to be evaluated with great caution.

It is difficult to explain the dichotomy between results showing that oncornavirus, particularly MuMTV-related RNA, but not proviral DNA,[36,37,39] is present in tumor cells, However, it is possible that a mechanism could exist whereby sporadic expression of a MuMTV-related sequence occurs in human breast tumor cells without the presence of a provirus. The most likely mechanism is one involving transcriptional "mistakes." RNA polymerases may be highly prone to error since they initiate transcription in the absence of a base-paired primer molecule.[69] In most of the experiments discussed previously, cDNA probes representing only the first 150-250 nucleotides at the 5'-end of the RNA were used, and a high degree of homology (40%) would be observed even if only 60 RNA nucleotides were hybridized. As a result, at present it is not known which regions of the MuMTV genome are similar to the MuMTV-like RNA sequences which have been found in human cells by molecular hybridization. Even in recent studies in which MuMTV-cDNA probes used at 10-fold excess annealed to MuMTV RNA, only 70% of the RNA sequences were protected from RNAse digestion,[39] suggesting that there was repetition and nonrepresentation of the genomic sequences. Thus, it is possible that oligomers as small as eight to ten nucleotides in length, may be randomly present in certain populations of tumor cells, and may be responsible for the observed annealing with MuMTV-cDNA. Why would these sequences generated, perhaps within the framework of other RNA sequences by transcriptional error, be present only in human tumor material and not in benign tumors or normal breast tissue? There is some evidence that DNA polymerases from tumor cells may be altered and more prone to error than the polymerases in normal cells.[70] These DNA polymerases may erroneously synthesize MuMTV-like RNA in the absence of proviral sequences and this RNA may then transcribe MuMTV-related proteins.

Conclusion

Many factors are involved in the development of cancer in the mammary gland. In the mouse it is known that a virus plays the dominant role. In other mammals, including humans, no single factor has been found to be a major cause of breast cancer, and the involvement of a virus related to MuMTV in human breast cancer is far from established. A collaborative study between different laboratories might help to resolve the question of whether or not MuMTV or any other virus is etiologically associated with human breast cancer. If it is shown conclusively that human breast tumors are caused by a virus, it may be possible to develop a vaccine against this virus. However, scientists have a special responsibility not to raise public hopes for a cure or a prophylaxis for breast cancer based on suggestive rather than conclusive data. In the past many scientists have expressed their own beliefs as if they were proven fact. For example, when "virus-like" particles were discovered in human milk, scientists voiced the opinion that women with a maternal history of breast cancer should avoid breast feeding their children because of the possible transmission of a cancer-causing virus from mother to daughter via the milk, as occurs in the mouse.

The public at large may still be concerned about this issue. Although no definite recommendation can be made at this time, it is highly unlikely that breast cancer is related to breast feeding for the following reasons: (a) as pointed out by Fraumeni and Miller,[71] in countries where breast feeding is common, breast cancer rates are relatively low, whereas in the United States, for example, the incidence of breast cancer has increased in recent years, although breast feeding has declined; (b) the correlation between the occurrence of virus-like particles, MuMTV-related antigen and DNA polymerase in the milk of women with or without a family history of breast cancer is poor and agrees with the epidemiological findings that breast cancer occurs equally in the maternal and paternal side of the family; and (c) even if a putative human breast cancer virus exists and is secreted into the milk, the virus would most likely be inactivated, since human milk has been shown to enzymatically inactivate a number of animal viruses, and would thus not be transmitted from mother to daughter.

An important point I would like to make is that scientists involved in cancer research should not feel that they must always justify their work with animal models in terms of discovering a viral etiology for human cancer. I think that it is important to remember that there are fundamental differences between humans and laboratory strains of animals. We should be able to accept the fact that human breast cancer may not be caused by a virus. An open-minded attitude on this question will provide the mental freedom that is essential to creative and innovative research into the cause of human breast cancer.

ACKNOWLEDGMENTS

Thanks are due to Dr. S.L. Marcus for discussion and to Dr. A.J. McClelland for editorial assistance. The author is supported, in part, by Public Health Service grants CA-17129 and CA-08748 from the National Institutes of Health.

References

1. Shimkin, M.B.: In: *Recent Results in Cancer Research; Breast Cancer: A Challenging Problem, Vol. 42,* M.L. Griem, E.V. Jensen, J.E. Ultmann and R.W. Wissler (eds.), Springer-Verlag, New York, 1973, p. 6.

2. Bittner, J.J.: *Science* 84:162, 1936.

3. Sarkar, N.H., Moore, D.H., Kramarsky, B., and Chopra, H.C.: In: *The Atlas of Virus Morphology,* A.J. Dalton and F. Haguenau (eds.), Academic Press, New York, 1973, p. 307.

4. Sarkar, N.H. and Moore, D.H.: *Nature* 236:103, 1972.

5. Moore, D.H.: *Cancer Research* 34:2322, 1974.

6. McGrath, C., Grant, P., Soule, H., Glancy, T., and Rich, M.: *Nature* 252:247, 1974.

7. Moore, D.H., Sarkar, N.H., Kelly, C.E., Pillsbury, N., and Charney, J.: *Texas Rept. Biol. Med.* 27:1027, 1969.

8. Sarkar, N.H. and Moore, D.H.: In: *Recent Results in Cancer Research; Breast Cancer: A Challenging Problem,* M.L. Griem, E.V. Jensen, J.E. Ultmann and R.W. Wissler (eds.), Springer-Verlag, New York, 1973, p. 15.

9. Chopra, H., Ebert, P., Woodside, N., Kvedar, J., Albert, S., and Brennan, M.: *Nature New Biol.* 243:157, 1973.

10. Temin, H.M. and Mizutani, S.: *Nature* 226:1211, 1970.

11. Baltimore, D.: *Nature* 226:1209, 1970.

12. Moore, D.H., Charney, J., Kramarsky, B., Lasfargues, E.Y., Sarkar, N.H., Brennan, M.J., Burrows, J.H., Sirsat, S.M., Paymaster, J.C., and Vaidya, A.B.: *Nature* 229:611, 1971.

13. Schlom, J., Spiegelman, S., and Moore, D.H.: *Nature* 231:97, 1971.

14. Gerwin, B.I., Ebert, P.S., Chopra, H.C., Smith S.G., and Kvedar, J.P.: *Science* 180:198, 1973.

15. Cavalieri, L.F. and Carroll, E.: *Biochem. Biophys. Res. Commun.* 67:1360, 1975.

16. Lewis, J.B., Abrell, J.W., Smith R.G., and Gallo, R.C.: *Science* 183:867, 1974.

17. Schlom, J., Spiegelman, S., and Moore, D.H.: *J. Natl. Cancer Inst.* 48:1197, 1972.

18. Das, M.R., Sadasivan, E., Koshy, R., Vaidya, A.B., and Sirsat, S.M.: *Nature New Biol.* 239:92, 1972.

19. Roy-Burman, P., Rongey, R.W., Henderson, B.E., and Gardner, M.B.: *Nature New Biol.* 244:146, 1973.

20. Dion, A.S., Vaidya, A.B., and Fout, G.S.: *Cancer Res.* 34:3509, 1974.

21. Schlom, J., Colcher, D., Spiegelman, S., Gillespie, S., and Gillespie, E.: *Science* 179:696, 1973.

22. Sarngadharan, M.G., Sarin, P.S., Reitz, M.S., and Gallo, R.C.: *Nature New Biol.* 240:67, 1972.

23. Knopf, K.W., Yamada, M., and Weissbach, A.: *Biochemistry* 15:4540, 1976.

24. Sarkar, N.H. and Moore, D.H.: *J. Virol.* 13:1143, 1974.

25. Kantor, J.A., Lee, Y., Chirikjian, J.G., and Feller, W.F.: *Science* 204:511, 1979.

26. Gerard, G.F., Rottman, F., and Green, M.: *Biochemistry* 13:1632, 1974.

27. Axel, R., Gulati, S.C., and Spiegelman, S.: *Proc. Natl. Acad. Sci. USA* 69:3133, 1972.

28. Gerard, G.F., Lowenstein, P.M., and Green, M.: *Fed. Proc. Fed. Am. Soc. Exp. Biol.* 35:1592, 1976 (abstract).

29. Ohno, T., Sweet, R.W., Hu, R., DeJack, D., and Spiegelman, S.: *Proc. Natl. Acad. Sci. USA* 74:764, 1977.

30. Ohno, T. and Spiegelman, S.: *Proc. Natl. Acad. Sci. USA* 74:2144, 1977.

31. Sarkar, N.H., Charney, J., Dion, A.S., and Moore, D.H.: *Cancer Res.* 33:626, 1973.

32. Fieldsteel, A.H.: *Cancer Res.* 34:712, 1974.

33. Schlom, J., Spiegelman, S., and Moore, D.H.: *J. Natl. Cancer Inst.* 48:1197, 1972.

34. McCormick, J.J., Larson, L.J., and Rich, M.A.: *Nature* 251:737, 1974.

35. Axel, R., Schlom, J., and Spiegelman, S.: *Proc. Natl. Acad. Sci. USA* 69:535, 1972.

36. Vaidya, A.B., Black, M.M., Dion, A.S., and Moore, D.H.: *Nature* 249:565, 1974.

37. Bishop, J.M., Quintrell, N., Medeiros, E., and Varmus, H.E.: *Cancer* 34:1421, 1974.

38. Varmus, H.E., Quintrell, N., Medeiros, E., Bishop, J.M., Nowinski, R.C., and Sarkar, N.H.: *J. Mol. Biol.* 79:663, 1973.

39. McGrath, C.M., Furmanski, P., Russo, J., McCormick, J.J., and Rich, M.M.: In: *Tumor Virus Infections and Immunity,* R.L. Crowell, H. Friedman and J.E. Prier (eds.), University Park Press, Baltimore, Maryland, 1976, p. 63.

40. Colcher, D., Spiegelman, S., and Schlom, J.: *Proc. Natl. Acad. Sci. USA* 71:4975, 1974.

41. Yeah, J., Ahmed, M., and Mayyasi, S.A.: *Science* 190:583, 1975.

42. Chan, E., Peters, W.P., Sweet, R.W., Ohno, T., Kufe, D.W., Spiegelman, S., Gallo, R.C., and Gallagher, R.E.: *Nature* 260:264, 1976.

43. Charney, J. and Moore, D.H.: *J. Natl. Cancer Inst.* 48:1125, 1972.

44. Priori, E.S., Anderson, D.E., Williams, W.C., and Dmochowksi, L.: *J. Natl. Cancer Inst.* 48:1131, 1972.
45. Bowen, J.M., Dmochowksi, L., Müller, M.F., Priori, E.S., Semen, G., Dodson, M. L., and Maruyama, K.: *Cancer Res.* 36:759, 1976.
46. Müller, M., Zotter, S., and Kemmer, C.: *J. Natl. Cancer Inst.* 56:295, 1976.
47. Hoshino, M. and Dmochowski, L.: *Cancer Res.* 33:2551, 1973.
48. Witkin, S.S., Egeli, A., Sarkar, N.H., Good, R.A., and Day, N.K.: *Proc. Natl. Acad. Sci. USA* 76:2984, 1979.
49. Voller, A.D., Bidwell, S., and Bartlett, A.: In: *Manual of Clinical Immunology*, N. Rose and W. Friedman (eds.), American Society for Microbiology, Washington, D.C., 1976, p. 506.
50. Witkin, S.S., Sarkar, N.H., Good, R.A., and Day, N.K.: *J. Immunol. Methods*, 1980 (in press).
51. Newgard, K.W., Cardiff, R.D., and Blair, P.B.: *Cancer Res.* 36:765, 1976.
52. Sarkar, N.H., Whittington, E.S., Racevskis, J., and Marcus, S.L.: *Virology* 91:407, 1978.
53. Müller, M. and Grossman, H.: *Nature New Biol.* 237:116, 1972.
54. Dion, A.S. and Moore, D.H.: In: *Recent Advances in Cancer Research: Cell Biology, Molecular Biology, and Tumor Virology, Vol. II*, R.C.Gallo (ed.), CRC Press, Inc., Cleveland, Ohio, 1977, p. 69.
55. Cardiff, R.D.: *J. Immunol.* 111:1722, 1973.
56. Sarkar, N.H., Nowinski, R.C., and Moore, D.H.: *Virology* 46:1, 1971.
57. LoGerfor, P., Silverstein, G., and Charney, J.: *Surgery* 76:16, 1974.
58. Mesa-Tejada, R., Keydar, I., Ramanarayanan, M., Ohno, T., Fenoglio, C., and Spiegelman, S.: *Proc. Natl. Acad. Sci. USA* 75:1529, 1978.
59. Ohno, T., Mesa-Tejada, R., Keydar, I., Ramanarayanan, M., Bausch, J., and Spiegelman, S.: *Proc. Natl. Acad. Sci. USA* 76:2460, 1979.
60. Zangerie, P.F., Calberg-Bacq, C.M., Colin, C., Franchimont, F., Francois, C., Gosselin, L., and Osterrieth, P.: *Cancer Res.* 37:4326, 1977.
61. Hendrick, J.C., Francois, C., Calberg-Bacq, C.M., Colin, C., Franchimont, P., Gosselin, L., Kozma, S., and Osterrieth, P.M.: *Cancer Res.* 38:1826, 1978.
62. Black, M.M, Moore, D.H., Shore, B., and Leis, H.P., Jr.: *Cancer Res.* 34:1054, 1974.
63. Black M.M., Zachrau, R.E., Shore, B., and Leis, H.P., Jr.: *Cancer Res.* 36:769, 1976.
64. Black M.M., Zachrau, R.E., Dion, A.S., Shore, B., Fine, D.L., Leis, H.P., Jr., and Williams, C.J.: *Cancer Res.* 36:4137, 1976.
65. Zachrau, R.E., Black, M.M., Dion, A.S., Shore, B., Williams, C.J., and Leis, H.P., Jr.: *Cancer Res.* 38:3414, 1978.
66. Fukuda, M., Wanebo, H.J., Tsuei, L., and Sarkar, N.H.: *J. Natl. Cancer Inst.*, 1980 (in press).
67. McCoy, J.L., Dean, J.H., Cannon, G.B., Jerome, L.J., Alford, T.C., Parks, W.P., Gilden, R.V., Oroszlan, S.T., and Herberman, R.B.: *J. Natl. Cancer Inst.* 60:1259, 1978.
68. Cunningham-Rundles, S., Feller, W.F., Cunningham-Rundles, C., DuPont, B., Wanebo, H., O'Reilly, R., and Good, R.A.: *Cellular Immunol.* 25:322, 1976.
69. Sternglanz, R. and Alberts, B.: *Nature* 269:655, 1977.
70. Loeb, L.A., Springgate, C.F., and Battula, N.: *Cancer Res.* 34:2311, 1974.
71. Fraumeni, J.F., Jr. and Miller, R.W.: *Lancet* 2:1196, 1971.

Malignancies in the Immunocompromised Human

Alexandra H. Filipovich, Beatrice D. Spector, and John H. Kersey

University of Minnesota, Minneapolis, Minnesota

Twenty years have passed since the hypothesis of immunosurveillance, presaged by Paul Ehrlich near the turn of the century, was proposed by Lewis Thomas.[1] This theoretical construct suggested that a primary role of the normally functioning (cell-mediated) immune system was to provide defense against malignant cells which were constantly arising throughout the body. Subsequent predictions that immunodeficiency states would give rise to frequent, multiple, and diverse tumors early in life have not generally been upheld by experience. However, the process of examining evidence from the human and murine systems[2] to support or refute this dominant concept has fostered two new theories which are in the forefront of current immunological research. The first deals with genetic restriction of specific immune responses to cells infected by viruses (including "oncogenic" viruses) or other intracellular parasites.[3] The second has to do with internal modulation of constituent subpopulations of the immune systems during periods of homeostasis and activation, referred to as immunoregulation.[4]

One or more of these theories may one day explain the unusual distribution of malignancies, and, in particular, the striking preponderance of lymphoreticular tumors which have been documented among immunodeficient individuals. The suggestion that partial immunodeficiency renders the host more susceptible to malignancy within the immune system itself is supported by experimental[5,6] and empirical data sources.[7-9]

This paper will concern itself with the current state of investigation into malignant outcomes in several populations of immunodeficient humans. The goals will be: to outline available descriptive information, to represent major theories linking immunodeficiency and malignancy, and to propose additional investigative approaches to the question.

The Study of Tumors in Immunodeficient Individuals

Reports of tumors arising in patients with genetic disorders associated with immunodeficiency appeared in increasing numbers in the late 1950's and early 1960's.[10−12] During the succeeding decade, attention was drawn to the significant number of *de novo* malignancies, particularly lymphomas occurring in organ allograft recipients,[13,14] and in patients who had received chronic immunosuppressive treatment for nonmalignant disorders.[15] Individuals who had been treated with immunosuppressive antimetabolites for primary malignancies ranging from ovarian cancer to Hodgkin's disease were noted to develop acute myeloid leukemia as a second malignancy.[16]

Persistent interest in the link between immunodeficiency and human cancer is reflected in the ongoing activities of two special cancer case registries which have been established within the United States for the retrospective collection of data regarding tumors diagnosed in immunocompromised persons.

The Immunodeficiency-Cancer Registry (ICR) was established at the University of Minnesota in Minneapolis in 1973.[7] This project has collected 303 cases of malignances (Table 1) which developed in individuals, with one of 14 different categories of naturally occurring immunodeficiency (classified as Primary Specific Immunodeficiencies by the WHO Committee on Immunodeficiency).[17] One hundred seventy-six or 63% of such ICR cases with known age at diagnosis of malignancy occurred in children less than 15 years of age.

An informal data base of malignancies among patients who had received immunosuppressive or cytotoxic treatment has been operated by Dr. Israel Penn at the Veteran's Hospital in Denver, Colorado, since 1968. This Denver Transplant Tumor Registry (DTTR) contains 733 tumors (Table 2) which occurred *de novo* in patients who had received allogeneic organ transplants for reasons other than prior malignancy.[8]

Analysis of data collected on malignancy in immunodeficiency is, however, complicated by the heterogeneity of the immunodeficiency states and malignancy types represented in these series. It is postulated that patients with naturally occurring immunodeficiencies (NOID's) represent a variety of distinct underlying defects. The 14 NOID's in the ICR differ from one another as to age of onset and severity of immunodeficiency symptoms, scope and degree of cellular abnormalities (which frequently affect several organ systems), prognosis and malignancy patterns. Patients with NOID typically suffer frequent, prolonged and

Table 1. Summary of Immunodeficiency-Cancer Registry (May 1979) (N = 303 Cases)[a]

Immunodeficiency Disease	Lymphomas					Leukemias				Epithelial Tumors	Other Tumors	Total
	Histiocytic	Lymphocytic	Hodgkin's	Others	Subtotal	Lymph	Myel	NOS[c]	Subtotal			
AT[c] (2.0-31) 9.0[b]	13	16	11	21	61	22	0	0	26	18	1	106
WAS[c] (1.5-22) 6.0	12	3	4	22	41	0	4	4	8	1	3	53
CVI[c] (2.0-69) 46.0	7	8	5	18	38	3	1	0	4	35	0	77
↓IgA[c] (3.0-62) 30.0	2	1	1	2	6	1	0	0	1	8	1	16
X-LA[c] (1.1-20) 8.0	1	1	1	2	5	3	2	2	7	2	1	15
SCID[c] (0.1-2.25) 0.9	4	2	1	4	11	1	3	0	4	0	0	15
↓IgM[c] (2.5-41) 11.0	3	1	1	1	6	0	0	0	0	2	0	8
Nl./Elv. Igs[c] (7.0-10) 9.0	1	1	0	1	3	0	0	0	0	0	0	3
Others[c] (1.5-71) 18.00	1	1	2	0	4	1	0	0	1	4	1	10
Totals	44	34	26	71	175 (58%)	31	10	10	51 (17%)	70 (23%)	7 (2%)	303 (100%)

[a] An additional 11 malignancies were observed in seven patients.

[b] Age range and median time of diagnosis of malignancy.

[c] Abbreviations: AT = ataxia-telangiectasia; WAS = Wiskott-Aldrich syndrome; CVI = common variable immunodeficiency; ↓IgA = selective IgA deficiency; X-LA = X-linked (Bruton's) agammaglobulinemia; SCID = severe combined immunodeficiency; ↓IgM = selective IgM deficiency; Nl./Elv. Igs = immunodeficiency with normal or elevated immunoglobulins; others = immunodeficiency with thymoma (4 cases), X-linked hyperimmunoglobulin M (2 cases), hyperimmunoglobulin E syndrome (1 case), episodic lymphopenia and lymphocytotoxin (1 case), DiGeorge syndrome (1 case), transient hypergammaglobulinemia of infancy (1 case); NOS = not otherwise specified.

Table 2. Summary from Denver Transplant Tumor Registry (DTTR) (N = 733 malignancies)[a]

	Lymphomas					Leukemias	Epithelial Tumors		Other Tumors	Total
	Histiocytic	Lymphocytic	Hodgkin's	Other	Subtotal		Skin and Lips	Other		
De novo tumors in allogeneic transplant recipients	93	10	3	44	150 20.5%	17 2.3%	277 37.8%	211 28.8%	78 10.6%	733 100%

[a] Forty patients had more than one variety of malignancy. Age at transplant: 5-70 yr; mean: 40 yr. Malignancy developed 1-158 m post-transplant; mean: 38 m. (From Penn, I., *Transp. Proc., Vol. XI*, p. 1047, March, 1979.)

repeated infections with bacterial and viral pathogens, the sources of chronic antigenic stimulation. Malignant events generally become apparent early in life and without exposure to immunosuppressive drugs, although many affected patients have received one or more courses of immunostimulatory or immunoreconstituting treatment.[18-22]

By contrast, in human allograft recipients, an immunodeficient state is induced shortly before surgery and sustained indefinitely by immunosuppressive or cytotoxic drugs. The allogeneic graft, as well as opportunistic or reactivated infectious agents, chronically stimulate the purposefully comprised immune system in these patients. Corticosteroids and azathioprine may have carcinogenic effects apart from their immunosuppressive potential.[8] Other factors that may compound the susceptibility of the transplant recipient to tumorigenesis include the nature of the predisposing disease[23] and chronic metabolic or hormonal abnormalities. The latency period to malignancy varies with tumor histology.

Little information is currently available which would permit comparison of variables of immunologic function among those patients in the several "susceptible" populations who do or do not eventually develop tumors.

Although there are serious limitations inherent in the analysis of data collected retrospectively, the descriptions of malignancy patterns can be used to generate hypotheses to be tested in future prospective clinical studies or in the laboratory.

Features of Tumors in Immunodeficient Individuals

Incidence

The cancer incidence for all NOID's has been estimated at 4.0, 3.1, and 1.7.[7,24,25] In the ICR, age at diagnosis ranges from one month to 69 years with a male-to-female predominance of 2:1. Twenty-five percent of the tumors reported occurred in syndromes felt to have an X-linked recessive inheritance. Thirteen family groupings of NOID have been collected, of which nine are concordant for histologic type and site of malignancy.[7]

For three of these disorders (ataxia-telangiectasia, Wiskott-Aldrich syndrome, selective IgA deficiency), similar cancer incidence rates were observed in registry-generated surveys.[7,24] The two syndromes with the highest incidence figures, Wiskott-Aldrich syndrome (WAS) and ataxia-telangiectasia (A-T), represent disorders which include phenotypic abnormalities outside the immune system. WAS had the highest cancer rate—12% for each of the series—a 118-fold age-adjusted excess risk compared to population-based figures (Perry, unpublished observations). Patients with this disease experience thrombocytopenia, eczema, variable immune dysfunction with a variety of pathogens and autoimmune reactions, and survive to a mean age of 6.5 years. Forty-one out of 53, or 76.9%, of tumors in WAS originated in cells of lymphoid origin.

The percentages of patients with A-T who develop cancer stand at 10.3 and 11.7, respectively.[7,24] This syndrome has an autosomal recessive inheritance presenting in early childhood with cerebellar ataxia and bulbar telangiectasia. Variable immunodeficiency of B and T cells is generally diagnosed beyond infancy and patients frequently survive into the second and third decades. Insulin-resistant diabetes and tumors may develop in later years.[26] Eighty-three out of 106, or 78%, of such neoplasms were lymphoid.

Comparatively low incidence rates of 1.2% and 2.4% were found among the most common primary specific immunodeficiency, selective IgA deficiency.[7,24] Epithelial tumors comprise the majority in patients with selective IgA deficiency, and are twice as common when cases associated by diagnoses with IgA deficiency as part of their disorder (hypogammaglobulinemia, dysgammaglobulinemia, A-T, and common variable immunodeficiency) are compared with those cases in the ICR assumed to have had normal or elevated levels of circulating IgA.

Lymphoproliferative disorders predominate in severe combined immunodeficiency, an etiologically diverse disorder. Acute leukemia was the most common diagnosis associated with Bruton's X-linked agammaglobulinemia, presumed to be an intrinsic disorder of B cells. The largest group of epithelial tumors, especially gastric carcinoma, was reported in common variable immunodeficiency, a heterogeneous disease category characterized by dysgammaglobulinemia and variable T-cell dysfunction, with onset of infectious complications and autoimmune phenomena frequently occurring in the second to fifth decades of life.

According to an earlier publication, the cancer mortality rate in immunodeficient children was estimated to be 100 times greater than for the general pediatric population.[27] Refined cancer incidence and mortality rates for naturally-occurring immunodeficiencies awaits more accurate estimates of the populations at risk.

Six percent of renal transplant recipients have developed *de novo* malignancy, an incidence rate which has been reported to be 100 times greater than in the general population.[28] Twenty-four percent of patients surviving five years after successful transplant have developed a malignant neoplasm.[29] Tumors of the skin and lips make up 37.8% of the DTTR total (277/733) and represent more than one-half of all epithelial cancers recorded; 20.5% of *de novo* tumors were submitted as lymphomas.[8] To date, all *de novo* lymphomas in which the genetic source of malignant cells could be identified were of recipient origin.[30] Overall cancer incidence in recipients of cardiac allografts is 8%, and 54% of these are lymphomas.[23]

Characteristics of Tumors

Malignant Lymphomas and Lymphoproliferative Disorders

General Associations. The striking predominance of lymphomas in immunocompromised individuals offers indirect evidence that a defective immune system renders its host susceptible to this class of tumors. There were 175 lymphomas among 303 patients in the ICR (Table 1) and 150 among 733 malignancies recorded in the DTTR (Table 2). These represent 58% and 20.5%, respectively, of reported tumor diagnoses. Age-specific cancer rates were available for two groups of immunocompromised patients: the relative risk of nodal malignancies in WAS was computed at 350 times that expected;[3] the risk of developing lymphoma increases 35-fold following renal transplantation.[14] In both the ICR and DTTR, lymphomas showed a shorter latency period than did other tumors,[14,31] and were diagnosed more often in children and relatively young adults.[7,23] Among cardiac allograft recipients studied at Stanford University in California, the six lymphomas were reported exclusively in individuals with the same pretransplant disease, idiopathic cardiomyopathy.[23] Malignant lymphomas have been associated with several autoimmune diseases,[15] such as Sjogren's syndrome, systemic lupus erythematosus, autoimmune hemolytic anemia, which may represent inherited or acquired diseases or immunoregulation and possible activation of endogenous viruses. The latent susceptibility to development of lymphoma may, in these latter diseases, be exacerbated by additional immunosuppressive treatment[15] or splenectomy.

Whereas exposure to benzene and other hydrocarbons has been perceived for a long time as a risk factor in carcinogenesis, it is only recently that a significant excess of deaths attributable to lymphomas following occupational benzene exposure has been reported.[32] Increased relative risks were noted for reticulum cell sarcomas, lymphosarcomas, and Hodgkin's disease in persons 45 years and older. The authors speculate that chromosomal damage, lymphopenia, and other immunologic aberrations, which have been shown to follow chronic benzene exposure in some humans, may contribute to this observed excess.[32]

It has also been shown that progressive cell-mediated immunodeficiency, such as that seen in late-stage and disseminated non-Hodgkin's lymphoma as well as Stage III and IV Hodgkin's disease occurring in the general population, portends a worse prognosis.[33] Data regarding the course of malignant lymphomas, response to therapy, and survival postdiagnosis in patients with NOID's is currently under analysis.

Site and Histology. Involvement of the central nervous system by lymphoma is an unusual characteristic seen in immunocompromised hosts. Eighty-seven percent of the 54 such cases in the DTTR (42% of all lymphomas) originated in and remained confined to the central nervous system. Among 40 WAS patients with lymphoma in the ICR, ten or 25% (mean age 6.6 years) developed a primary lymphoma of the brain; 80% carried a diagnosis compatible with the hystiocytic lymphoma of Rappaport.[34] Less than 2% of the lymphomas from patients in the general population arise in the central nervous system,[8] the mean age of such patients in one large study was 52 years and only 15% of all primaries of the brain were of the "histiocytic" type.[35] It is unclear why lymphomas in immunocompromised individuals should favor the central nervous system. Absence of a lymphatic drainage system and decreased effectiveness of immunity within the central nervous system have been proposed to explain the seemingly "immunologically privileged" nature of this site.[36] Furthermore, neurotropic viruses (e.g., the Herpes group) may serve as antigenic stimuli at this location. A hemagglutinating strain of papovirus was isolated from one such "reticulum cell sarcoma" of the brain as well as from the urine of a patient with WAS at the time of diagnosis.[37]

The 350-fold excess of the diffuse histiocytic type (reticulum cell sarcoma) determines almost entirely the overall increased risk of lymphoma following renal transplantation.[14] Application of the Lukes and Collins classification for the non-Hodgkin's lymphomas showed that some of the post-transplant diffuse histiocytic tumors, and similar tumors from patients with WAS, were classified as B immunoblastic sarcomas.[38] This tumor type, presumed to involve transformed committed lymphocytes, is not only rare in large series of lymphomas, but has previously been reported only in adults.[39,40] Recently, a monoclonal immunoblastic sarcoma of donor origin was reported as the first example of a lymphoma arising in a human with documented graft versus host disease following allogeneic bone marrow transplantation.[41]

Twenty cases of Kaposi's sarcoma, accounting for 13% of post-transplant lymphomas, has been recorded in the DTTR.[42] It has been postulated that this tumor of skin and visceral organs, histologically comprised of several cell types, represents the result of an immunologic reaction between normal and antigenically altered lymphocytes.[43] A herpes-type virus has been isolated from such tumors.[44] This tumor is endemic to malaria-infested regions of Africa, but in the United States and Europe it is most prevalent among patients receiving immunosuppresive therapy.[45] Alteration of immunosuppression in some of the 20 renal transplant patients resulted in regression of lesions in both benign and malignant forms.[42] We are unaware of Kaposi's sarcoma occurring in patients with naturally-occurring immunodeficiency diseases.

Hodgkin's disease, the most frequently-occurring tumor of lymphoid tissue in the general population, may represent a primary neoplasm of the monocyte-macrophage series. Activation of the immune system to eradicate the tumor appears to be a critical prognostic variable.[46] Twenty-five cases of Hodgkin's disease have been collected in the ICR with the greatest number of cases—11 of these—associated with A-T. Pathologic material from eight of the 26 cases of Hodgkin's disease has recently been submitted to an independent morphologic evaluation. Results showed 50% to be of the rare lymphocytic-depletion type.[47] This type, extremely uncommon under ten years of age, comprises a small minority of the Hodgkin's disease cases in the population at large[48] and is associated with poor prognosis due to lowered resistance to the disease and intercurrent infection.[46] Three of four of this type were observed in patients with A-T who were four, eight, and ten years old at the time of diagnosis.[47]

Tumors such as histiocytic lymphoma and lymphocytic depletion-type Hodgkin's disease are most frequently diagnosed in the older age group, characterized by the most consistent evidence of "immunologic involution."[49]

Lymphoproliferative Processes Associated with EBV. An interesting facet of the link between immunodeficiency and lymphoma is the number and types of such neoplasms arising in patients with the X-linked lymphoproliferative syndrome (XL-P), a condition involving ineffective response to Epstein-Barr virus (EBV). Dr. D. Purtilo, working out of the University of Massachusetts at Worcester, has studied the cases of 50 males in two kindreds thought to represent this newly proposed inherited immunodeficiency. He reports that 40% of the patients with this diagnosis have developed malignant lymphomas including American Burkitt's, histocytic lymphoma, and B immunoblastic sarcoma as well as plasmacytoma.[50] Variable phenotypic expression within a given family, findings of subtle immune defects to several pathogens, as well as an increased incidence of cardiac and neurological congenital anomalies in relatives,[51] has led to speculation that this syndrome may involve several organ systems.

In other cases of immunoblastic proliferation and/or hypergammaglobulinemia associated with EBV infection, findings of associated humoral and cell-mediated immunodeficiency,[52] or failure to generate immune interferon[53] in response to the organism, have been implicated.

EBV has been recovered from patients with renal allografts, or from those receiving immunosuppressive treatment with two to three times the frequency of isolates from the normal population.[54] A polyclonal "immunoblastic sarcoma" clinically simulating malignant lymphoma has been reported in a renal transplant recipient who had been exposed to infectious mononucleosis shortly prior to surgery (Houlihan et al., unpublished observations). The extent to which other examples of atypical infectious mononucleosis or other viral disorders and aggressive "benign" polyclonal, or "premalignant" but fatal lymphoproliferative processes, contribute to the overall number of lymphomas occurring in immunodeficient patients has not yet been determined.

Other Lymphoproliferative Processes. Another four of six post-transplant lymphomas examined at the University of Minnesota were found to be polyclonal by the determination of intracytoplasmic immunoglobulin by the immunoperoxidase technique.[38] The remaining two were negative for immunoglobulins of any class. A fatal lymphoproliferative disorder and concomitant polyclonal gammopathy have developed in four patients with SCID following transfer-factor[20] therapy or intraperitoneal cultured thymic epithelial grafts.[21] Many of the lymphoid tumors reported to the ICR are submitted as "unclassifiable" malignancies. In addition, the behavior of some "lymphomas" in NOID's may be unusual. For example, we recently observed a patient with common variable immunodeficiency whose "malignant" follicular center cell lymphoma (diagnosed, incidentally, three years prior to death) had spontaneously disappeared at the time of autopsy (Snovar et al., unpublished observations).

Leukemias

The proportion of leukemias is noticeably greater than the 3.3% of the general population[55] for the following two groups: patients with naturally occurring immunodeficiency diseases (17%, 50/292, Table 1), and patients with various autoimmune diseases who had received some form of immunosuppressive therapy (18%, 15/83 patients).[63] In another review, 58 patients treated with alkylating agents (and in most cases corticosteroids) for non-neoplastic diseases who had developed variants of acute myelogenous leukemia were reported.[9] The rising number of such cases apparent in the 1970's are being attributed to the broader application of cytotoxic drugs. Overall, patients treated for primary tumors with a multiplicity of chemotherapeutic agents appear to carry a 50-fold increased long-term risk of developing acute nonlymphocytic leukemias. For patients who have received treatment for multiple myeloma the risk rises to 100-fold.[16]

Seven of 10 lymphocytic leukemias from patients with A-T which have been studied with immunologic markers have been shown to be of T-lymphocyte origin; three of seven cases are known to be associated with abnormalities of the 14q chromosome. This small series of leukemias in one NOID evaluated by functional markers suggests that the proportion of T phenotypes is somewhat higher than that seen in other series of lymphoid malignancies, in presumably nonimmunodeficient patients.[57,58]

Acute myelogenous leukemia was associated with WAS and SCID.

Carcinomas

Skin and lip carcinomas are the most frequently reported tumors of epithelial origin in transplant recipients (277/488 in the DTTR, Table 2). In one study where the comparison population was drawn from the same geographic area as the cases, the risk of skin cancer in renal transplant recipients was 7.1 times the expected rate, due primarily to squamous cell carcinoma (relative risk, 36.4).[59] Although skin cancers in general are inconsistently reported, and are not even reported by the U.S. Third National Cancer Survey, it is known that in the public at large, basal cell carcinomas outnumber squamous cell carcinomas 2:1. Multiple skin tumors were found more often in the DTTR than in the general population (43%, 22%, respectively) and occurred in much younger individuals.[60] "Premalignant" hyperkeratoses associated with exposure to solar irradiation are a frequent finding in transplant recipients.

Carcinomas of the gastrointestinal tract in the ICR have affected only patients presumed to have IgA deficiency as part of the immunodeficiency disease. Of these, gastric carcinomas were the most common epithelial tumor reported to the ICR overall (45%, 26/55); 72% (18/26) of these malignancies arose in patients with common variable immunodeficiency at a median age of 54 years (range 15-67 years).

Other Features

Except for the excess number of skin and lip cancers, cervical cancer, *in situ,* in the DTTR, is the only other common malignancy of the general population (e.g., lung, colon, breast) that figures predominantly in either cancer case registry. Multiple primaries have not been reported in excess in patients reported to the ICR.[7]

Theories Relating Immunodeficiency with Malignancy

Theories regarding the etiologies of malignances in the heterogenous populations of immunodeficient patients must take into account the various findings of these cancer registries. In general terms, immunodeficiency is associated with unusual sites and histologies of tumors, many of which can be viewed as malignancies of the immune system itself.

The preponderance of unusual lymphomas leads us to hypothesize that these malignancies arise when immunocytes proliferate due to failure of immunoregulation. We further posit that selected diffuse histiocytic lymphomas which occur in post-transplant patients and some naturally occurring immunodeficiency diseases (especially those lymphomas identified as B-immunoblastic sarcomas) represent a subtype of lymphoma that reflects such underlying defects of immunoregulation. Immunoregulation is a normal function of the immune system which operates in conjunction with that intact system's critical role of protecting the rest of the organism from extracellular infectious agents. It is generally recognized that the immunoregulatory function rests primarily among T lymphocytes. Two distinct populations of "helper" and "suppressor" T cells comodulate the expansion of subpopulations of B and T cells which are stimulated, and in many cases, overstimulated by a variety of antigens. Resident lymphocytes in the immunocompromised host undergo an initial response to pathogens and/or an allograft. This process may result in polyclonal proliferation which is, in a sense, promoted by a lack of normal suppressive signals. Such a state of polyclonal proliferation may progress to a polyclonal tumor mass or give rise to a monoclonal malignancy if a new irreversible cytogenetic defect occurs.

This sequence of events is quite analogous to that proposed for the evolution of frankly malignant immunoblastic lymphomas in alpha-chain disease.[61] In this primary disorder of immunoglobulin synthesis, there is an early stage characterized by proliferation of plasma cells, typically infiltrating the small intestine, which produces a "presumably" homogenous population of immunoglobulin molecules, abnormal alpha-heavy chains. It is sometimes possible to reverse this phase with antibiotic therapy, which may clear the intestinal infection which has stimulated replication of alpha-chain secreting plasma cells. In the second stage, there is progressive deterioration of the patient's general condition associated with the development of a "malignant" immunoblastic tumor which is thought to arise from the same B cell clone responsible for the plasmacytosis. Dissemination of this tumor outside of the abdomen is rare, and occasionally the malignant cells no longer appear to have the capacity to produce alpha-chain disease protein. There is some evidence that certain cases of alpha-chain disease represent progression from a benign monoclonal state to a true malignancy;[61] however, the universality of this model remains to be proven.

Dysfunction of immunoregulation has also been postulated and to some extent demonstrated in human graft versus host disease[62,63] and in systemic lupus erythematosus.[64] Except for a documented absence of Con A suppressor function in three patients with SCID who subsequently developed lymphoproliferative disorders, no comprehensive prospective studies of the integration of enhancing and suppressing lymphocyte populations have yet been carried out on patients with the various NOID's.

Another example of an immunoregulatory defect, that of suppressor cell dysfunction prior to transplantation and chemical immunosuppression, has been observed in patients with idiopathic cardiomyopathy, the same disease associated exclusively with postcardiac transplant lymphomas.[23,65] Immunosuppressive therapy of a host chronically stimulated by his allograft could affect immunoregulation by depressing overall immune function.

A related issue in the discussion of immunologic defense against cancer is its role in limiting proliferation of endogenous and exogenous oncogenic viruses. It has been proposed that one of the evolutionary imperatives in the refinement of immunoregulation was the advantage to the host of preventing expression of virogenes (RNA tumor viruses) carried in the lymphocytes. Experimentally, activation of these oncogenic viruses occurs with activation and proliferation of lymphocytes, particularly in conjunction with murine graft versus host disease.[54] A similar process has been suggested to account for the greatly increased risk of lymphoma in allograft recipients (host stimulated by graft) as compared to patients receiving similar immunosuppressive therapy for other indications.[54]

On the other hand, failure to eradicate cells infected with exogenous or reactivated DNA viruses has been documented in association with several aggressive lymphoproliferative disorders in transplant patients (EBV) (Houlihan et al., unpublished observations) and XL-P (EBV),[50] and in two patients with A-T (Influenza virus) who were not harboring a malignancy.[66] A systematic study of the abilities of immunosuppressed and immunodeficient patients to mount cytotoxic T-cell responses to virus-bearing cells may prove useful in ultimately evaluating the role of this specific defect in the susceptibility to malignancy.

The once dominant idea of immunosurveillance, the process of eliminating small foci of malignantly transformed cells which express "foreign" surface antigens, stands to make at least a brief theoretical recovery with the current interest in natural killer cells (NK). These "null" cells, possibly a variety of pre-T cells, have been isolated from spleens and peripheral blood of humans. They have the capacity to lyse a wide variety of cultured and malignant cells without presensitization.[67] They show preferential activity against human tumor and virus-infected cells,[68] and their efficiency is increased following viral infections and interferon production. While a role for the NK cell *in vivo* remains to be defined, lack of *in vitro* activity has been demonstrated in one patient with SCID,[69] one patient with systemic lupus erythmatosus,[68] as compared to normal cytotoxic activity in patients with common variable immunodeficiency, Bruton's agammaglobulinemia,[69] and in persons undergoing intensive immunosuppressive therapy.[69]

Amplification of a genetically restricted, cytotoxic response against presumed tumor-associated antigens (acute myelogenous leukemia) has been accomplished *in vitro* using cells obtained from patients during remission.[70] This manipulation holds some promise for future immunotherapeutic intervention, but the potency of this T cell-mediated function *in vivo* during primary escalation of the leukemia must still be questioned.

Finally, consideration should be given to the possibility that immunodeficient states and their associated malignancies are both manifestations of the same predisposing event. For the purpose of exposition, we will use the example of ataxia-telangiectasia. With this disease, ineffective repair of damaged DNA has been demonstrated *in vitro*. Immunodeficiency is rarely apparent early in life and is an inconsistent clinical feature. Chromosomal defects, including a "characteristic" break at the 14q 12, are present in many cells and have been detected in subpopulations of nonmalignant T cells. The extent to which these dictate "acquired" or progressive T-cell dysfunction in some patients has not yet been shown. Translocations 14q 32 have been associated with a variety of lymphoid malignancies, including the three T-cell leukemias in A-T mentioned previously, and in Burkitt's lymphoma. It is of interest that three of five Burkitt lymphomas reported to the ICR occurred in patients with A-T.

Bloom's syndrome is also marked by frequent chromosomal rearrangements and has findings of immunodeficiency as well as a marked predisposition to lymphoid malignancy and gastric carcinoma,[71] a pattern similar to that seen in A-T.

It is also possible that metabolic errors such as adenosine deaminase deficiency (ADA) associated with SCID may independently result in both immunodeficiency and malignancy.

It should be kept in mind that within a given immunodeficiency syndrome, excess cancer risk for differing tumors may be due to varying proportions of several contributing factors.

Future Studies

Several directions can be pursued in the study of the role of immunodeficiency in human malignancy. The first, a careful retrospective examination of clinical and histological case material, is currently being conducted by the ICR. As homogenous groupings and potential risk factors are identified among the heterogenous immunodeficiency populations, case/control studies may present feasible approaches to the examination of such variables as infection, *in vitro* correlates of immunoregulatory function, and premalignant conditions and lesions. Immunoreconstitution, including bone marrow transplantation, a method of permanently correcting a variety of inherited defects resulting in immunodeficiency, should be investigated as an approach to the "prevention" of malignancies peculiar to immunodeficiency states.

ACKNOWLEDGMENTS
This work was supported in part by a contract from the United States Public Health Service (CP-43384).

References

1. Thomas, L.: In: *Cellular and Humoral Aspects of the Hypersensitivity States,* H.S. Lawrence (ed.), Harper, New York, 1959, p. 529.

2. Kersey, J.H., Spector, B.D., and Good, R.A.: In: *Advances in Cancer Research, Vol. 10,* G. Klein and S. Weinhouse (eds.), Academic Press, New York, 1973, p. 211.

3. Meruelo, D. and McDevitt, H.O.: *Semin. Hematol.* 15:399, 1978.

4. Schwartz, R.S.: *N. Engl. J. Med.* 293:181, 1975.

5. Cornelius, F.A.: *Transplantation* 12:531, 1971.

6. Outzen, H.C., Custer, R.P., Eaton, G.J., and Prehn, R.T.: *J. Reticuloendothel. Soc.* 17:1, 1975.

7. Spector, B.D., Perry, G.S., III, and Kersey, J.H.: *Clin. Immunol. Immunopathol.* 11:12, 1978.

8. Penn, I.: *Transplant. Proc.* 11:1047, 1979.

9. Grunwald, H.W., and Rosner, F.: *Arch. Intern. Med.* 139:461, 1979.

10. Good, R.A., Kelly, W., and Gabrielson, A.E.: *IInd International Symposium on Immunopathology,* P. Babor and P. Miescher (eds.), Benno Schwabe and Co., Basel, 1962, p. 353.

11. Page, A.R., Hansen, A.E., and Good, R.A.: *Blood* 21:197, 1963.

12. Boder, E. and Sedgwick, R.: *Cerebellum Posture and Cerebral Palsy, Vol. 8,* G. Walsh (ed.), Little Club Clinics Developmental Medicine, National Spastics Society, Medical Education and Information Unit, London, 1963, p. 11.

13. Penn, I.: In: *Malignant Tumors in Organ Transplant Recipients; Recent Results in Cancer Research, Vol. 35,* I. Penn (ed.), Springer-Verlag, New York, 1970, p. 1.

14. Hoover, R. and Fraumeni, J.F., Jr.: *Lancet* 3:55, 1973.

15. Louie, S. and Schwartz, R.S.: *Sem. Hematol.* 15:117, 1978.

16. Casciato, D.A. and Scott, J.L.: *Medicine* 58:32, 1979.

17. WHO Report: Immunodeficiency, Report of a WHO Scientific Group, *Clin. Immun. Immunopathol.* 13:296, 1979.

18. Spitler, L.E.: *Am. J. Med.* 67:59, 1979.

19. Stoop, W., Eijsvoogel, V.P., Zegers, B.J.M., Blok-Schut, B., van Bekkum, D.W., and Ballieux, R.E.: *Clin. Immun. Immunopath.* 6:289, 1976.

20. Gelfand, E.W., Baumal, R., Huber, J., Crookston, M.C., and Shumak, K.H.: *N. Engl. J. Med.* 289:1385, 1973.

21. Borzy, M.S., Hong, R., Horowitz, S., Gilbert, E., Kaufman, D., DeMendonca, W., Oxelius, V.A., Dictor, M., and Pachman, L.: *N. Engl. J. Med.* 301:565, 1979.

22. Dutau, G., Corberand, J., Abbal, M., Blanc, M., Claverie, P., and Rochiccioli, P.: *J. Genet. Hum.* 23:281, 1975.

23. Anderson, J.L., Bieber, C.P., Fowles, R.E., and Stinson, E.B.: *Lancet* 2:1174, 1978.

24. Aiuti, F., Giunchi, G., Bardare, M., et al.: *Immunol. Clin.* 25:7, 1978.

25. Hayakawa, H., Iizuba, N., Yata, J., Vamada, K., and Kobayashi, N.: In: *Immunodeficiency, Its Nature and Etiological Significance in Human Disease,* Japan Medical Research Foundation (ed.), University of Tokyo Press, Tokyo, 1978, p. 271.

26. Levin, S. and Perlov, S.: *Isr. J. Med. Sci.* 7:1535, 1971.

27. Kersey, J.H., Spector, B.D., and Good, R.A.: *J. Pediatr.* 84:263, 1974.

28. Penn, I.: In: *The Immunopathology of the Lymphomas, Comprehensive Immunology,*

Vol. 4, J.J. Twomey and R.A. Good (eds.), Plenum Medical Book Co., New York, 1978, p. 223.

29. Sheil, A.G.: *Transplant. Proc.* 9:1133, 1977.

30. Penn, I.: *N. Engl. J. Med.* 301:385, 1979.

31. Spector, B.D., Perry, G.S., III, Good, R.A., et al.: In: *The Immunopathology of the Lymphomas, Comprehensive Immunology, Vol. 4,* J.J. Twomey and R.A. Good (eds.), Plenum Medical Book Co., New York, 1978, p. 203.

32. Vianna, N.J. and Polan, A.: *Lancet* 1:1394, 1979.

33. Gupta, S. and Good, R.A.: In: *The Immunopathology of the Lymphomas, Comprehensive Immunology, Vol. 4,* J.J. Twomey and R.A. Good (eds.), Plenum Medical Book Co., New York, 1978, p. 565.

34. Rappaport, H.: *Tumors of the Hematopoietic System, Atlas of Tumor Pathology, Section II, Fasc. 8,* H. Rappaport (ed.), Armed Forces Institute of Pathology, Washington, D.C., 1966, p. 99.

35. Henry, J.M., Heffner, R.R., Jr., Dillard, S.H., Earle, K.M., and Davis, R.L.: *Cancer* 34:1293, 1974.

36. Barker, C.F. and Billingham, R.E.: In: *Advances in Immunology, Vol. 25,* H.G. Kunkel and F.J. Dixon (eds.), Academic Press, New York, 1977, p. 1.

37. Takemoto, K.K., Rabson, A.S., Mullarkey, M.F., Blaese, R.M., Garon, C.F., and Nelson, D.: *J. Natl. Cancer Inst.* 53:1205, 1974.

38. Frizzera, G.: Presented at the Symposium on Iatrogenic Cancer, Joint ASCP-CAP Meeting, New Orleans, March, 1979.

39. Lichtenstein, A., Levine, A.M., Lukes, R.J., Cramer, A.D., Taylor, C.R., Lincoln, T.L., and Feinstein, D.I.: *Cancer* 43:343, 1979.

40. Lukes, R.G. and Collins, R.D.: Lukes-Collins classification and its significance. *Cancer Treat. Rep.* 61:971, 1977.

41. Gossett, T.C., Gale, R.P., Fleischman, H., Austin, G.E., Sparkes, R.S., and Taylor, C.R.: *N. Engl. J. Med.* 300:904, 1979.

42. Penn, I.: *Transplantation* 27:8, 1979.

43. Warner, T.F.C.S. and O'Loughlin, S.: *Lancet* 2:687, 1975.

44. Giraldo, G., Beth, E., Haguenau, F., Noury, G., Puissant, A., and Huraux, J.M.: *Ann. de Dermatol.* 100:283, 1973.

45. Editorial: Disentangling Kaposi's Sarcoma. *Br. Med. J.* 2:1044, 1978.

46. Twomey, J.J., Good, R.A., and Case, D.C., Jr.: In: *The Immunopathology of the Lymphomas, Comprehensive Immunology, Vol. 4,* J.J. Twomey and R.A. Good (eds.), Plenum Medical Book Co., New York, 1978, p. 585.

47. Frizzera, G., Rosai, J., Dehner, L.P., Spector, B.D., and Kersey, J.H.: *Federation Proc.,* Abstract #5529, 1979.

48. Rosenberg, S.A. and Kaplan, H.S.: *California Med.* 113:23, 1970.

49. Yunis, E.J., Gernandes, G., and Good, R.A.: In: *The Immunopathology of the Lymphomas, Comprehensive Immunology, Vol. 4,* J.J. Twomey and R.A. Good (eds.), Plenum Medical Book Co., New York, 1978, p. 53.

50. Purtilo, D.T.: *Semin. Oncol.* 4:335, 1977.

51. Purtilo, D.T., Sullivan, J.L., and Paquin, L.A.: In: *Biological Markers in Cancer,* H. Lynch and H. Gurgis (eds.), Van Nostrand Reinhold Co., Div. of Litton Publishing Inc., New York, 1980 (in press).

52. Britton, S., Andersson-Anvret, M., Gergely, P., Henle, W., Jondal, M., Klein, G., Sandstedt, B., and Svedmyr, E.: *N. Engl. J. Med.* 298:89, 1978.

53. Virelizier, J.L., Lenoir, G., and Griscelli, C.: *Lancet* 2:231, 1978.

54. Schwartz, R.S.: *Lancet* 1:1266, 1972.

55. Third National Cancer Survey: Incidence Data, National Cancer Institute Monograph 41, DHEW Publ. No. (NIH) 75-787, Bethesda, Maryland, 1975.

56. Penn, I.: *Surgery* 83:492, 1978.

57. Spector, B.D., Perry, G.S., III, Gajl-Peczlaska, K.J., Coccea, P., Nesbit, M., and Kersey, J.H.: In: *Birth Defects, Original Article Series, Vol. 14:* R.L. Summitt and D. Bergsma (eds.), Alan R. Liss, Inc., New York, 1978, P. 85.

58. Bloomfield, C.D., Gajl Peczalska, K.J., Frizzera, G., Kersey, J.H., and Goldman, A.I.: *N. Engl. J. Med.* 301:512, 1979.

59. Hoxtell, E.O., Mandel, J.S., Murray, S.S., Schuman, L.M., and Goltz, R.W.: *Arch. Dermatol.* 113:436, 1977.

60. Penn, I.: In: *Advances in Cancer Research, Vol. 28,* G. Klein and S. Weinhouse (eds.), Academic Press, New York, 1978, p. 31.

61. Seligmann, M. and Rambaud, J.C.: In: *The Immunopathology of Lymphomas, Comprehensive Immunology, Vol. 4,* J.J. Twomey and R.A. Good (eds.), Plenum Medical Book Co., New York, 1978, p. 925.

62. Reinherz, E.L., Parkman, R., Rappaport, J., Rosen, F.S., and Schlossman, S.F.: *N. Engl. J. Med.* 300:1061, 1979.

63. Graze, R.R. and Gale, R.P.: *Am. J. Med.* 66:611, 1979.

64. Horowitz, S., Borcherding, W., Moorthy, A., Chesney, R., Schulte-Wisserman, H., Hong, R., and Goldstein, A.: *Science* 197:999, 1977.

65. Fowles, R.E., Bieber, C.P., and Stinson, E.B.: *Circulation* 59:483, 1979.

66. Nelson, D.L. Biddison, W.E., and Shaw, S.: *Pediatr. Res.* 13:758, 1979.

67. Herberman, R.B. and Holden, H.T.: In: *Advances in Cancer Research, Vol. 27,* G. Klein and S. Weinhouse (eds.), Academic Press, New York, 1978, p. 305.

68. Santoli, D. and Koprowki, H.: *Immunol. Rev.* 44:125, 1979.

69. Koren, H.S., Amos, D.B., and Buckley, R.H.: *J. Immunol.* 120:796, 1978.

70. Zarling, J.M. and Bach, F.H.: *Nature* 280:685, 1979.

71. German, J.: In: *Human Genetics,* S. Arnendares and R. Lisker (eds.), Excerpta Medica, Amsterdam, 1977, p. 64.

Monoclonal Antibodies as a Tool in Research on Oncogenic Viruses

Ullrich Hämmerling, Abraham Pinter, and
Paul V. O'Donnell

Memorial Sloan-Kettering Cancer Center, New York, New York

The purpose of this presentation is a demonstration of the scope and strength of monoclonal antibodies as an analytical tool. Monoclonal antibodies are so named because of their derivation from cloned lines of plasmacytoma cells. These, in turn, are obtained by cell fusion of normal immunocytes with myeloma cells.[1] Whereas conventional antisera can be made monospecific by absorption with a series of antigens, they will always consist of mixtures of antibodies, and hence their definition will remain imprecise. By contrast, because of the clonal nature of the hybridoma cells, monoclonal antibodies are homogeneous and of defined specificity. They can be considered the tool par excellence for the analysis of complex antigenic systems. Furthermore, as the result of separating, during cloning, and perpetuating even a minority of plasma cells present in the lymphoid tissues of immunized mice, antibodies to new antigenic determinants are emerging with ease. A case in point is the murine major histocompatability complex (MHC), which has been extensively studied for more than a decade by serologists, biochemists, immunologists and geneticists. However, within a few months after introduction of monoclonal antibodies to H-2 and Ia,[2] there has been such an influx of information with regard to new antigenic determinants, subdivisions of previously described determinants or crossreactivities between known determinants, that a revision of the taxonomy of the entire system seems inescapable. It is to be expected that similar revisions of other polymorphic antigen systems, such as HLA antigens, or most bacterial and viral antigens, are in store for us. But, beyond use as taxonomical devices, monoclonal antibodies are becoming an indispensable tool in genetic studies. Data pertaining to this point are the development and analysis of monoclonal antibodies to murine leukemia virus (MuLV) encoded antigens. On fusion with myeloma cells, rats immunized with whole ecotropic virus of AKR mice, or with purified protein antigens derived thereof, yielded three anti-gp70, four anti-p30, and one anti-p15E antibody secreting hybridomas. The salient points of a serological survey of over 30 different ecotropic, xenotropic and dualtropic MuLV isolates are: (a) As all three anti-gp70 and all four p30 display distinct patterns of reactivities, it must be concluded that they are all directed to unique, noncrossreactive determinants, bringing the number of recognizable determinants of AKR MuLV to at least three on the gp70 molecule, and to four on the p30 molecule. (b) The p30 antigen appears to be as polymorphic as the gp70 antigen. (c) As there is no evidence of linkage of any two of the determinants in dualtropic viruses, the recombination of ecotropic and xenotropic MuLV, thought to be the mechanism which gives rise to the dualtropic viruses, is not restricted to gp70, but is likely to encompass p30. (d) In one case, the presence or absence of a particular p30 determinant (identified by clone 60/35) is tightly correlated with N or B tropism of eco MuLV.

References

1. Köhler, G. and Milstein, C.: *Nature* 256:495, 1975.
2. Hämmerling, G., Hämmerling, U., and Lemke, H.: *Immunogenetics* 8:433, 1979.

A Possible Approach to the Therapy of Cancer: Interferon

F. Kingsley Sanders

Memorial Sloan-Kettering Cancer Center, New York, New York

Over the last few years it has become apparent that interferon offers great promise for the treatment of several different forms of neoplasia in man. It is, moreover, entirely fitting that an International Congress of Viral Oncology should consider interferon, since the name itself derives from the discovery by Isaacs and Lindenmann in 1957[1] that virus-infected chicken cells released substances that could protect other cells from infection by several different viruses. It has since been found that a capacity to produce substances resembling interferons is a property of cells from virtually every eukaryotic species that has been tested. Not only birds and mammals, but lower vertebrates such as tortoises and fish, as well as several higher plants, produce materials with at least some of the characteristics of interferons.

The latter are now known to be glycoproteins, synthesized and secreted by cells in response to virus infection as well as stimulation by various chemical "inducers," of which more later.[2] None can be detected in cells prior to induction, following which interferon production is turned on, rises to a peak level, and is then shut off. Following this, cells go into a state of "hyporesponsiveness" during which they fail to respond to a new interferon-inducing stimulus. For mouse cells this refractory period is 24–48 hours, but with human cells it can last for several days.[3]

The interferons secreted by cells in response to induction can be termed intercellular "messages"—that is, they are released by cells; then, after binding to specific receptors on other target cells, they can direct the latter to alter the expression of one or more of their specialized functions.

Among the alterations that interferons can induce in their target cells is resistance to a broad spectrum of viral infections. Chronologically, this was the first property of interferons to be studied intensively, and gave rise to the belief that interferons were just substances that interfered with viral replication, and that was all that they did! This rapidly became a dogma, so that as more and more interferon activities other than the antiviral effect became recognized, these other activities were automatically attributed to "impurities" in what were at the time still rather crude interferon preparations. However, in recent years, advances in the purification and characterization of interferons, including an ability to separate them by electrophoresis on gels in the presence of SDS, have shown that some of these other biological activities will pass through the steps of purification, and migrate on gels, coincidentally with the antiviral activity. This strongly suggests that these activities, in addition to the antiviral one, are in fact properties of the same set of molecules.[4] It is only fair to point out, however, that the pendulum may now have begun to swing the other way. Consequently, many of the more recently described attributes of interferon preparations have not yet been rigorously shown to be properties of the interferon molecules themselves.

Table 1 lists some of the nonantiviral activities of interferons. For my purpose here, I should like to concentrate on only three of them: (a) the antitumor effect: This is the reputed ability of interferons to inhibit the growth of tumors both in animals and in man; (b) the ability of interferons directly to suppress the growth of cells in culture; and (c) the various effects of interferons on cells of the immune system. These second and third categories are important since either, or both, may be involved in the antitumor properties of interferons, and must, at any rate, be allowed for when we attempt to plan any rational interferon therapy of tumors. For example, if suppression of cell multiplication is the more important component of interferon's action against tumors, then direct intralesional injection is likely to be more effective against solid tumors than any kind of systemic administration. Conversely, if interferon works mainly by inducing cells of the immune system to attack tumor cells, that mode of systemic administration which is most effective in delivering the interferon stimulus to the effector cell population would be preferred.

Before proceeding to a detailed consideration of the results so far obtained with interferon treatment of tumors in both experimental animals and man, I should like to expand on the nature of the active molecular species in interferon preparations. It is still widely believed that interferons are "species-specific," i.e., they are active only on cells from the same species as those in which the interferon was induced. It is now known that this is not always true. Interferons are usually more active on cells from their species of origin, but they are also often capable of exerting considerable biological activity on cultured cells from

Table 1. Some Effects of Interferon Other Than the Induction of Resistance to Virus Infection[a]

---

1. *Priming.* Pretreatment with small amounts of interferon augments the yield of interferon from cells subsequently stimulated to produce it.

2. *Blocking.* Treatment with large amounts of interferon reduces the yield from cells subsequently stimulated to produce it.

3. *Toxicity enhancement.* Interferon enhances the toxicity to cells of vaccinia, influenza, and vesicular stomatitis viruses; double-stranded RNA; DEAE-dextran, protamine sulfate, methylated albumin, concanavalin A.

4. *Depression of synthesis.* Uninduced protein and DNA synthesis; also induced syntheses of tyrosine amino-transferase, glycerol-3-phosphate dehydrogenase, glutamine synthetase.

5. *Enhancement of syntheses.* Uninduced products (Hyaluronic acid prostaglandin-E). Induced products (tRNA methylase, Aryl-hydrocarbon hydroxylase, histamine).

6. *Effects on cell surfaces.* For example, toxicity depression, alteration of surface charge, increased Con A binding, increased surface antigen expression; enhanced cytotoxicity of lymphocytes for target cells (both specific and nonspecific); enhanced sensitivity of target cells to cytotoxic antibody; enhanced phagocytosis by macrophages; macrophage "activation"; reversible metamorphosis of human ammion cells.

7. *Immunosuppression:* Effects on: antibody production both *in vitro* and *in vivo*; delayed-type hypersensitivity; heterologous adoptive cutaneous anaphylaxis; graft-vs-host reaction; complement fixation.

8. *Antitumor activity.*

---

[a] Condensed from Stewart.[3]

phylogenetically distant species.[5] We now know that each interferon possesses a range of cross-species activity, sometimes so characteristic that it is a property by which they can be identified.[3] *In vivo,* however, interferons are able to stimulate the production of IF-neutralizing antibody in heterologous species, even those whose cultured cells they are able to affect biologically.[6] This would seem to put a limit on the use, in therapy, of repeated injections of interferons from a heterologous source. It is not true of "native" interferons, however, since they are neither antigenic nor allergenic in their species or origin, so that it is possible to use them to treat patients repeatedly at high dose levels without eliciting the production of neutralizing antibody or allergic reactions.[7] This means it is necessary to use mouse interferon to treat mouse tumors, and human interferon to treat human tumors. Another complication is that several different interferons—differing antigenically as well as in molecular weight—can be produced by different kinds of cells within the same animal species. Thus in man, interferons produced by fibroblasts are antigenically distinct from those produced by lymphocytes. Peripheral blood leukocyte interferons are indistinguishable from those inducible from cultured human lymphoblastoid cell lines, although each contains a small and different amount of an interferon that can be identified immunologically as fibroblast interferon. In addition, within one species, even the same cell can produce more than one molecular form of interferon, distinguishable by their migratory behavior on SDS gels.[3] Distinct molecular forms of this kind may be the expression of different degrees of glycosylation of the same basic interferon polypeptide. Since interferons which have been deglycosylated (interferoids) still possess interferon properties, the carbohydrate moiety is not obviously necessary for the expression of biological activity *in vitro*.[4]

Still, an important function may yet exist to be found for the carbohydrate *in vivo* (perhaps to target the interferon to specific cells?), and this may raise problems regarding the production of therapeutically effective interferons in systems other than cultured human cells.

Yet another class of human interferons can be distinguished on the basis of their resistance to low pH. The leukocyte, lymphoblastoid, and fibroblast interferons already mentioned are all resistant to pH 2 and are designated Type I interferons. Interferons produced by mitogen or antigen-stimulated lymphoid cells are labile at pH 2, and are called Type II interferons; they are also antigenically distinct from Type I interferons.[8]

Interferons induced from various sorts of mouse cells either *in vitro* or *in vivo* also contain more than one molecular form of interferon.[3] While Type II mouse interferon differs from Type I, both antigenically and with respect to pH lability, the mouse does not appear to possess a "leukocyte" or "lymphoblastoid" type of interferon with properties analogous to that of the human. Nevertheless, as with human leukocyte IF, the different molecular species within preparations of mouse Type I interferon can be distinguished by their range of activity in heterologous cells.

Interferons as Antitumor Agents: Animal Experiments

In animals, interferon preparations of different kinds and degrees of purity have been shown to be active antitumor agents, not only against experimental virus-induced tumors, but against spontaneous, transplantable, and both chemically and radiation-induced tumors.

Virus-induced tumors which have responded to interferon treatment include Friend and Rauscher leukemia[9-17] and Moloney sarcoma (Harvey) in the mouse;[18] Shope fibroma in the rabbit;[19] polyoma virus-induced tumors in the hamster;[20] Rouse sarcoma in chickens;[21] as well as herpesvirus saimiri-induced lymphomas in the marmoset and the owl monkey.[22,23] However, interferon does not necessarily inhibit the development of all virus-induced tumors by means of the same mechanism. Where the cells which become transformed by virus infection are nonproducers (Rous, polyoma, and Shope viruses), and where the amount of oncogenicity is proportional to the size of the viral inoculum, there is probably some early virus-dependent event which is the point at which inhibition by interferon occurs. As *in vitro,* this is probably inhibition of the act of cell transformation itself. As a result, interferon given just before, together with, or immediately after virus inoculation is effective in reducing the number of tumors per animal, as well as protecting many from developing tumors at all. Given later, when transformation has already occurred, interferon has only a negligible effect. By contrast, in tumors caused by the injection of Friend and Rauscher leukemia viruses, interferon treatment was only effective when given after virus inoculation, at a high dose level, and for prolonged periods of time. Then it did delay tumor appearance, and slow down the development of those tumors which did eventually appear.

Among spontaneous tumors, the effect of interferon on AKR mouse leukemia and spontaneous mammary carcinoma[24-31] has been studied. Given at relatively high doses ($1-2 \times 10^4$ antiviral units daily) over a long period of time, interferon has been effective in delaying the development of AKR leukemias. When treatment was begun with preleukemic animals and continued for one year, survival following the appearance of leukemia was prolonged by about 100 days, while the total incidence in treated animals was reduced from 95% to 63%. When very high daily doses ($\geq 10^5$ units) were given, a doubling of the life span was observed, even when treatment was not started until after the onset of clinically observable leukemia. Although we call these doses high, they, in fact, represent an antitumor effect obtainable with about 0.1 μg interferon protein per day on a tumor load of some 10^9 cells.

With spontaneous mammary carcinoma and a comparable schedule of interferon administration, there was a similar delayed appearance of tumors, together with a modest increase in the life span. Paradoxically, no decrease was found in the amount of viral "gs" antigen produced in interferon-treated animals [mouse mammary carcinoma is a tumor in whose genesis a virus (MMTV) is involved]. However, it is now known that with C-type retroviruses, interferon affects viral assembly and/or release rather than the amount of virally-specified proteins synthesized.[24] As long as interferon-treatment is continued, release of C-type viruses is suppressed, but after its cessation they may perhaps be released in a burst of short duration. This may explain why interferon treatment of mouse leukemias and spontaneous tumors of viral etiology (AKR leukemia, mammary carcinoma) has to be continued throughout the life of the animal at high doses in order to be effective.

In view of the well-established effect of interferons on virus/host cell interactions, it was to be expected that interferons would be active against virally-induced tumors. However, it was a surprise to find that interferons were also highly effective against a number of transplantable mouse tumors, whose progressive growth is due to tumor cell multiplication and not to "tumor cell recruitment" through viral infection and transformation of formerly uninfected host cells. Among them are the EA, EL_4, L1210, and RC19 tumors, which have been extensively studied by Gresser.[33-38] All are highly malignant, and with the Ehrlich ascites (EA) (where the LD_{50} corresponds to ≤ 10 cells), inoculation of 10^4 cells killed 100% of control animals in 22 days. By contrast, 90% of animals treated daily for several weeks with 2×10^4 units of interferon survived more than six months. With the Lewis lung carcinoma, a metastasizing mouse tumor highly resistant to conventional chemotherapy, interferon was active against both the primary tumor and its metastases.[39] Other mouse tumors susceptible to inhibition by interferon were Ehrlich carcinoma, L1210 lymphoma, sarcoma 180, polyoma-induced transplantable sarcoma, Friend leukemia cells, and osteosarcoma.[40-45] With the latter, as with the Lewis lung carcinoma, interferon was active against both primary tumors and metastases.[45]

All of these studies were carried out with mouse Type I interferons. Very few studies have yet been done with Type II. In the few which have been done, $3-6 \times 10^2$ units daily were found as effective as $\geq 10^4$ units of Type I interferon.[45] But we must not conclude from this that Type II interferons are more powerful antitumor agents than Type I, since, to date, most Type II preparations used have been relatively crude; containing a rich brew of various lymphokines in addition to interferons, their high activity cannot as yet be attributed to interferon alone.

Recently, it has been claimed that the growth of tumor cells of human origin [Hela, RD4 (bladder cancer), mammary carcinoma, melanoma, osteosarcoma] in nude mice, can be inhibited by treatment with human, but not mouse interferons.[46-48] If correct, this would suggest a direct effect of interferon on tumor cells which is not mediated by the host cells; and its confirmation is awaited with interest.

Tumor induction in the mouse by a chemical carcinogen, 3-methylcholanthrene (3MCA), has been either delayed or completely inhibited by interferon treatment.[49,50] Similarly, treatment with small amounts of interferon, begun immediately following X-irradiation, significantly decreased the incidence of radiation-induced lymphoma in mice.[51] Both 3MCA and radiation may induce tumors in rodent species through "activating" an endogenous C-type virus, so that the effect may be due to interferons' antiviral activity.

Synergistic effects have also been reported to follow interferon therapy combined with other methods to reduce the tumor load. In two mouse leukemias [one transplantable (LSTRA) and one spontaneous (AKR)], as well as transplanted mammary carcinoma, sequential treatment with various cytoreductive drugs (BCNU, cyclophosphamide, vincristine, cytoxan, adriamycin) has resulted in much more prolonged survival than after either chemotherapy or interferon alone.[52-55] Similarly, surgical resection of a primary mammary carcinoma followed by interferon-treatment was three times as effective in prolonging life than surgery alone.[31]

There is even some evidence that endogenously produced interferon (perhaps produced in response to induction by endogenous C-type viruses) may play a part in limiting the growth of tumors in untreated animals. Tumor production in Moloney sarcoma and Rauscher leukemia virus-infected mice was markedly enhanced in mice treated with anti-interferon globulin.

To sum up the animal data, while the antitumor activity of interferons in experimental animals is real, it may be effected through several mechanisms. With some tumors there seems to be a direct action on tumor cells, with others the effect is mediated through the tumor-bearing host. In viral oncogenesis, the antitumor activity seems to be exerted mainly through its antiviral effect. However, even in some virally-induced tumors (Friend leukemia), direct inhibition of cell multiplication, as well as an antibody-dependent cytotoxic reaction, may also play a role. More relevant to human cancers is the example of transplantable mouse tumors, since both sorts of tumor, as far as we know, grow only through the multiplication of tumor cells. The important factors determining interferon's effectiveness against transplantable mouse tumors, besides interferon concentration and dose schedule, are tumor load, together with a route of administration guaranteed to bring about an intimate contact between the interferon and host cells. A direct effect on tumor cells does appear to occur, perhaps through inhibition of cell multiplication; indeed, prior cultivation of mouse L1210 cells for as little as 24 hours in the presence of interferon was associated with a hundred-fold decrease in their tumorigenicity.[56] Nevertheless, there is good evidence that host-mediated mechanisms are also involved. When mice were inoculated with mutant L1210R cells that had become resistant to both interferon's antiviral and cell growth inhibitory actions *in vitro,* they remained susceptible to interferon's antitumor activity *in vivo.*[57] When the transplanted cells were recovered from tumors and cultured once more *in vitro,* they were found to have retained their characteristic resistance to the antiviral and cell growth inhibitory effects of interferon. Perhaps relevant to this aspect of the antitumor effect are interferon's abilities to enhance the cytotoxicity of both sensitized T lymphocytes and natural killer (NK) cells, and to stimulate increased phagocytosis by macrophages.[3] All these effects have been noted *in vivo* as well as *in vitro.* So interferons may not only be able to slow tumor cell growth and "normalize" tumor cell behavior, they may also give host cells the ability to recognize them as "foreign."

Further research is needed to clarify these important questions. In the meantime, what can antitumor studies in the mouse tell us about the prospects for interferon therapy of cancer in man?

1. Mouse interferon does not kill tumor cells directly, either in animals or in culture; and although tumor cell killing by host cells primed by interferon has been repeatedly demonstrated, there has been no evidence of massive cell death in interferon-treated animals.

2. To be maximally effective, mouse interferon must be given so that it comes into close contact with the tumor cells.

3. It cannot be used prophylactically, but must be used therapeutically, repeatedly, at extremely high doses relative to those needed to achieve protection against virus infection, and for a considerable length of time; but long-term, high-dose therapy is well tolerated except in newborn animals.

4. There appears to be an optimum dose below which very little antitumor effect occurs, but above which immunosuppressive effects may negate the benefits of treatment.

5. The effect obtained is inversely proportional to tumor load, but the latter can be effectively reduced, prior to interferon treatment, through surgery or by means of cytoreductive drugs.

6. Mouse interferon, from a pharmacological standpoint, appears to be like human fibroblast interferon. Since the mouse does not produce the equivalent of human leukocyte on lymphoblastoid interferon, one should not plan human trials with either of these based on a rigid extrapolation from mouse to man.

7. It is clear that under the most favorable conditions of treatment, mouse tumors have occasionally been prevented from appearing, or else achieved long-term survival approaching a normal life span.

The results in animals lead one to hope that success may one day be attained in the treatment of human tumors. What has been achieved so far is considered in the next section.

Interferons as Antitumor Agents: Experience in Man

At the present time all attempts to demonstrate antitumor activity following the systemic administration of human interferon have used human leukocyte interferon (HuLeIF). Through research lasting many years, a single investigator, Dr. Kari Cantell of the State Serum Institute in Helsinki, Finland, has developed a set of procedures for the large-scale production of HuLeIF, using leukocyte-rich buffy coats obtained from Blood Centers, where blood is routinely processed to separate packed cells from plasma and platelets. His laboratory is, at present, the largest production center of HuLeIF for clinical use in the world today, and most of the interferon used in the clinical investigation which I shall describe comes from this one source.

Human Fibroblast Interferon (HuFIF), suitable for human use, is far more expensive to produce than HuLeIF. So far it has only been produced in relatively small amounts, and has been used on a limited scale for inoculations into, or near, superficial tumor nodules. Superficial tumor metastases of melanoma, breast carcinoma, and prostate cancer have been studied following the administration of 0.5×10^5 antiviral units/day for 30 days.[58,59] About half the treated nodules were markedly inhibited in their growth, several being reduced to 25% of their original size within two weeks of beginning treatment. With melanoma nodules, which normally grow rapidly, this amounted to an eight-fold difference in size between treated and untreated tumor nodules. All treated nodules became heavily infiltrated with lymphocytes, and melanoma cells were fewer than expected.

Good clinical effects have also been reported following the topical administration of HuLeIF in cervical cancer and condyloma acuminata.[60] Direct intralesional injection of $1-3 \times 10^6$ units of HuLeIF daily into six patients with metastatic mammary carcinoma caused the lesion to disappear in two patients, no histological evidence of tumor cells being found after treatment, while pretreatment biopsy had been positive in both instances. In three other patients, tumors injected with interferon were observed to regress in size by more than 50%, with electron microscopic evidence of morphological changes in the tumor cell membranes.[61]

By far the most extensive evidence for the effectiveness of HuLeIF in the treatment of human cancer is the experience of Dr. Hans Strander and his colleagues in Stockholm with classical osteogenic sarcoma. This is a highly malignant spindle cell tumor occurring between ten and 25 years of age, and originating within bone tissue among cells which form membrane bone. Primary treatment is normally by disarticulation or amputation of the affected part. Among a historical series of controls, multiple gross pulmonary metastases predictably develop within 12 months following diagnosis of the primary lesion, and in the natural course of the disease such patients invariably die.[62] A proportion of those receiving only surgical treatment, however, fail to develop metastases, and have a normal life span. The proportion of such long-term survivors (originally 17%) seems to have increased to 25–30% in recent times, probably accounted for by the inclusion of more cases with the worst prognoses (e.g., on the average, larger tumors at the time of primary treatment) among historical controls.

Strander's trial began in 1972 on a carefully selected group of patients.

Included were only those who had (a) a primary tumor located in the
long bones or the pelvis; (b) a normal chest X-ray on admission, and (c)
a concurring histological diagnosis of classical osteogenic sarcoma by
several pathologists. At present the study encompasses 38 interferon-
treated patients, 30 contemporary control patients, and 35 historical
control patients. HuLeIF treatment (3×10^6 units i.m. daily for one
month, then three times weekly for 17 months) begins at diagnosis, prior
to surgery. Apart from the latter, no other treatment is given. The results
so far are given in Figure 1. The effects of IF treatment, both on survival

Figure 1. Effect of interferon treatment on classical osteogenic sarcoma. △ - △
= "historical" controls; □ - □ = "contemporary" controls; ○ - ○ = interferon-
treated patients. (For schedule of treatment see text.)

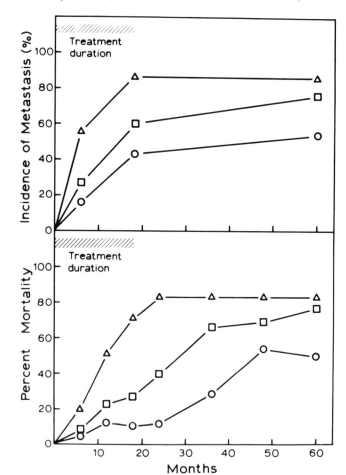

and on the occurrence of metastases, are obvious. In those patients who did develop metastases, there were also differences between the patients in each group concerning the time between recurrence and death. In interferon-treated patients the time was 25 months; in contemporary control patients, 20 months; and in historical controls, 13 months.[63,64] However, interpretation of these results is still difficult because of the nonprospectively, randomized design of the trial.

Particular interest attaches to a group of seven patients with recurrent laryngeal papilloma,[64] since virus-like inclusions can be seen histologically, in the laryngeal epithelium. The only treatment was to give 3×10^6 units HuLeIF either once, twice, or three times weekly. Interferon-induced complete regressions occurred in all seven patients over a period of several months. Relapses were noted within two months of the cessation of treatment, but upon its resumption, regression occurred once more. Here there is no doubt as to a cause-and-effect relationship between HuLeIF treatment and the regression of laryngeal papillomas. Results with bladder papillomas are no less spectacular.[65] Regression was obtained with three of three patients after two to 17 months on high-dosage HuLeIF therapy, although they have not yet been followed long enough to find out whether recurrence is likely.

Encouraging results have also been obtained in Stockholm[66] and elsewhere[67] with multiple myeloma. Out of a total of 16 patients treated, 12 had had no prior therapy. Of these, four had advanced disease, and were already severely debilitated when interferon treatment began; they did not respond to treatment. All except one of the remaining eight showed a response to interferon, three patients showing striking improvements resulting in complete remission; the last four had partial remissions including one in whom a large cranial soft tumor regressed completely within seven weeks. Ten patients with multiple myeloma have also been treated by Dr. J. Gutterman of the M. D. Anderson Hospital in Houston, Texas. In six of them, there was a clear-cut antitumor response (more than a 50% decrease in serum paraprotein and/or Bence Jones protein excretion). The nature of an individual's previous response to chemotherapy did not predict his response to interferon. However, there was a strong correlation between response to interferon and the total tumor mass at the time of the beginning of treatment. Five out of six patients with intermediate tumor masses responded; none of those with very large tumor masses did. Individual patients showed spectacular responses, including a case with a scalp lesion similar to one of Strander's patients. It began to regress two weeks after the start of therapy and eventually disappeared. With multiple myeloma, it appears that the stage of the disease at which treatment is begun is more important than whether patients have received prior treatment, or whether or not they are resistant to other therapies.

In addition, a series of lymphomas and leukemias have been treated with HuLeIF. In Sweden, four cases of Hodgkin's disease responded: one patient had temporary but considerable improvement; among the other three there were one complete and two partial remissions.[68] Six B-cell lymphomas were treated for 30 days with 10^7 units HuLeIF/day by Dr. T. Merigan in California.[69,70] Three cases with rapidly advancing diffuse histocytic lymphoma responded poorly. The other three, with indolent, nodular, lymphocytic, poorly differentiated lymphomas, responded with dramatic resolution of abnormal lymph node masses. Dr. Gutterman has had a similar experience with lymphomas in Texas.[71] A patient with diffuse histiocytic lymphoma did not respond to 3×10^6 units/day, but when the dose was raised to 9×10^6 units, one of the two large tumor masses disappeared. In nodular lymphocytic lymphomas either a partial or complete remission was obtained, as in four out of six cases, and in three of the four, complete disappearance of all evidence of disease was achieved. Five children with acute leukemia, both lymphocytic and granulocytic, have been treated with high doses of HuLeIF $(0.25-2 \times 10^6$ units/kg) intravenously. An antileukemic effect was observed in three of three patients with ALL and one of two with AGL.

Very little work has been done so far with HuLeIF on patients with solid tumors. Gutterman and his colleagues, however, have begun an investigation on 17 patients with breast cancer,[71,72] most of whom had been primarily heavily treated, had failed to respond to conventional therapy, and who had superficial metastases which allowed serial measurements of tumor size. Following HuLeIF treatment, at $3-9 \times 10^6$ units daily, seven women responded positively. Regressions were seen in soft tissue metastases, bone deposits, and marrow infiltrations. Some of these patients who showed a positive response to interferon treatment, had previously become resistant to several chemotherapeutic agents during treatment. However, out of six patients who had always been resistant to chemotherapy, none responded to interferon.

Interferons, thus, have been clearly shown to have therapeutic effects against tumors in both animals and man. In the latter, these include tumor regressions. However, the number of cancer patients studied so far has been small, and most investigations uncontrolled. Neither the degree, nor the duration of the possible benefit of interferon treatment to the patient can be estimated as yet. It is clear, however, that HuLeIF can be administered to man at high dosage (in terms of antiviral units) over prolonged periods without serious side effects. However, as yet, neither the maximum effective dose, nor the optimum regimen of treatment has been worked out for any one tumor. No evidence has yet been found of tumor cells which develop resistance to interferon treatment, the emergence of resistant cells being a commonplace of chemotherapy. The major obstacle to continued experimental therapy with interferons, both in animal model systems and in man, is the scarcity of interferon preparations.

The Supply of Interferons

Very early in the history of interferons, it was realized that they had unique promise as agents for the treatment of many common infectious diseases. However, since the most clinically effective interferons are those induced in human cells, the problem of producing enough interferon to treat the many thousands having these common diseases seemed insoluble.

Thus, the discovery of effective nonviral inducers in the 1960's raised the hope that all the antiviral and other properties of interferon could be exploited clinically, simply by stimulating the patient to produce his own interferon—by injecting him repeatedly with an interferon-inducer.

Unfortunately, while several inducers, particularly poly I:C, a synthetic double-stranded RNA, proved effective against many virus infections in mice, and in addition showed antitumor and immunomodulatory activities in that species, they have largely failed in man. This has been due, first, to the phenomenon of hyporesponsiveness I mentioned earlier—the failure of cells to respond to a second treatment with an interferon-inducer, which tended to negate the effect of repeated injections.

Second, those inducers, such as double-stranded RNA's, which were most promising on the basis of their behavior in mice, proved surprisingly poor inducers of interferon in primates, including man. This is because an active nuclease in primate serum, which destroys poly I:C, is able to prevent the inducer from reaching the target tissues where it can induce interferon.

Thirdly, all inducers have considerable toxicity in man at the levels of dosage that would be required to induce enough interferon to have a therapeutic effect. For these reasons attempts to use interferon inducers in man have been disappointing.

Recently a nuclease-resistant complex of poly I:C with polylysine, stabilized in carboxymethyl cellulose, has been developed which is able to induce high levels of interferon in primates, and which also has an antiviral effect in these animals. At present it is being tested clinically. Its use, however, may still be limited by hyporesponsiveness to repeated induction, and perhaps by toxicity. The progressive failure with interferon-inducers as therapeutic agents has disillusioned many investigators regarding interferon's great clinical potential. However, in recent years there has been widespread, renewed interest in the use of exogenous interferons, that is interferon-induced, in cells either propagated or maintained in cell culture systems.

The most urgent task basic to the clinical evaluation and eventual exploitation of interferons is to procure them in sufficient quantity, and at a sufficiently low cost, to allow extensive *in vivo* investigation in man. The following is an example of the magnitude of the problem. In Dr. Strander's trial of the efficacy of interferon treatment in osteosarcoma, patients were given 3×10^6 antiviral units of HuLeIF three times a week for 18 months (a total of 7×10^8 units). Fully induced cell cultures produce about 10^4 units per cm^3 of medium, so some 70 liters of culture must be processed to provide the interferon needed to treat one patient. At present, the largest world source of clinically acceptable HuLeIF is the production facilities of the Central Public Health Laboratory in Helsinki, Finland, and the Finnish Red Cross Blood Transfusion Service; together they can produce about 2×10^{11} units per annum—enough to treat some 250 cancer patients throughout the world. Moreover, since the culture media used contain many expensive ingredients (e.g., serum), the cost of a single course of treatment can run as high as $35,000 per patient.

Whatever improvements may be made in the techniques of cell culture, present-day production methods, thus, can only be a stop-gap, since the most they can hope to achieve is the production of enough interferon to satisfy demands for clinical testing in both viral and neoplastic disease. For general, widespread use of interferons, they must be produced in quantity at low cost; so the future lies with "second-generation" methods.

The most obvious of these is "Recombinant DNA" technology. It has been shown many times that RNA containing molecules with the message for the synthesis of interferons can be detected, translated, and assayed in heterologous systems. This raises the exciting prospect of the eventual purification of the interferon "messenger RNA" and the coping of it, using the enzyme reverse transcriptase, into a complementary DNA (cDNA). The latter could then perhaps be inserted, with appropriate additions and/or modifications, into a bacterium or other easily- and cheaply-grown prokaryotic cell for production in tanks of several thousand liters capacity, as penicillin is today.

Transfer of genetic information from human mRNA $\rightarrow$ cDNA $\rightarrow$ bacterial plasmid DNA $\rightarrow$ protein in this way has already been achieved with human pituitary growth hormone. This route towards increased interferon production is being actively followed in several laboratories today.

A second way to use recombinant DNA technology would follow the total purification of interferon, which apparently has now been achieved in the case of HuLeIF. Knowledge of the amino-acid sequence, which will come in the near future, might allow synthesis of a DNA expressing this sequence in terms of codons which bacteria "like." Insertion of this synthetic DNA into a bacterial plasmid might result in a strain of bacteria capable of making molecules with the biological properties of HuLeIF. This method of "persuading" bacteria to produce human proteins has already been achieved with the peptide hormones somatostatin and β-endorphin.

One of the objections to the use of transformed bacteria to produce alien products is that the yield is generally low. In the case of interferon, this possibility is not necessarily a serious disadvantage. The biological activity of interferons is so high ($> 10^9$ units/mg of interferon protein) that even if each bacterium "programmed" to make interferons produced only ten molecules of interferon protein, ten fermentors would have the capacity to produce as much interferon in one run as the entire annual production of Finland—and at a fraction of the cost.

A more serious obstacle to the use of bacteria for producing interferons would be the possibility that the carbohydrate moiety of the interferon glycoprotein has some part to play in its biological activity; for example, to give the molecule stability in body fluids. Any product made by bacteria would not be glycosylated.

However, recent demonstrations that certain interferons can be deglycosylated without loss of activity *in vitro,* or of stability *in vivo,* renders it unlikely that any product made by bacteria would be totally inactive because it lacked carbohydrate.

In addition, the total purification of interferons and their eventual sequencing raises a third possibility—whether it would be possible to produce them directly by chemical synthesis, either by solution or solid-state methods. This has already been achieved with molecules the size of ribonuclease (124 amino acids) and is theoretically possible with interferons, which are about twice as large. An objection to this method would be its probable very high cost. Beyond small peptides, the addition of every extra amino acid adds astronomically to the cost of the product. However, in view of its very high biological activity, even if synthetic interferon cost $1,000,000 a gram, interferon for a single course of treatment, according to Strander's procedure, would still only cost $700 as compared with $35,000 at today's going rate. Finally there is the strong suspicion that "interferoids," or interferons without carbohydrates, may not be the end of the story. Activity may not require the total amino-acid sequence of interferon. There may be a much shorter "active fragment" within the interferoid molecule itself in which, theoretically, the same biological activity resides. This would be much cheaper to synthesize and reduce the cost of treatment still further.

References

1. Isaacs, A. and Lindenmann, J.: *Proc. R. Soc., B.* 147:258, 1957.
2. Ho, M. and Armstrong, J.A.: *Ann. Rev. Microbiol.* 29:131, 1975.

3. Stewart, W.E., II: *The Interferon System,* Springer-Verlag, New York, Wien, 1979.
4. Stewart, W.E., II: *Proc. of the IVth Int. Cong. Virology,* Amsterdam, 1978 (in press).
5. Desmyter, S., Rawls, W.E., and Melnick, S.L.: *Proc. Natl. Acad. Sci. USA* 59:69, 1968.
6. Levy-Koenig, R.E., Golgher, B.R., and Paucker, K.: *J. Immunol.* 104:791, 1970.
7. Strander, H., Cantell, K., Carlstrom, G., and Jakobsson, P.A.: *J. Natl. Cancer Inst.* 51:733, 1973.
8. Valle, M.J., Jordan, G.W., Haahr, S., and Merigan, T.C.: *J. Immunol.* 115:230, 1975.
9. Gresser, I., Coppey, J., Falcoff, E., and Fontaine, D.: *Proc. Soc. Exp. Biol. Med.* 124:84, 1967.
10. Gresser, I., Coppey, J., Fontaine-Brouty-Boyé, D., and Falcoff, R.: *Nature* 215:174, 1967.
11. Gresser, I., Falcoff, R., Fontaine-Brouty-Boyé, D., Zajdela, F., Coppey, J., and Falcoff, E.: *Proc. Soc. Exp. Biol. Med.* 126:791, 1967.
12. Gresser, I., Coppey, J., Fontaine-Brouty-Boyé, D., Falcoff, E., Falcoff, R., Zajdela, F., Bourali, C., and Thomas, M.T.: In: *Ciba Symposium on Interferon,* G.E.W. Wolstenholme and M. O'Connor (eds.), Churchill, London, 1967, p. 240.
13. Wheelock, E.F. and Larke, R.P.B.: *Proc. Soc. Exp. Biol. Med.* 127:130, 1968.
14. Gresser, I., Berman, I., de-Thé, G., Brouty-Boyé, D., Coppey, J., and Falcoff, E.: *J. Natl. Cancer Inst.* 41:505, 1968.
15. Glasgow, L.A. and Friedman, S.B.: *J. Virol.* 3:99, 1969.
16. Toth, F.D., Vaczi, L., and Berencsi, C.: *Acta Microbiol. Acad. Sci. Hung.* 18:23, 1971.
17. Toth, F.D., Vaczi, L., and Berencsi, C.: *Acta Microbiol. Acad. Sci. Hung.* 18:109, 1971.
18. Berman, L.D.: *Nature* 227:1349, 1970.
19. Kishida, T., Kato, S., and Nagano, Y.: *C. R. Soc. Biol.* 159:782, 1965.
20. Atanasiu, P. and Chany, C.: *C. R. Acad. Sci. (Paris)* 151:1687, 1960.
21. Strandstrom, H., Sandelin, K., and Oker-Blum, M.: *Virology* 16:384, 1962.
22. Laufs, R., Steinke, H., Jacobs, C., Hilfenhaus, J., and Karges, H., *Med. Microbiol. Immunol.* 160:235, 1974.
23. Rabin, H., Adamson, H.R., Neubauer, R.H., Cicmanec, J.L., and Wallen, W.C.: *Cancer Res.* 36:715, 1976.
24. Gresser, I., Coppey, J., and Bourali, C.: *C. R. Acad. Sci. (Paris)* 267:1900, 1968.
25. Gresser, I., Coppey, J., and Bourali, C.: *J. Natl. Cancer Inst.* 43: 1083, 1969.
26. Graff, S., Kassel, R., and Kastner, D.: *Trans. N. Y. Acad. Sci.* 32:545, 1971.
27. Gresser, I., Maury, C., and Tovey, M.: *Int. J. Cancer* 17:647, 1976.
28. Came, P.E. and Moore, D.H.: *Proc. Soc. Exp. Biol. Med.* 137:304, 1971.
29. Came, P.E. and Moore, D.H.: *J. Natl. Cancer Inst.* 48:1151, 1972.
30. Bekesi, J.G., Roboz, J.P., Zimmerman, E., and Holland, J.F.: *Cancer Res.* 36:631, 1976.
31. Bekesi, J.G.: In: *Report of the IInd International Workshop on Interferons,* M. Krim, W.E. Stewart, II, H.P. Oettgen and V.G. Edy (eds.), The Rockefeller Univ. Press, New York, 1980 (in press).
32. Billiau, A.: *Tex. Rep. Biol. Med.* 35:406, 1977.
33. Gresser, I. and Bourali, C.: *Nature* 223:844, 1969.

34. Gresser, I., Bourali, C., Levy, J.P., Fontaine-Brouty-Boyé, D., and Thomas, M.T.: *Proc. Natl. Acad. Sci. USA* 63:51, 1969.
35. Gresser, I., Bourali, C., Chouroulinkov, I., Fontaine-Brouty-Boyé, D., and Thomas, M.T.: *Ann. N. Y. Acad. Sci.* 173:694, 1970.
36. Gresser, I.: *Symp. Series Immunobiol. Standard* 14:209, 1970.
37. Gresser, I. and Bourali, C.: *J. Natl. Cancer Inst.* 45:365, 1970.
38. Gresser, I., Maury, C., and Brouty-Boyé, D.: *Nature* 239:167, 1972.
39. Gresser, I. and Bourali-Maury C.: *Nature New Biol.* 236:78, 1972.
40. Ferris, P., Padnos, M., and Molomut, N.: *Fed. Proc.* 30:341, 1972.
41. Takeyama, H., Nishiwaki, H., Yamada, K., Ito, Y., and Nagata, I.: In: Gresser, I.: *Cancer—A Comprehensive Treatise, Vol. 5,* F. Becker (ed.), Plenum Press, New York, 1977, p. 525.
42. Yokota, Y., Kishida, T., Esaki, K., and Kawamata, J.: *Biken J.* 19:125, 1976.
43. Coragio, F., Coto, V., Fantoni, V., Galeota, C.A., and Lavegas, E.: *Boll. Ist. Sieroter. Milanese* 44:64, 1965.
44. Rossi, G.B., Marchegiani, M., Matarese, G., and Gresser, I.: *J. Natl. Cancer Inst.* 54:993, 1975.
45. Glasgow, L.A.: In: *Report of the IInd International Workshop on Interferons,* M. Krim, W.E. Stewart, II, H.P. Oettgen and V.G. Edy (eds.), The Rockefeller Univ. Press, New York, 1980 (in press).
46. Horoszewitz, J.: In: *Report of the IInd International Workshop on Interferons,* M. Krim, W.E. Stewart, II, H.P. Oettgen and V.G. Edy (eds.), The Rockefeller Univ. Press, New York, 1980 (in press).
47. Taylor-Papadimitriou, J.: In: *Report of the IInd International Workshop on Interferons,* M. Krim, W.E. Stewart, II, H.P. Oettgen and V.G. Edy (eds.), The Rockefeller Univ. Press, New York, 1980 (in press).
48. Kishida, T.: In: *Report of the IInd International Workshop on Interferons,* M. Krim, W.E. Stewart, II, H.P. Oettgen and V.G. Edy (eds.), The Rockefeller Univ. Press, New York, 1980 (in press).
49. Kishida, T., Toda, S., Toida, T., and Hattori, T.: *C. R. Soc. Biol. (Paris)* 165:1489, 1971.
50. Salerno, R.A., Whitmire, C.E., Garcia, I.M., and Huebner, R.J.: *Nature New Biol.* 239:31, 1972.
51. Lieberman, M., Merigan, T.C., and Kaplan, H.S.: *Proc. Soc. Exp. Biol. Med.* 138:575, 1971.
52. Chirigos, M. and Pearson, J.W.: *J. Natl. Cancer Inst.* 51:1367, 1973.
53. Chirigos, M.: In: *Report of the IInd International Workshop on Interferons,* M. Krim, W.E. Stewart, II, H.P. Oettgen, and V.G. Edy (eds.), The Rockefeller Univ. Press, New York, 1980 (in press).
54. Gresser, I.: In: *Cancer—A Comprehensive Treatise. Chemotherapy, Vol. 5,* F. Becker (ed.), Plenum Press, New York, 1977, p. 525.
55. Frei, E., III, Schabel, F.M., Jr., and Goldin, A.: *Cancer Res.* 34:184, 1974.
56. Gresser, I., Bandu, M.T., and Brouty-Boyé, D.: *J. Natl. Cancer Inst.* 52:553, 1974.
57. Gresser, I., Thomas, M.T., and Brouty-Boyé, D.: *Nature* 231:20, 1971.
58. Horoszewicz, J.S., Leong, S.S., Ito, M., Buffett, R., Karakousis, C., Holyoke, E., Job, I., Dolan, J., and Carter, W.A.: *Cancer Treat. Rep.* 11:1899, 1978.

59. Horoszewicz, J.S.: In: *Report of the IInd International Workshop on Interferons,* M. Krim, W.E. Stewart, II, H.P. Oettgen and V.G. Edy (eds.), The Rockefeller Univ. Press, New York, 1980 (in press).

60. Ikic, D., Bosnic, N., Smerdel, S., Jusic, D., Soos, E., and Delimar, N.: In: *Proceedings of the Symp. on Clinical Use of Interferon,* Yugoslav Acad. of Sciences and Arts, Zagreb, 1975, p. 299.

61. Habif, D.: In: *Report on the IInd International Workshop on Interferons,* M. Krim, W.E. Stewart, II, H.P. Oettgen and V.G. Edy (eds.), The Rockefeller Univ. Press, New York, 1980 (in press).

62. Marcove, R.C., Miké, V.; Hajek, J.V., Levin, A.G., and Hutter, R.V.P.: *J. Bone Joint Surg. Am.* 52-A:411, 1970.

63. Strander, H.: *Blut* 35:277, 1977.

64. Strander, H.: In: *Report of the IInd International Workshop on Interferons,* M. Krim, W.E. Stewart, II, H.P. Oettgen and V.G. Edy (eds.), The Rockefeller Univ. Press, New York, 1980 (in press).

65. Osther, K.: In: *Report of the IInd International Workshop on Interferons,* M. Krim, W.E. Stewart, II, H.P. Oettgen and V.G. Edy (eds.), The Rockefeller Univ. Press, New York, 1980 (in press).

66. Mellstedt, H., Bjorkholm, M., Johansson, B., Ahre, A., Holm, G., and Strander, H.: *Lancet* 1:245, 1979.

67. Gutterman, J.U., Blumenshine, G.R., and Alexanian, R.: In: *Report of the IInd International Workshop on Interferons,* M. Krim, W.E. Stewart, II, H.P. Oettgen and V.G. Edy (eds.), The Rockefeller Univ. Press, New York, 1980 (in press).

68. Blomgren, H., Cantell, K., Johansson, B., Lagergren, C., Lingborg, U., and Strander, H.: *Acta Med. Scand.* 199:527, 1976.

69. Merigan, T.C., Sikora, K., Breeden, J.H., Levy, R., and Rosenberg, S.A.: *N. Engl. J. Med.* 299:1449, 1979.

70. Merigan, T.C.: In: *Report of the IInd International Workshop on Interferons,* M. Krim, W.E. Stewart, II, H.P. Oettgen and V.G. Edy (eds.), The Rockefeller Univ. Press, New York, 1980 (in press).

71. Gutterman, J., Yap, Y., Buzdar, A., Alexanian, R., Hersh, E., and Cabanillas, F.: *Abstract #674, Proc. Amer. Assoc. Cancer Res.* 20:167, 1979.

72. Gutterman, J.: In: *Report of the IInd International Workshop on Interferons,* M. Krim, W.E. Stewart, II, H.P. Oettgen and V.G. Edy (eds.), The Rockefeller Univ. Press, New York, 1980 (in press).

A Summing Up

Ariel C. Hollinshead

The George Washington University Medical Center, Washington, D.C.

We are entering the year 1980 within a few months. Exactly 100 years ago, in 1880, Louis Pasteur started his work on rabies. He had already had a very full life—full of discoveries. These were well documented by Dubos,[1] and his observations summarized by Porter.[2] It is of interest to read them once more: (a) He found the symptoms of rabies disease varied greatly, but in all cases (animal and human) the positive agent was the same; (b) saliva of human patients may contain other microbial pathogens, a fact that complicated experimental results with rabbits; (c) the brain, spinal cord and probably the entire nervous system of persons who succumb to rabies contained the same agent, as was the case in animals with the disease; (d) the incubation of the disease could be shortened from weeks to several days by injecting rabies material through the skull and directly onto the brain of animals, and (e) the intravenous injection into healthy animals of the saliva or blood from a diseased animal did not confer immunity on the healthy one. He also showed that the virulence of rabies virus could be altered by passing it through animals. If he passed the diseased brain or spinal cord of a dog to a monkey and then from monkey to monkey, the virulence decreased not only for monkeys but also for other animals, and protected the animals. However, if he passed the material from rabbit to rabbit the virus became much more virulent both for the rabbit and for the dog. He then made the amazing discovery that the virulence, but not the immunizing ability, of the rabies virus in the spinal cord of the rabbit would gradually decrease if suspended and stored in dry air, but would keep if stored at low temperatures. This heralded a new era in methods of immunization.

He inoculated dogs with 15-day-old material known to be avirulent and, at two-day intervals thereafter, he used increasingly fresher cord material, in the final inoculation using the fresh, highly virulent material. These dogs were resistant to rabies even when inoculated on the surface of the brain. Five years later, when Pasteur was 63 years of age, he made an important scientific and medical decision while working with a physician, Dr. Grancher, in a series of inoculations of a nine-year-old boy, Joseph Meister, who had been bitten two days before by a rabid dog.

Six years later, Dr. William Coley, an American surgeon, began injecting cancer patients with mixed bacterial toxins, and in 1893, he injected his toxin into a 16-year-old boy with inoperable cancer. The tumor shrank and disappeared.[3] He improved the survival of 250 other patients, but his work was, in general, unrecognized. Unlike Pasteur and Jenner, who inoculated against smallpox in 1796, Coley stimulated the general immune response by nonspecific means. Seventy years later, in 1963, Georges Mathé administered a live bacteria tuberculosis vaccine called BCG (Bacillus Calmette-Guérin) into patients with acute lymphoid leukemia.[4] He reduced the tumor burden with chemotherapy and followed this with nonspecific active immunotherapy in order to alter the patient's immune system as Coley had done. Like Jenner and Pasteur, we tested animals in the 1950's, and humans with disease-related purified tumor antigens in 1968, beginning an era of specific, active immunotherapy of cancer.

Fruton has suggested that a prominent feature of the interplay between chemistry and biology "has been a competition between two styles of molecular explanation of biological phenomena, one in which molecules were considered to be units of physical motion, while in the other they were viewed as units of chemical reaction."[5] He points out that in 1806 Berzelius understood the intimacy of this connection, and there followed several notable achievements in the study of chemical dynamics of physiological function, and that by 1850 "this emphasis had promoted the emergence of a physiological chemistry more closely linked to medical physiology than to pure chemistry."[5] He points out that up through the first half of this century biological and chemical interest seemed to diverge, and that it was not until after World War II that "the use of electron microscopy and differential centrifugation erased this separation, and the mode of assembly of the macromolecular components of living cells is now a subject of intense biological studies." Similarly, "the interface of biochemistry and genetics is one of the most flourishing areas of science."

In 1964, I heard a lecture at the National Institutes of Health by Dr. Christian B. Anfinsen[6] in which he described some biological implications of protein structure. His description remains the best statement I have seen on this subject:

> The polypeptide chains that make up the covalent structures of proteins are long, linear polymers. These chains are folded and coiled into complex three-dimensional configurations, unique for each kind of protein molecule, in which amino-acid residues separated by considerable distances along the chains are brought into close proximity to form "active centers." Experiments *in vitro* have shown that full disorganized and inactive protein structures may be refolded efficiently to yield the original native materials. Furthermore, an enzyme system has been found which facilitates the formation of correct three-dimensional structure. The present view suggests that proteins as one finds them in Nature, are the most stable possible arrangements of the polypeptide chain starting with the selection of amino-acid sequences that are precisely 'coded' for eventual folding into a unique geometric solution to the biological problem. During evolution, a sequence may be changed by mutation of the corresponding gene. An acceptable three-dimensional configuration is ensured by natural selection of organisms having amino-acid sequences that are so coded that they fold into a geometric arrangement very similar to that existing before mutation. Various biological mechanisms such as gene duplication and aggregate formation from dissimilar protein subunits serve to maintain and stabilize biological suitability in many instances.

Some of the most important work in helping to elucidate this interplay has been achieved by studying unique biological markers of plasma cell-lymphocyte tumors, and this includes the study of myeloma proteins. Waldenström macroglobulins and the Bence-Jones proteins.[7] These studies not only helped with an understanding of the serum proteins, but, conversely, the important strides in understanding tissue proteins have, reciprocally, been a combination of the use of good biological studies coupled with the use of chemical techniques which had been found useful for the study of serum proteins. In recent years, there have emerged numerous classes and subclasses of cell surface antigens coded for by the HLA major histocompatibility complex.[8]

Thanks to crystalographer Rosalind Franklin, photographic plates of DNA diffraction patterns gave Watson and Crick the key they needed for elucidation of the structure of DNA in 1953.[9] However, molecular biologists were not able to explain how information is encoded in parts of DNA that are not structural genes. By 1976, it was possible to determine DNA sequences fairly rapidly.[10] These studies have helped in understanding the role of mammalian cell DNA, the major part of which is not incorporated in structural genes. Just how viral genetic information is integrated into mammalian cells has been a subject for elegant studies in recent years. Baltimore has pointed out that the DNA viruses cause various infectious diseases while one class of RNA viruses, the biochemically defined retroviruses, are known only to cause cancer.[11] However, he points out that retroviruses direct the synthesis of "Two critical classes of proteins: proteins for replication and proteins for constructing the virus particle. By encoding the reverse transcriptases, retroviruses have evolved the ability to integrate themselves into cell chromosomes as proviruses." Occasional mutations, he postulates, interfere with the transmission of the provirus, and cells do not necessarily possess the viral genome at all times. In short, the virus could live as a separate entity, reinfecting and causing the existence of proviruses once again. A very rare mutation might be connected with transformation leading to cancer cells, but this would be an accident.

Dr. Price[12] stated that when these accidents occur, it is possibly the result of a carcinogen-induced change in the chronically-infected cell. He feels that "antibody" to recombinant ecotropic and xenotropic virus or to a common tumor antigen is effective in inhibiting cellular oncogene induction and that "cancers regardless of causative agent may be preventable." It is probable that the effects of tumor-associated antigens (TAA) which are ascribed to "antibody," result from a more complex series of events related to immunoprevention. The TAA are varied and it would seem that host-cell gene control and immunologic recognition differ for the tumor-specific surface antigens (TSSA) of avian sarcoma, the Moloney or Gross cell surface antigens (MCSA, GCSA) of mouse lymphoma, etc.

We have evidence from Dr. Hardy[13] that the feline oncornavirus-associated cell membrane antigens (FOCMA) are present on feline lymphoid tumor cells independent of the presence of infectious virus, in contrast to the antigen on normal mouse cells which crossreacts with one induced by Abelson murine leukemia virus (MuLV), for example. Similarly, the differences may be related not only to host differences, but also to the differences between the types of cells involved, the types of tumors and variations in host immune status in inbred and random-bred mammalians during different stages of development, and of disease progression. Precancerous states and the emergence of a host of immunoevasive changes are under study in man.

Dr. Sarkar[14] discussed the interplay of several factors in the etiology of human breast cancer and was justifiably cautious in describing the poor correlation between family history of breast cancer and the presence of B-type virus-like particles or reverse transcriptase in human milk. He has correlated the number of damaged B-type particles in human milk to nonspecific enzymatic destruction. He also reported that no murine mammary tumor virus (MuMTV)-related nucleotide sequences in the DNA or human breast cells MCF-7 were detectable by a sensitive technique which could detect less than one genome per cell. Furthermore, he described a nonspecific presensitization to MuMTV antigens by leukocytes from patients with various forms of breast disease.

In the study of DNA viruses, we have pointed out that it is important to think not only of genetic evolution but also of genetic revolution.[15] The expression of the highly sophisticated herpesviruses are different in human tumors than in animal models, and it would be important to study those models which reflect changes similar to man. Dr. Munk[16] has described a new experimental model, the tree shrew, in which he is investigating virus latency as one of the prerequisites for virus-induced carcinogenesis. Moreover, the cooperation of herpesviruses and their expression in relation to other viruses should be studied; and it is possible that the retroviruses might be involved in the transformation of some tissue types but not others. Cocultivation of whole and defective particles associated with many different forms of wild-type viral strains in appropriately selected normal tissues may afford a better understanding of these associations.

Since 1968, we have been concerned with careful identification of herpesvirus-related antigens associated with human squamous carcinomas, and with a thorough testing of the relationship of these antigens to the malignant process. The relationship of herpesvirus-tumor-associated antigens (HSV-TAA) to squamous carcinomas is accompanied by what appears to be a lack of relationship to sex, age, race and tumor status, and the preponderance of data suggests that HSV-TAA expression precedes the impaired cellular immunity associated with these cancers.[15] Dr. Filipovich[17] pointed out that squamous cell carcinomas occur in immunodeficient populations, but the sequence of events is less understood than in lymphomas. It stands to reason that the herpesvirus would not depend upon replication in the very tissue which it might destroy. Thus, it has been shown that herpesviruses have a preference for existence and latent infection in cells of the central nervous system. It is highly possible that a small fragment of herpesvirus below the level of detection of present annealing experiments, or a defective herpesvirus that produces nonstructural thymidine kinase antigens and induces a virus-specific DNA polymerase could be involved in squamous cell transformation with or without new enzymatic conditions either at the genetic or epigenetic level.[15] The identification, separation and characterization of the two polypeptide chains which comprise HSV-TAA, with molecular sizes of approximately 40,000 daltons and 60,000 daltons, permitted the production of highly specific hyperimmune antisera to these antigens. Recent studies in cooperation with Dr. Auersperg permitted us to determine whether the preferential expression of HSV-TAA observed in squamous cell carcinoma *in vivo* persisted after long-term culture.[18] We used the HSV-TAA antisera for a study to determine whether or not cell lines from human cervical carcinomas, established

within the last 15 years (up to 90 passages), as well as other lines derived
from malignancies other than cervical carcinomas and from nonmalignant
tissues, had the HSV-TAA marker. Our studies suggest that the expression of HSV-TAA may be a very stable biological marker for cultured
cervical cell populations. It is of interest that one of the control lines,
HT-29, was positive even though the cells were derived from colon
adenocarcinoma. Subsequent to the completion of this study, we learned
that the HT-29 cells we were studying had been reported by others to be
expressing squamous characteristics in culture, as indicated by the
presence of well-formed desmosomes and very long tonofibrils. This
raises the interesting possibility that HSV-TAA may be acting as a
marker for squamous cell characteristics independently of the tissue
origin of the cells.[18] It should be possible to correlate these expressions
associated with the cancer cell with those genetic fragments of HSV
which have become incorporated into the squamous cancer cell. Much
work is being conducted in the mapping of the genome of the mature
herpesvirus, and it is possible that we will soon be able to correlate the
specific HSV-TAA proteins with the regions which code these markers.
Dr. Aurelian[19] and Dr. Tarro[20] described elegant work in these proceedings. A sensitive ELISA will aid our progress.[21]

A list of important studies of HSV-TAA and antibodies and those
which have exchanged reagents is of interest: Evidence for herpesvirus-
tumor association in humans came from Kvasnicka in 1956; Wyburn-
Mason in 1957; Rawls, Tompkins, Figueroa and Melnick in 1968; and
Naib, Nahmias, Josey, and Kramer in 1969. Evidence for herpesvirus-
tumor-associated antigens in humans came from Tarro in 1970; Hollins-
head, Melnick and Rawls in 1971; Centifanto, Dryle, Deardourff and
Kaurman in 1972; Aurelian, Schuman, Marcus and Davis in 1973;
Collard, Thornton and Green in 1973; Frenkel, Roizman, Cassai and
Nahmias in 1972; Lin and Munyon in 1974; Specher-Goldberger and
Thiry in 1974; Anzai et al. in 1976; Notter and Docherty in 1976; Kato
and Torigoe in 1977; Sato, Urade, Yoshida et al., in 1978; Ito and
Nishimura in 1978; and Ibrahim and Nahmias in 1978. Several of these
investigators have exchanged reagents and information.

One of the DNA viruses has an easier target, namely the human B
lymphocyte, and most if not all B lymphocytes have specific Epstein-
Barr virus (EBV) receptors.[22] EBV causes infectious mononucleosis, but
it is not clear whether or not virus-converted cell lines arise in the
mononucleosis patients or in healthy seropositive individuals and are
held dormant, or whether the cells are transformed by released infectious
virus from the blood of the infected donor.[23] Both nasopharyngeal
carcinoma and African Burkitt's lymphoma are associated with EBV.
An important documentation of this latter discovery was presented by

Dr. Burkitt[24] in these proceedings. If one accepts the fairly strong evidence of these associations, then it is possible, as Klein has suggested,[22] that EBV may act in connection with "a special form of cellular competence, perhaps a genetic deficiency in some regulatory mechanism, before fully autonomous cancer cells can emerge." Furthermore, he suggested that nasopharyngeal carcinoma may be associated with a viral subtype, and that similar explanations may be pertinent with regard to this form of cancer.

Dr. Vonka[25] discussed the relationship of EBV to tonsillar carcinoma and the types of studies necessary for confirmation. It is of interest that a small percentage of lymphoma cells can, at any given time, produce mature EBV, indicating that the entire virus genome is present in the tumor cells. This raises the question of how EBV induces a malignant state in only a very small percentage of patients infected by this virus. Dr. Karpas[26] described the existence of virus-like particles in the cytoplasmic inclusion bodies of fresh human leukemic cells. A look at preleukemic states may be useful. Dr. Becker[27] discussed the role of retroviruses and EBV in human leukemia and lymphoma.

Dr. Padgett[28] concluded that current evidence does not indicate an association of human papovaviruses, JCV and BKV, to human cancers but indicated the need for further investigation, particularly on young patients, and for studies on episomal viral DNA. JCV virus, discovered by Padgett in 1971, is associated with a rare progressive multifocal leukoencephalopathy. While both viruses produce tumors in lower animals, recently London et al.[29] demonstrated that JCV also induces glioblastomas in nonhuman primates (owl monkeys). Virus infection of humans occurs early in life, and 70 to 80% of adults have antibodies to the virus, while few sera of cancer patients or controls seem to react with tumor (T) antigen. There is conflicting evidence in hybridization studies.

Dr. Schmidt-Ullrich[30] has obtained evidence that plasma membranes of cells transformed or infected by simian virus 40 (SV40) express modified T antigen (90,000–100,000 daltons), which is encoded by the virus genome, and a 44,000–60,000 dalton protein, which is host cell-specific. BKV-transformed cells yielded similar results and he found crossreactivity between both virus systems.

The demonstration of the enormous potential in new procedures concerning monoclonal antibody production was described by Dr. Hämmerling.[31] Whereas conventional antisera can be made monospecific by absorption with a series of antigens, they will always consist of a mixture of antibodies. By contrast, monoclonal antibodies are homogenous, of defined specificity and often high titered. Thus, they can be looked at as among the most useful tools for the analysis of complex antigenic systems. Similarly, genetic engineering has come of age, and large batches of insulin, albumin, etc. are now being produced by genetic recombinations of cells and bacteria.

Cytomegaloviruses (CMV) have been associated with various human tumors, especially sarcomas, best documented by Dr. Giraldo and Dr. Beth.[32] One of these, Kaposi's sarcoma (KS), is a potentially interesting model in the research for virus-associated human malignancies. "The cluster-type of occurrence of KS in endemic areas is suggestive of the involvement of infectious, environmental or genetic factors." Furthermore, data were obtained on a series of 92 patients with KS and of 4,517 patients with double primaries, including all sites. The latter group was studied, since 37% of KS patients had other primary malignancies. In the series of double primaries, lymphoreticular malignancies were involved in 8% of cases; for KS alone the corresponding figure was 58%. Recent studies demonstrated the presence of CMV-associated early antigens and CMV DNA in tumor biopsies. In cooperative studies with Dr. Bernice Eddy, we have also isolated viruses with the mixed characteristics of CMV and herpesviruses from lung cancer tissues.[33] Moreover, Rapp et al.[34–36] have been able to transform hamster and human cells in tissue culture with CMV, and they showed that a human prostate cancer line had certain antigens in common with those seen in CMV-transformed hamster cells. Nucleic acid hybridization studies revealed about 10 to 15 genome equivalents of CMV DNA in cultured human cells of prostatic origin. It was suggested that the cells either had been transformed by CMV or were chronically infected with the virus.[35]

Smith and de Harven studied HSV and CMV replication in human lung fibroblast cells.[37] HSV replicated and progeny virus was released within eight hours postinfection, whereas CMV required four days. There was a greater tendency of HSV to produce membrane alterations, whereas they noted the appearance of cytoplasmic dense bodies in CMV- but not HSV-infected cells. It is possible that in nature, mixed wild-type viruses containing features of both types of herpesvirus may be necessary for survival, particularly during the process of transformation. This would permit a second interpretation of the events observed in squamous cell carcinomas. However, virus isolations are very rare, and it is possible that these isolations are from other forms of cells, since isolations from cloned cells in long-term culture with squamous characteristics have not yet been possible.

Notkins has shown how herpesviruses pass directly from cell to cell through "intercellular bridges" just one step ahead of the herpesvirus antibodies and complement which attack and destroy cells which have developed the viral antigens.[38] If leukocytes were added prior to the addition of antibody and complement, the infected cells could not form bridges, and the infection was cured. Whether or not this might have been the result of interferon production is not known. White blood cells are well known as a rich source of interferon.

Dr. Prince[39] presented several lines of evidence which indicate an important role for hepatitis B virus (HBV) in the development of hepatocellular cancer in chronic hepatitis B-carriers. Ever since 1957, when Isaacs and Lindenmann discovered interferon,[40] we have seen an array of intermediate cell products, including interferon analogues, produced by different cell types after stimulation, not only by virus infections, but also by re-encounter with foreign antigens. They may be produced in lymphocytes exposed to tumor cells, and those made by T-suppressor lymphocytes are highly active in immune cell regulation. Merigan showed that interferon may be useful in the treatment of chronic hepatitis B patients and possibly in cancer patients who develop a severe case of shingles (herpes zoster). This raises certain questions relative to the nature of interferon action. The chemical nature of interferon is not known. However, because of the new advances in genetic engineering, it is now possible to produce large quantities of proteins of medical importance using recombinant DNA techniques. The structure of interferon will soon be understood. In 1973 it was reported that interferon might be useful in the treatment of osteosarcoma.[41] Very little is known at this time as to just why interferon might be useful in the treatment of cancer. There is some concern about just what the long-term effects of such treatment might be, since there are no model studies in higher animals. According to one recent popular article,[42] "it still takes hundreds of gallons of white cells to produce frustratingly small amounts of usable interferon." As reviewed more completely by Dr. Sanders,[43] in 1978 Merigan et al.[44] reported the usefulness of interferon in the treatment of B-cell lymphoma. Gutterman et al.[45] reported in May, 1979, that they had seen complete remission in six of 17 breast cancer patients and three of ten patients with B-cell neoplasms, with partial remissions seen in four additional patients. Thus, there was some benefit for 13 of 27 patients with advanced cancers. They suggested that the use of interferon in the treatment of earlier stages of cancer may be even more beneficial. Some of the questions at an upcoming conference on interferon indicate the state of the art. With regard to the treatment of viral infections, the question is asked as to whether interferon is capable of regulation of persistent infection, and what is the long-term effect upon normal genes? With respect to cancer, the question asked is whether or not interferon is a part of the cellular immune host response to tumor antigens. This question has been asked for a number of nonspecific substances used for immunorestoration or immunostimulation of the immune system in cancer patients. Are cancer effects virus-related?

The continual need for productive interface studies, indicated so many years ago, continues. We now know that it is not the virus oncogene but the oncogene products —proteins —that induce transformation. The continual need for interplay and the furtherance of knowledge in biology and chemistry by the multimodality approach, as Fruton so wisely suggested, is the key to progress.

References

1. Dubos, R.J.: *Louis Pasteur: Free Lance of Science,* R.J. Dubos (ed.), Little, Brown, Boston, 1950, reissued by Scribners, 1976.

2. Porter, J.R.: *Science* 178:1249, 1972.

3. Coley, W.B.: *Med. Rec.* 43:60, 1893.

4. Mathé, G., Amiel, J.L., Schwartzenberg, L., Schneider, M., Caltan, A., Schlumberger, J.R., Havat, M., and de Vassal, F.: *Rev. Franc. d'Etudes Clin. et Biol.* 13:454, 1963.

5. Fruton, J.S.: *Science* 192:327, 1976.

6. Anfinsen, C.B.: *Some Biological Implications of Protein Structure,* Lecture given at the National Institute of Health, October 21, 1964.

7. Solomon, A.: *N. Engl. J. Med.* 294:17, 1976.

8. Carpenter, C.B.: Editorial, *N. Engl. J. Med.* 294:1005, 1976.

9. Watson, J.: *The Double Helix,* J. Watson (ed.), Atheneum, New York, 1968.

10. Kolata, G.B.: *Science* 192:645, 1976.

11. Baltimore, D.: *Science* 192:632, 1976.

12. Price, P.J.: This volume.

13. Hardy, W.D., Jr. and McClelland, A.J.: This volume.

14. Sarkar, N.H.: This volume.

15. Hollinshead, A.C., Chretien, P.B., Lee, O., Tarpley, J.L., Kerney, S.E., Silverman, N.A., and Alexander, J.C.: *Cancer Res.* 36:821, 1976.

16. Munk, K.: This volume.

17. Filipovich, A.H., Spector, B.D., and Kersey, J.H.: This volume.

18. Auersperg, N., Hollinshead, A.C., Lee, O., and Wong, K.: 1980, submitted for publication.

19. Aurelian, L., Jariwalla, R.J., Donnenberg, A.D., and Sheridan, J.F.: This volume.

20. Tarro, G., Flaminio, G., Cocchiara, R., d'Alessandro, G.D., Mascolo, A., Papa, G., di Gioia, M., and Geraci, D.: This volume.

21. Tarro, G., Flaminio, G., Cocchiara, R., di Gioia, M., and Geraci, D.: *Cell Mol. Biol.,* 1980 (in press).

22. Klein, G.: *N. Engl. J. Med.* 293:1353, 1975.

23. Klein, G.: *Nature* 252:348, 1974.

24. Burkitt, D.P.: This volume.

25. Vonka, V., Hirsch, I., Suchánková, A., Břicháček, B., Závadová, H., Kuchlerová, L., and Sibl, O.: This volume.

26. Karpas, A.: This volume.

27. Becker, Y.: This volume.

28. Padgett, B.L.: This volume.

29. London, W.T., Houff, S.A., Madden, D.L., Fucillo, D.A., Gravel, M., Wallen, W.C.,

Palmer, A.E., Sever, J.L., Padgett, B.L., Walker, D.L., zu Rhein, G.M., and Ohashi, T.: *Science* 201:1246, 1978.

30. Schmidt-Ullrich, R.: This volume.

31. Hämmerling, U., Pinter, A., and O'Donnell, P.V.: This volume.

32. Giraldo, G., and Beth, E.: This volume.

33. Hollinshead, A., Miller, H., Tanner, K., Lee, O., and Klausia, J.: *Cancer Immunol., Immunother.* 5:93, 1978.

34. Albrecht, T. and Rapp, F.: *Virology* 55:53, 1973.

35. Rapp, F., Geder, L., Murasko, D., Lausch, R., Ladda, R., Huang, E.-S., and Webber, M.: *J. Virol.* 16:982, 1975.

36. Rapp, F. and McCarthy, B.A.: In: *Antiviral Mechanisms in the Control of Neoplasia,* P. Chandra (ed.), Plenum Press, New York, 1979, p. 263.

37. Smith, L.D. and de Harven, E.: *J. Virol.* 12:919, 1973.

38. Notkins, A.: *J. Exp. Med.* 137:706, 1973.

39. Prince, A.M.: This volume.

40. Isaacs, A. and Lindenmann, J.: *Proc. Roy. Soc. B.* 147:258, 1957.

41. Strander, H., Cantell, K., Carlström, G., and Jakobsson, P.A.: *J. Natl. Cancer Inst.* 51:733, 1973.

42. Rosenfeld, A.: *Life Magazine* 7:55, 1979.

43. Sanders, F.K.: This volume.

44. Merigan, T.C., Sikora, K., Breeden, J.H., Levy, R., and Rosenberg, S.A.: *N. Engl. J. Med.* 299:1449, 1978.

45. Gutterman, J., Yap, Y., Buzdar, A., Alexanian, R., Hersh, E., and Cabanillas, F.: *Am. Soc. Clin. Oncol.* 674:15, 1979.

Author Index

Subject Index